MICROSCOPY
AND
MICROTECHNIQUE

MICROSCOPY
AND
MICROTECHNIQUE

R. MARIMUTHU

Principal (Retd.)
Arignar Anna Government Arts College,
Attur, Salem
Formerly, Reader and Head of Applied Botany
Periyar University, Salem
Tamilnadu

Chennai   New Delhi   Tirunelveli

ISBN 978-81-8094-035-4   **MJP Publishers**

All rights reserved   No. 44, Nallathambi Street,

Printed and bound in India   Triplicane, Chennai 600 005

MJP 037   © Publishers, 2017

Publisher :   C. Janarthanan

Project Editor :   C. Ambica

To

The sweet memories of my parents Mrs. Vedhavalli and Mr. M. Ramanathan

My Guru Prof. V. Krishnamurthy, the Doyen of Indian Algology and a rare combination of a researcher and teacher

The Lotus Feet of the Lord Kalki whose Divine Grace makes us to flower in every moment in our lives

FOREWORD

The microscope is the instrument most used by biologists, and students are introduced to it even at higher secondary school level. However, it is surprising to find that very few are aware of its construction, optical properties and the proper care and use of the same. Even at the secondary school level, students of biology are shown objects under the microscope but I am not sure whether they are given any instructions about its use, much less about its construction. Students of biology at the college level (undergraduate students) do use the microscope, but most of them learn only to use the focusing screws and the light source.

Some years back, a worshop on microscopy was organized, which was attended by a number of college teachers and research scholars. It was then felt that a book on microscopy and microtechnique was a dire necessity. At the time the most popular book on Plant Microtechnique was that of Johansen. A less commonly used book was that of Sass.

In the present millennium, these books would seem out of date. Developments in the manufacture of microscope and newer applications of microscopic technique have necessitated an updating of information and a more practical guide to the use and care of the microscope and to microtechnique.

In this context, Dr. Marimuthu's book is most welcome. The book is organized in four parts. The first part deals with Microscopy wherein the principles involved in light microscopes, the properties of lenses, formation of images, concepts of magnification and resolution and factors governing resolution are given. Significance of angular aperture and numerical aperture of lenses is highlighted. Also included in this part are details regarding the nature and functions of various types of substage condensers and of the illuminating systems, types of oculars and objectives and how these have to be used. The second part deals with different types of light microscopes using bright field, phase contrast, fluorescence, dark field and polarized light. Accounts are also given of UV microscope, interference microscope, confocal microscope and electron microscope. The third part deals with the documentation of images obtained in microscopes such as drawing, photomicrography, digital imaging and micrometry. An account of the use of the different types of microscopes will not be complete without the science and art of microtechnique. Therefore, the fourth part deals with this subject. This part is of the nature of a practical manual for preparation of material for microscopy. The author gives valuable tips about mounting specimens whole, fixation of specimens, sectioning, staining and mounting of fixed material and gives step-by-step procedures for micropreparation of biological material. This part cannot be exhaustive as numerous methods, stains and reagents have been used by microscopists the world over, but the author has given good details about the more common procedures and has given practical advice on many aspects of microprepa-rations. Students will benefit by the thoughtful provision of review questions at the end which are exhaustive. Although the book refers to plant microtechnique, the information given in this book will be useful for all biologists.

The author should be congratulated for coming out with a very useful book on microscopy and microtechnique and I am sure this book will be a valuable acquisition to biological libraries.

I congratulate Dr. Marimuthu on this valuable book of reference and wish the book the rich success it deserves.

V. Krishnamurthy

Director

Krishnamurthy Institute of Algology

Chennai-40.

PREFACE

The need for a textbook solely devoted to microscopy and microtechnique has long been felt by the teachers and the taught in biological sciences in Indian universities.

It is towards fulfilling this long-felt need that the present book is ventured. Chapters are so schemed and topics so sequenced to suit the requirements and needs of the end user.

I am indebted to the inspiring works/books of Johansen, Peter Gray, John R Baker and many others whose works have been extensively consulted and used.

Some of the figures in the present book were made by me and some have been borrowed with thanks from the references listed.

I fervently hope that the book is useful to the undergraduate and postgraduate students, research scholars and teachers as well.

Constructive criticism and suggestions for improvement are welcome. Feedback may be mailed to the publisher or to botany_marimuthu2000@yahoo.co.in

R. Marimuthu

ACKNOWLEDGEMENTS

It is the pleasant duty of an author to place on record his thanks to all the good souls who have been inspiring him.

I wish to sincerely thank the following who have been instrumental in some way or the other to get this book completed:

The publisher Mr. Chidambaram Pillai (MJP Publishers) who had been constantly encouraging and persuading me to complete the assignment through the periods of my road accident and heart surgery. His genuine interest in getting the book out in print is thankfully acknowledged.

Sajeesh Kumar, Managing Editor; Radha, Revathi and Ramalakshmi of the editorial department; and Yamuna Devi, Uma Maheswari and Lissy John of the typesetting department for their active interaction with me during the proof correction and final formatting stages.

The authors of all the references cited in the book for having generously made available ideas, facts, presentations and illustrations, some of which could be used with academic liberty. Thank ye all... Grammarians!

My Guru Prof. V. Krishnamurthy who encouraged me all along telling that such a book is very much needed and that he wanted to see my book in print.

My revered teachers, Prof. (Late) S. Sundaram, the all-time-great teacher in Botany, Dr. A. Balasundaram and Dr. R. Sundaram who have been role-models to many students and who have inspired me greatly during my student days and service as a teacher.

My wife Vijayalakshmi for the secretarial assistance she has rendered and for having tolerated my keeping late hours with my computer despite my doctor's advice.

My children who have been constantly encouraging me in getting the book completed. My especial thanks to my son-in-law Dinesh Kumar who pointed out some inconsistencies in the equations in sections on Numerical Aperture and Angular Aperture so that they could be put in order.

Last but not the least, to all my students who continue to oxygenate the flame in me.

R. Marimuthu

CONTENTS

List of Figures   xxvii

List of Tables   xxxv

1

MICROSCOPY

Introduction   1

Image Formation   2

    Deviated and Undeviated Light Rays   4

LIGHT MICROSCOPY   5

PRINCIPLES OF LIGHT MICROSCOPY   5

LENS   6

    Refraction   6

    Dispersion of Light   8

    Aberrations of Lenses   9

        Spherical Aberration   10

        Chromatic Aberration   10

    Theoretical Basis and Correction of Aberrations   11

        Correction of Spherical Aberration   11

        Correction of Chromatic Aberration   12

        Approaches Generally Followed in Correction of

          Aberrations (Distortions) of Images   13

    Images   14

        Intricacies of Seeing (Viewing) Objects on a Magnified Scale   14

        Image Quality   17

MAGNIFICATION   19

    Magnification—The Concept   19

        Imaging Scenario 1   20

        Imaging Scenario 2   21

Imaging Scenario 3   21
Imaging Scenario 4   21
Imaging Scenario 5   22
Expression of Magnification   23
Other Aspects of Magnification   24
   Range of Useful Magnification   24
   Magnification as Related to Microscope and Human Eye   25
   Infinite Magnification   25
   Thumb Rule for Recommended Magnification of Microscope   27
   Choice of Eyepiece/Objective Combinations
      to Ensure Optimal Magnification   27

RESOLUTION AND RESOLVING POWER   28
Resolution—The Phenomenon   28
Mathematical Expression of Resolution and Resolving Power   29
Factors Governing/Limiting Resolution   32
Resolving Power of Microscope   33
Factors that Determine Resolution in Optical Light Microscopes   35
Methods of Increasing the Resolving Power of a Lens System   35
   Increasing the Resolution Using Short Wavelengths   35
   Increasing the Resolution Using Immersion Objectives   36
   Increasing the Resolution Using Inclined Light   37
Angular Aperture (AA) of Lens   38
Numerical Aperture (NA)   40
Resolving Power of Objective and Size of the Airy Diffraction Pattern   44
Resolution and Numerical Aperture   44
Different Equations for NA found in Literature   45
Airy Discs and Upper Limit of Resolution   45
Contrast and Resolution of Images   47

CONDENSERS   49
Structural Description of a Substage Condenser   50
Types of Condensers   51
   Abbe Type Condenser   52
   Aplanatic Condenser   53
   Achromatic Condenser   54
   Achromatic-Aplanatic Condenser   55
Value Addition to Condensers   55
   Flip-Top Lens (Swing-Out Top Lens) Condenser   55

         Immersion Condenser   56
         Movable and Fixed Condensers   57
      Points/Tips on Optimal use of Condensers   57
ILLUMINATING SYSTEMS OF A MICROSCOPE   60
      Illuminating Systems Suitable for Various Microscopy Needs   60
         Axial Reflected Light   61
         Condensed Reflected Light   62
         Inclined or Unilaterally Reflected Light   62
         Circular Ringlike Light   63
      Illuminating Systems Involving Additional Condensers   63
         Critical Illumination   64
         Kohler Illumination   64

LENS SYSTEMS USED IN MICROSCOPES   **66**

OBJECTIVE LENS SYSTEMS   66
      Structural Description of an Objective   67
      Corrective Arrangements in Objective Lens System   69
         Correction for Optical Aberration   70
         Correction for Field Curvature   73
         Correction/Compensation for Variations in Cover Glass   75
         Infinity-Corrected Objectives   80
      Long Working Distance (LWD) Objectives   84
      Immersion Objectives/Oil-immersion objectives   85
      Parfocality and Parcentricity   87
      Field Diameter   88
         Working Distance and Depth of Focus of an Objective   88
         Depth of Field   90
      Conclusion   91
OCULAR LENS SYSTEMS (OCULARS/EYEPIECES)   92
      Types of Oculars   94
         Positive Type of Oculars   94
         Negative or Huygenian Oculars   98
      Other Advanced/Improved Types of Oculars   100
         Periplan Oculars   100
         A Typical Modern Ocular   100
      Inscriptions Found on Oculars   101
      Tips on Choosing and Using Oculars   102
      Ramsden Disc   103

Vignetting   104
    Mechanical Vignetting   104
    Optical Vignetting   104
Review Questions   105

2

MICROSCOPES

Introduction   109
History and Evolution of Microscopes   109
    Earliest Version of Compound Microscope   110
    Robert Hooke's Microscope   111
    Leeuwenhoek's Microscope   112
    Binocular Microscope of Rhieta   112
    Horizontal Microscope of Bonannes   112
    Wilson's Screw Barrel Type Microscope   113
LIGHT MICROSCOPY   **113**
Simple Microscopes   113
    Basics of How to use a Simple Magnifier   115
    Magnifying Power and Field of View of a Simple Magnifier   116
    Quality of the Image   116
TYPES OF OPTICAL LIGHT MICROSCOPES   117
Students' Dissection Microscope   117
    Structure/construction of Dissection Microscope   117
Stereoscopic Microscope   119
    Principle   119
    Construction/Description of a Stereo-Binocular
       Dissection Microscope   119
    Uses   121
Compound Microscope   122
    Construction and Optical Principles Involved in Light Microscopes 122
    Optical Systems and the Optic Principle of the Light Microscope 128
Working of an Optical Light Microscope   129
    Choice of Suitable Eyepiece/Objective Combination   132
Bright-field Microscopy   133
    Limitations   133
    Advantages   133
Basic Concepts and Formulae in Microscopy   134
Phase Contrast Microscopy   137

Phase Shift   137
Principle   139
Applications   141
Fluorescence Microscopy   141
Types of Fluorescence   142
Photoluminescence, Fluorescence and Phosphorescence   143
Fluorescence Light Microscope   144
Trans-illumination Fluorescence Microscope   145
Epi-illumination Fluorescence Microscope   146
Applications   147
Dark-field Microscopy   148
Improvising the Ordinary Light Optical Microscope   149
for Dark-Field Microscopy   149
Principle   150
Advantages   150
Limitations   151
Applications   151
Polarized Light Microscopy   151
Principle   151
Polarimetry and Polarimeter   153
Applications   156
UV Microscopy   156
Interference Microscopy   157
Principle   157
Differential Interference Microscopy   158
Principle   158
Components of Differential Interference Contrast (DIC) Microscope   159
Working/Functioning of the DIC Microscope   160
Advantages   162
Limitations   162
Confocal Microscopy   163
Working Principle of CFM   164
Construction of a Confocal Microscope   166
Improvements over Conventional Light
Microscopy and Fluorescence Microscopy   167
Advantages   168
Important Aspects of Confocal Microscopy   168
Objectives of a CFM   170

Scanning Systems   170
Signal-to-Noise Considerations   171
Electronic Light Detectors   171
Specimen Preparation for CFM   172
Spectral Bleed-through Artefacts in CFM   173
Laser Safety   173
Useful Tips on how to use and Maintain Microscopes   173
General Guidelines   173
Guide to a Beginner   174
General Tips on Usage of Microscope   176
Attributes/Parts that are to be Checked
    while Purchasing a Microscope   177
Technical Tips for Oil-immersion Microscopy   181
Some Useful Tips for Comfortable Microscopy   182
Basic Requirements for Successful Microscopy   183

ELECTRON MICROSCOPY   183
Particulate and Wave Properties of Electrons   184
Components of Electron Microscope (EM)   185
Source of Electrons   185
Electromagnetic Lenses   187
Aberrations of Electron Lenses   188
Resolving Power of Electron Microscope   189
Vacuum System   189
Image Formation in Electron Microscope   190
ELECTRON MICROSCOPES   191
Transmission Electron Microscope (TEM)   192
Electron-Generating Arrangement   193
Electromagnetic Lenses   194
Specimen Chamber   195
Viewing Chamber   196
Photographic Arrangement   196
Vacuum System   196
Electrically Operated Mechanical Controls   197
Dimension of the Microscope   197
Other Versions of Transmission Electron Microscopes   197
Applications   198
Limitations   198
Scanning Electron Microscope (SEM)   198

Optical System and Components of SEM   200
Review Questions   200

3

DOCUMENTATION OF IMAGES OBTAINED IN MICROSCOPY

Introduction   203
Camera Lucida   203
   Principle   204
   Camera Lucida—Mirror Type   204
   Camera Lucida—Prism Type   205
   Useful Tips on Using Camera Lucida   206
PHOTOMICROGRAPHY   **206**
   Principle   207
   Image Obtained in Microscope   208
      Photoeyepiece   208
   Photographic Films   209
      Film Speed   209
      Film Types   211
      Balancing of Film for Illumination   212
      Film Size Formats   212
      Useful Tips on Selection and Use of Films for Photomicrography   214
      Critical Information to be Sought about the Film   215
      Use of Polaroid Films   215
      Preservation of Old Transparencies and Negatives for Posterity   216
   Art of Photography in Photomicrography   216
   Cameras Available for Photomicrography   217
   Adapting any Available Camera to the Microscope   217
      Makeshift Arrangements   217
      Use of Specially Designed Camera Adapters   219
DIGITAL IMAGING—NEW OPPORTUNITIES
FOR PHOTOMICROGRAPHY   224
   Why Digital Imaging?   225
   Advantages and Attributes of Digital Cameras   226
   Software for digital imaging   227
   Types of digital cameras available   228
   Purchase of Digital Camera   229
      Nature of Output   229

Transference of Digital Signals to a Computer   229
Speed of Transferring the Images to the Computer   229
Resolution   230
Using an Advanced Digital Photomicrographic Configuration   231
MICROMETRY   235
Principle   235
Micrometers   236
Ocular Micrometer   236
Stage Micrometer   238
Calibrating the Ocular Scale and the Microscope   240
Micromeasurements   242
Marking the Scale of Magnification on Camera Lucida
Drawings and Photomicrographs   243
Review Questions   248

4

MICROTECHNIQUE

INTRODUCTION   251
Purpose of Microscopic Examination   251
Kinds of Preparations for Microscopic Observation   253
Whole Mounts   253
Smears   253
Squashes   253
Sections   253
MATERIALS AND EQUIPMENT   254
Glassware   255
Plain Microslides   255
Coverslips or Cover Glass   255
Cavity Slides/Depression Slides/Culture Slides   257
Specimen-Transferring Tools   257
Containers for Handling Specimens/Sections
Stuck to Slides   257
Cleaning Slides and Glassware   260
Slide Containers   261
Equipment   262
Hot-Air Oven   262
Slide-Warming Table   264
Section Cutting Devices (Microtomes)   265

MICROTOME   265
  Hand Microtome   266
  Rotary Microtome   267
    Operating the Microtome   269
  Sledge Microtome   270
    Sectioning Procedure   272
  Microtome Knives and their Maintenance   273
    Tips on Use and Maintenance of Microtome Knives   275
FIXATION AND FIXATIVES   276
  Introduction   276
  Fixation—Aim and Advantages   277
  Agents Employed in Fixing Biological Materials   277
    Fixation by Using Physical Factors   278
    Fixation by Using Chemical Factors   278
  Coagulant Fixatives   278
  Non-coagulant Fixatives   279
  Chemical Fixative Mixtures   280
    Acetic Acid–Alcohol Mixtures   280
    Formalin–Acetic Acid–Alcohol Mixtures   281
    Chrome–Acetic Acid Mixtures   282
    Chrome–Acetic–Formalin Mixtures   283
    Picric Acid Fixative Mixtures   284
    Potassium Chromate Mixtures   285
  Various Plant Groups or Plant Parts and
    Fixatives Ideal for them   286
  Points to be Kept in Mind While Fixing
    Biological Materials For Microtechnique   287
STAINS AND STAINING   288
  Principles of Staining   288
  Principle of Differential Staining   289
  Direct and indirect Staining   290
  Use of Mordants   290
  Solvents for the Stains   293
  Strength of Stain Solutions   294
  Bleaching   294
  Progressive and Regressive Staining   296
    Progressive Staining   296
    Regressive Staining   296
  Differential Acidification   297

General and Specific Stains 297

    General Stains 297

    Specific Stains 297

Stains used in Plant Microtechnique 297

Natural Dyes 298

    Brazilin 298

    Haematoxylin 298

    Haematein 302

    Cochineal and its Derivatives 302

    Indigocarmin 303

Coal-tar Dyes 303

Acid Fuchsin 304

Aniline Blue Water-soluble 304

Crystal Violet 305

Erythrosin Bluish 306

Fast Green FCF 306

Light Green SF 306

Safranin O 307

Sudan IV 308

STAINING SCHEDULES 308

Safranin and Fast Green 308

Safranin and Haematoxylin 310

Safranin, Crystal Violet and Orange G 310

    Typical Schedule 311

    Stockwell's Variation 312

Quadruple Staining 313

OTHER USEFUL SCHEDULES 315

Crystal Violet and Erythrosin Combination 315

    Procedure 316

Johansen's Methyl Violet–Erythrosin Schedule 316

Foster's Tannic Acid–Iron Chloride Staining Schedule 317

DEHYDRATION 318

Dehydrating Agents 319

    Ethyl Alcohol (Ethanol) 320

    Isopropyl Alcohol 320

    Butyl Alcohol 321

    Tertiary Butyl Alcohol 322

    Tertiary Butyl Alcohol Series 322

Hygrobutol 322
Acetone 323
Cellosolve 323
Dioxan(e) 323
Glycerine 325
Points to be Kept in Mind while Dehydrating
Materials for Microtechnique 325
CLEARING OR REMOVAL OF DEHYDRATING AGENT 325
Procedure for Using Clearing Agent 326
Procedure for Hard Tissues 327
Procedure for Soft Tissues 327
Clearing Agents used for Whole Mount 327
Terpineol 328
Clove Oil 328
Bergamot Oil 329
Cedar Wood Oil 329
Clearing Agents Used for Materials to be Embedded in Wax 330
Benzol 330
Toluol 331
Xylol 331
Trichloroethylene 333
Chloroform 333
Carbolxylene 333
Points to be Kept in Mind while Clearing Material for Microtechnique 334
Floatation Method 334
MOUNTING AND MOUNTANTS 335
Attributes of a Liquid Mounting Medium 336
Types of Mounting Media 337
Hydrophil Media 337
Hydrophobe Media 338
Adhesive and Non-adhesive Mounting Media 339
Some Important Mounting Media 339
Glycerol (Glycerine) as a Mounting Medium 339
Ferrant's Medium 340
Methyl Salicylate 341
DPX 341
Gum Arabic 342
Dammar Balsam 342

Canada Balsam   343
Euparol   343
Styrax   344
Hyrax   344
Cedar Wood Oil   344
Lactophenol   344
Clarite   344
Glycerine Jelly   345

MICROSLIDE PREPARATION   345

WHOLE MOUNTS   345
Temporary Whole Mounts   346
Procedure   346
Semi-permanent Whole Mounts   347
Procedure   347
Permanent Whole Mounts   349
Hygrobutol Method   349
Glycerine–Xylol Method   351

SMEARS   352
Smearing Technique   353
Alternative Method   353
Staining the Smear   354
Belling's Iron–Acetocarmine Method   354
Johansen's Methyl Violet Method   355
McClintock's Acetocarmine Method   356

SQUASHES   357
Warmke's Method   357
Hillary's Method   358

SECTIONING OF BIOLOGICAL SPECIMENS   360
Introduction to Methods of Sectioning   360
Free-hand Sections   362
Free-hand Sections of Fresh Specimens Using a Razor Blade   362
Free-hand Sections using a Hand Microtome   363
Free-hand Sections using a Sliding Microtome/Sledge Microtome   365
Sectioning   365
Processing and Staining Schedule   365
Microtome Sections   366
Paraffin Infiltration   366
Embedding   369

Use of 'L' Shaped Metallic or Wooden Blocks ... 369

Use of Paper Boat to Embed Materials ... 370

Use of the Lids of Coplin Jars ... 371

Precautions to be Followed While Embedding Materials in Wax ... 372

Fixing the Wax Block on the Specimen Holder ... 372

Microtoming ... 374

Problems Met with During Microtomy/
Defects in the Ribbons of Serial Sections and
Rectification of the Defects ... 375

Fixing the Ribbon Containing Microsections on Slides ... 377

Cleaning of Microslides ... 377

Adhesives to Fix the Ribbons on to Slides ... 377

Application of Adhesive and Fixing the
Ribbons on to the Slide ... 378

Dewaxing and Staining of the Sections ... 380

MACERATION ... 380

Jeffrey's Method ... 381

FIXING COVERSLIPS AND RINGING ... 382

Mechanism Involved in Binding the Coverslip to the Slide ... 383

Application of the Coverslip ... 384

Sealing the Coverslip ... 384

Review Questions ... 386

Appendix ... 393

Glossary ... 403

References ... 417

Index ... 419

FIGURES

Figure 1.1   Light waves   3

Figure 1.2   Image formation by deviated rays   4

Figure 1.3   Path of the light (a) without object (b) with object   5

Figure 1.4   Types of lenses   6

Figure 1.5   Light rays passing through a convex lens   7

Figure 1.6   Light rays passing through a concave lens   7

Figure 1.7   The electromagnetic spectrum   8

Figure 1.8   Refraction and dispersion of light, and formation of
              normal spectrum   9

Figure 1.9   Spherical aberration   10

Figure 1.10   Chromatic aberration   11

Figure 1.11   Correcting spherical aberration   12

Figure 1.12   Correction of chromatic aberration   13

Figure 1.13   Resolving power line through various imaging devices   16

Figure 1.14   Photomicrograph images of leaf of *Elodea* at magnifications of
              40×, 100× and 400× respectively.   18

Figure 1.15   Magnification versus resolution: images of microsection
              depicting the effects of magnification with resolution
              on the quality of image as compared to the effect
              of magnification alone.   18

Figure 1.16   Magnification with a simple lens   19

Figure 1.17   Imaging scenario 1: Object farther away from 2F; image—real,
              very small, inverted, on 'F' on the other side of lens   21

Figure 1.18   Imaging scenario 2: Object nearer 2F; image—real, small,
              inverted, between 'F' and '2F' on the other side of lens   21

Figure 1.19   Imaging scenario 3: Object at 2F; image—real, as big as object,
              inverted, at '2F' on the other side   21

Figure 1.20   Imaging scenario 4: Object in between F and 2F; image—real,
              larger than object, inverted beyond 2F on the other side of lens 22

Figure 1.21   Imaging scenario 5: Object in between F and optic centre;
              image—virtual, larger than object, erect and on the same
              side as object   22

Figure 1.22   Increasing the resolution using immersion oil   36

Figure 1.23   Direct, inclined and converged light rays   38

Figure 1.24   Angular aperture (AA) and semi-angle of the cone (μ, also
designated as α)   38

Figure 1.25   Natural light or "resultant light"—a combination of deviated and
undeviated rays   39

Figure 1.26   Numerical aperture of an objective lens when a condenser
is not used   41

Figure 1.27   Numerical aperture of the objective lens increased by use of a
substage condenser   42

Figure 1.28   Numerical aperture of objectives of different powers   42

Figure 1.29   Airy discs and intensity distribution (a) Unresolvable point
(b) Two different points at resolvable distance
(c) Two points at the limit of resolvable distance   46

Figure 1.30   Numerical aperture and airy disc size   47

Figure 1.31   Parts of a substage condenser with iris diaphragm   50

Figure 1.32   Abbe type condenser   52

Figure 1.33   Optical pathway of Abbe condenser   53

Figure 1.34   Aplanatic condenser   54

Figure 1.35   Achromatic condenser   54

Figure 1.36   Achromatic-aplanatic condenser   55

Figure 1.37   Swing-top lens condenser   56

Figure 1.38   Vertically movable condenser   57

Figure 1.39   Reflection mirror   58

Figure 1.40   Use of condenser and iris diaphragm to control illumination   59

Figure 1.41   Inclined or unilaterally reflected light and eccentric diaphragm   62

Figure 1.42   Effect of circular ringlike light   63

Figure 1.43   Critical illumination   64

Figure 1.44   Kohler illumination (a) Image of the filament of the bulb
(b) Image of the iris of the additional condenser   65

Figure 1.45   Objective lens system   67

Figure 1.46   Various types of corrected objectives   72

Figure 1.47   Apochromat objectives of various powers   73

Figure 1.48   Correction of an achromat objective for field curvature   74

Figure 1.49   Objectives with correction collar (a) Collar adjusted for
cover glass thickness 0.20 mm (b) Collar adjusted
for cover glass thickness 0.13 mm   76

Figure 1.50   Mechanical tube length   78

Figure 1.51   Mechanical tube length in inverted reflected light microscope   79

Figure 1.52   Infinity-corrected objective system   81

Figure 1.53   Different types of additional optical components
introduced in the light path of infinity-corrected
microscopic system for different applications   82

Figure 1.54   Different types of infinity-corrected objectives   83

Figure 1.55   Long working distance (infinity-corrected) apochromat   84

Figure 1.56   Aplanatic refractions occurring in oil-immersion objective   86

Figure 1.57   Working distance and depth of focus   90

Figure 1.58   Ranges of depth of field   91

Figure 1.59   Ocular lens system   92

Figure 1.60   Anatomy of simple oculars (a) Ramsden type ocular
(b) Huygenian type ocular   93

Figure 1.61   Longi-section view of a simple positive ocular
(Ramsden ocular)   95

Figure 1.62   Corrected simple oculars (Kellner design)
(a) corrected Ramsden ocular (b) corrected Huygenian ocular   96

Figure 1.63   Longi-section of a compensative positive ocular   97

Figure 1.64   Longi-section of a Huygenian ocular   99

Figure 1.65   Periplan ocular   100

Figure 1.66   A typical modern ocular (aberration-free 10× ocular
with dioptre adjustment)   101

Figure 2.1   Jansen and Hans microscope   111

Figure 2.2   Robert Hooke's microscope   111

Figure 2.3   Leeuwenhoek's microscope   112

Figure 2.4   Wilson's screw barrel type microscope   113

Figure 2.5   Different types of simple magnifiers (simple microscopes)
(a) Illuminated loupe (b) Stamp loupe (c) Foldable field lens
(d) Measuring and inspecting magnifier (e) Binocular loupe   114

Figure 2.6   Dissection microscope   118

Figure 2.7   Hand-rest of dissection microscope   118

Figure 2.8   Ocular lens system of a dissection microscope   119

Figure 2.9   Stereo-binocular microscope (a) Drawing
(b) Photograph of neopta stereo-binocular microscope   120

Figure 2.10   Compound microscope   123

Figure 2.11   (a) Compound microscope with disc diaphragm (without
                   condenser) (b) Disc diaphragm   124

Figure 2.12   Compound microscope with disc diaphragm and artificial
                   illuminator attachment   125

Figure 2.13   Rack-and-pinion   126

Figure 2.14   Inclined binocular microscope with fixed body
                   and movable stage   127

Figure 2.15   Optic principle of light compound microscope   128

Figure 2.16   Schematic representation of the working of a light
                   compound microscope   130

Figure 2.17   Typical NA values for objectives of various powers   134

Figure 2.18   (a) Deviated and undeviated rays forming the resultant light
                   (b) Phase shift   138

Figure 2.19   Phase contrast microscope   140

Figure 2.20   Schematic representation of the light path and
                   the components in fluorescence microscopy   145

Figure 2.21   Optical principle of fluorescence microscope
                   (a) Trans-illumination fluorescence microscope
                   (b) Epi-illumination fluorescence microscope   146

Figure 2.22   Types of condensers used in dark-field microscopy
                   (a) Condenser with opaque stop (b) Paraboloid condenser
                   (c) Cardioid condenser   149

Figure 2.23   A wire grid polarizer converting normal light
                   (unpolarized beam) into one with a single linear polarization   151

Figure 2.24   Polarization of light   152

Figure 2.25   Components of a polarimeter   153

Figure 2.26   Polarized light microscopy—optical principle
                   1. Polarizer and analyser are set at right angles;
                   object is turned to −45°. 2. Polariser and analyser
                   are set parallel to each other; object is turned to +45°   155

Figure 2.27   Interference light microscopy   157

Figure 2.28   A Wollaston prism   159

Figure 2.29   Optical path and working of the NDIC microscope   161

Figure 2.30   Principle of confocality   164

Figure 2.31   Optical path and working principle of confocal microscope   165

Figure 2.32   Confocal microscope   167

Figure 2.33   Diagram of electron gun   186

Figure 2.34   Electron lens (a) Entire (b) Sectional view   187

Figure 2.35   Diffraction/scattering of electrons by different
areas of the specimen   188

Figure 2.36   Layout of a simple electron microscope   192

Figure 2.37   (a) Siemens Elmiscop 102 TEM (b) A high-resolution
transmission electron microscope (a vertical sectional view)   193

Figure 2.38   Scanning electron microscope (SEM) (a) Optical path
(b) Philips PSEM 500   199

Figure 3.1   Camera lucida—mirror type   205

Figure 3.2   Camera lucida—prism type   205

Figure 3.3   35-mm film cassette   213

Figure 3.4   Film holders for photomicrography   214

Figure 3.5   Photomicrography using an integral lens camera   218

Figure 3.6   SLR camera mounting accessories   220

Figure 3.7   Manual photomicrographic camera (eyepiece camera)   223

Figure 3.8   DXM 1200 digital eclipse ACT-1 control software window
elements   228

Figure 3.9   Nikon eclipse E800 microscope with DXM 1200
digital camera system   231

Figure 3.10   An advanced digital photomicrographic configuration   232

Figure 3.11   Olympus DP-10 digital camera with SmartMedia card   233

Figure 3.12   DP-10 digital camera hand switch   233

Figure 3.13   Various types of ocular scales (a) Crosslines (b) Horizontal
micrometer (c) Crossed micrometer (d) Indexed squares
(e) Patterson globe and circle   236

Figure 3.14   Ocular micrometer reticle (a) Ocular micrometer and rings
(b) Ocular micrometer as viewed in the microscope   237

Figure 3.15   (a) Stage micrometer (b) Micrometer scale 1 mm long
divided into 100 equal parts (c) Micrometer scale 2 mm long
divided into 200 equal parts (d) Stage micrometer scale for
metallurgical studies (1 mm divided into 50 equal parts).   239

Figure 3.16   Stage micrometer scale as seen under different magnifications
(a) Low power (b) High power (c) Oil-immersion   240

Figure 3.17   Ocular scale superimposed on stage micrometer scale   241

Figure 3.18   Scale line showing magnification in a camera lucida drawing 244

Figure 3.19   Scale line showing magnification in a photomicrograph   247

Figure 4.1   Tools for transferring the specimen (a) Pipette with rubber
teat (b) Section lifter   257

Figure 4.2   Various types of containers for handling specimens   258

Figure 4.3   Slide submission tray   261

Figure 4.4   Slidebox   261

Figure 4.5   Slide storage cabinets (a) Vertical storage cabinet
(b) Flat storage cabinet   262

Figure 4.6   Electrically operated hot-air oven   263

Figure 4.7   Radiant-heat embedding oven   264

Figure 4.8   Electrical slide-warming table   265

Figure 4.9   Manual slide-warming table   265

Figure 4.10 Hand microtome   267

Figure 4.11 Rotary microtome   268

Figure 4.12 Arrangement to decide thickness of the section cut   268

Figure 4.13 Sledge microtome   271

Figure 4.14 Microtome knife (a) A microtome knife with its handle
(b) Split cylinder (c) Types of cutting edges (d) Cutting
facet and clearance angle   274

Figure 4.15 Honing stone and strop (a) Setting the cutting facet
(b) Stropping a microtome knife   275

Figure 4.16 Outline drawing of microslide to guide mounting
in the central point   346

Figure 4.17 Applying the coverslip over the specimen (a) and
(b) Correct methods of applying the coverslip
(c) Incorrect way of applying the coverslip   347

Figure 4.18 Cutting a hand section. The razor is drawn across
the specimen with gentle pressure, and the section
is then washed into a stender dish.   363

Figure 4.19 Sectioning specimens using hand microtome (a) Fixing the
specimen (b) Cutting sections   364

Figure 4.20 Embedding with 'L' shaped blocks (a) Two 'L' blocks
(b) Reservoir made by 'L' blocks (c) Size of the reservoir
thus varied   369

Figure 4.21 Making a paper boat (a) using pre-determined lines
(b) using a wooden block   371

Figure 4.22 Embedding specimens in wax (a) Pouring molten
wax in the reservoir (b) Wax block containing specimens   372

Figure 4.23 Specimen holders   373

Figure 4.24 Cutting sections with a microtome (a) Starting paraffin
ribbon (b) Laying out the paraffin ribbon   374

Figure 4.25   Problems met with during sectioning (a) Curved ribbon
(b) Longitudinal streaks in the ribbon (c) Alternate thick and
thin sections (d) Shrunken sections (e) No ribbon formation
(f) Microsection separates from wax (g) Ribbon gets
stuck to wax block   375

Figure 4.26   Adhesive for fixing the ribbons (a) Canada balsam bottle
(b) Application of adhesive   378

Figure 4.27   Mounting the ribbons on slides   379

Figure 4.28   Macerated angiosperm wood   381

Figure 4.29   Ringed slide   385

Figure 4.30   Turn table   386

Figure A.1   Section cutting for electron microscopy (a) Plate Glass
(b) Making tape boat (c) Specimen in the plastic block
(d) Sectioning   395

Figure A.2   Recommended range of condenser iris   400

TABLES

Table 1.1   Viewing systems and their resolution   2

Table 1.2   Characteristics of real and virtual images   8

Table 1.3   Range of useful magnification (500–1000 × NA of objective)   25

Table 1.4   Refraction indices of different media and the numerical aperture and angular aperture they yield   37

Table 1.5   Numerical aperture versus optical correction   43

Table 1.6   Substage condenser applications   59

Table 1.7   Equivalent foci and their magnification   68

Table 1.8   Objective types and corrections of optical aberrations   71

Table 1.9   Maximum resolving power and depth of focus   89

Table 3.1   Sample calibration value sheet   242

Table 3.2   Magnification sample chart   246

Table 4.1   Coverslips of various thicknesses and their uses   256

Table 4.2   Coverslips of different shapes and dimensions and their uses   256

Table 4.3   Some coagulant fixatives and their properties   279

Table 4.4   Some non-coagulant fixatives and their properties   279

Table 4.5   Fixatives for various plant parts   287

Table 4.6   Differences between direct and indirect staining   290

Table 4.7   Ethyl alcohol–butyl alcohol series as suggested by Sass (1964)   321

Table 4.8   Ethyl alcohol–tertiary butyl alcohol series (Sass, 1964)   322

Table 4.9   Series to be followed for materials fixed in aqueous fixative   324

Table 4.10   Series to be followed for materials fixed in alcoholic fixative   324

Table 4.11   Clearing agents in botanical microtechnique   326

Table 4.12   Series to be followed for hard and large tissues   331

Table 4.13   Series to be followed for softer tissues   331

Table 4.14   Differences between hydrophobe and hydrophil mounting media   338

Table 4.15   Differences between non-adhesive and adhesive mounting media   339

Table 4.16   Composition of lactophenol   344

Table 4.17   Primary stains and counterstains recommended for some specimens   350

1

MICROSCOPY

INTRODUCTION

Sight is our dominant sense and the sensory world is primarily a "visual one". Magnifying glasses, microscopes and telescopes provide extension of our visual sense. They enable us to see, and more important, to see clearly small or distant objects. The invention and gradual perfection of these instruments permitting the exploration of the Universe not accessible to our own naked eyes is a major and well known theme in the history of science. Much of the progress in the field of biology in the last hundred years or so is closely bound up with improvements in the microscope (Grimstone, 1968).

Microscope (Gr. *Mikro* = small, minute; *scopia* = observation) is an instrument consisting essentially of a lens or a combination of lenses, designed to magnify very small objects such as microorganisms, to look larger so that they can be seen and studied.

Viewing or seeing depends mainly on the resolving power of the human eye lens. **Resolving power** is nothing but the capability of the lens to show two different points or lines or objects or dots lying very close to each other, as separate.

The resolving power of the human eye is 0.1 mm, i.e., points or lines at a distance of less than 0.1 mm will appear as a single point or line to our eyes.

Cells of plants and animals as well as cell organelles are of dimensions less than 0.1 mm. Therefore, it becomes necessary to use some sort of magnifying device to see them.

In ancient times, glass globes filled with water were used as simple magnifying lenses. Following this, lenses made of glass or other transparent materials were made for use as magnifiers.

When the resolution of simple lenses was not sufficient, lens systems, consisting of more than one lens, were designed for use. Gradually, compound microscopes, phase contrast microscopes, etc. were developed.

All these use visible light to create the image. Therefore, all these were called **light microscopes**. Electron microscope was developed when the magnification and resolution of light microscopes were not sufficient.

Different viewing systems and their resolutions are given in Table 1.1.

Table 1.1   Viewing systems and their resolution

Viewing system	Resolution
Eye	$100\ \mu$ (0.1 mm)
Light microscope	$1\ \mu$ (0.001 mm)
Electron microscope	$0.001\ \mu$ (10 Å)

Researches on lenses have been conducted right from 13th century, when man knew glass. Leonardo da Vinci, the Italian genius (1452–1519) was the first to recommend that lenses can be used to view objects that are too small to be seen with naked eye. The magnifying lenses used in this period were called filimicroscropes (*fili* = insects). Thus lenses were largely used to study insects.

Several improvements were made from simple lenses. Step-by-step, several microscopes were designed. Finally, in the beginning of the 20th century, the present-day compound microscope using light for viewing was designed. Of all these, the simplest one is the students' compound microscope which uses light to create the image.

IMAGE FORMATION (HOW THINGS ARE SEEN)

In order to understand how things are seen, one has to understand how images are formed. It is a common knowledge that light is essential to form images of things. Therefore, an account of the properties of light is imperative at this juncture.

Light is said to travel as **sine** waves. Long wavy lines denote the same. A more appropriate definition of light is that "Light is a series of energy particles travelling at a speed of 186,000 miles per second in a wavy snakelike path".

As millions of such particles travel alongside in a light ray, they can be diagrammatically shown as continuous wavy lines. Each wave is a sine wave (Figure 1.1) with two dimensions:

1. *Amplitude*   The depth of the trough.
2. *Wavelength*   The distance between adjacent peaks.

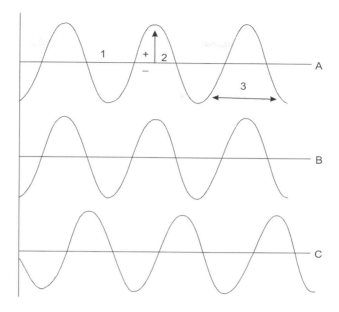

1. Main axis; 2. Amplitude; 3. Wavelength

A and B—waves in phase; C—wave out of phase with A and B

Figure 1.1   Light waves

Our eyes perceive amplitude as brightness, and wavelength as colour. The composite light comprising all the different wavelengths is seen as white light. Longer wavelengths falling on our eyes are perceived as red light and shorter wavelengths are perceived as blue light.

The objects (microsections) observed under microscopes, have varying degrees of transparency. Our eyes can see their images only if these images differ from their background (field of vision) in brightness and/or colour.

When there is no obstacle in the path of light in a microscope all the light rays travel undeviated and a bright filled of vision is obtained.

When a transparent blue colour filter is placed in the path of light, all the light rays passing outside the filter travel uninterrupted. Out of the light rays passing through the filter, the blue waves (shorter waves) are allowed to pass through without any change, while all other wavelengths are absorbed. So the blue filter creates a blue-coloured image in a white background (Figure 1.2). On the other hand, when a neutral density filter is placed in the path of light in the microscope, the amplitude of all the wavelengths passing through it is reduced. Therefore, this object (the neutral density filter) appears like a dull image compared to the brighter background.

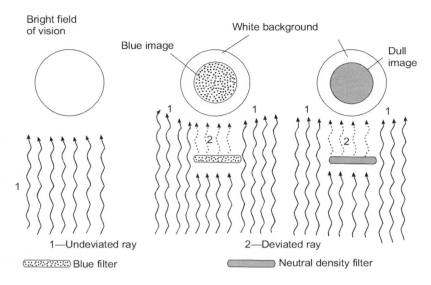

Figure 1.2   Image formation by deviated rays

Deviated and Undeviated Light Rays

Knowledge of the deviated rays and undeviated rays is essential for a proper understanding of the principles of microscopy.

When there is no object placed in the path of the light in the microscope, all the light rays travel without any hindrance. The field of vision is seen as a bright circle. The entire field of vision is filled with undeviated rays.

On the other hand, when an object is placed in the path of the light, the light rays falling on the object are deviated. The objective lens system converges all the deviated rays on the other side to form the primary image. The ocular lens system captures this primary image and forms an image at the plane of vision (Ramsden disc). Our eye captures this image and we see this image (Figures 1.3a and b).

It is the deviated rays that form the image of the object in the eye point (plane of vision). The image is bright or dull according to the degree of transparency of the object examined. The light that passes around the object is undeviated and it forms the background of the image.

The image will be seen clearly only if it differs from its background in its brightness as well as colour. In other words, the deviated rays should be different from the undeviated rays either in amplitude or wavelength or in both.

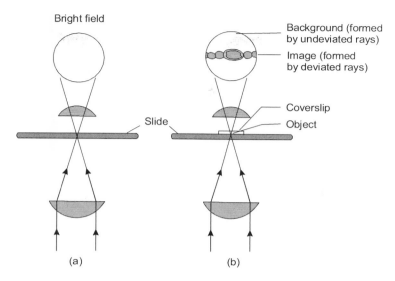

Figure 1.3 Path of the light (a) without object (b) with object

If the objects (microsections) observed in the microscopes have natural colours, the amplitude as well as the wavelength of the deviated rays is changed. Therefore, the image of the object will be seen clearly against the white background. On the other hand, if the object observed is colourless, we can stain it artificially, and obtain a clear image of it.

LIGHT MICROSCOPY

PRINCIPLES OF LIGHT MICROSCOPY

The invention and development of even more perfect microscopes and the associated techniques of specimen preparation lead to the following achievements in the field of biology.

⊙ Study of bacteria and protozoa
⊙ Identification of cells as fundamental constituents of plants and animals
⊙ Recognition and understanding the functional role of cell organelles
⊙ Recognition of chromosomes as units of heredity
⊙ Understanding of organogenesis

Light microscopes using a simple lens system are referred to as simple microscopes, while those using a combination of multiple lens systems are referred to as compound microscopes. The type of microscope which most of us are familiar with is the "ordinary" compound microscope and there are some more kinds of microscopes such as phase contrast microscope, interference and polarizing microscopes.

The "ordinary" compound microscope which is also called light microscope consists of a light source and three sets of lenses. The lens of the condenser focuses light on to the object. By their combined action, the objective and ocular lens systems form a magnified image of the object. For a proper understanding of the principles of light microscopy, knowledge on the following aspects is essential.

1. Lenses, their types, aberrations of images formed by lenses, and resolving power of lenses
2. Condensers, illuminating systems and the lens systems used in microscopes

LENS

A lens is a mass of glass or other transparent mineral substance with one surface plane and the other surface curved or with both the surfaces curved.

A lens is usually a segment of a sphere or a segment of two or more imaginary intersecting spheres (Figure 1.4).

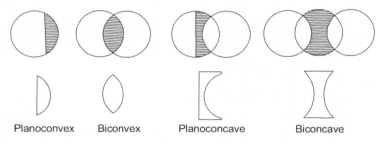

| Planoconvex | Biconvex | Planoconcave | Biconcave |

Figure 1.4   Types of lenses

Every lens possesses an optical centre, a primary axis, secondary axis and a principal focus. Refraction is an important property of lenses. It is the refraction that makes it possible for the lens to produce images. The second important property of lenses is dispersion of light.

REFRACTION

When light rays travelling in a medium enter into another medium of a different optical density, they deviate slightly from their path. This is called refraction. For example, a long pole, partly introduced into water at an angle, appears bent or broken.

Light rays travelling in parallel lines undergo refraction when they pass through a lens. They become converged on the other side of a convex lens (Figure 1.5) and become diverged on the other side of a concave lens (Figure 1.6).

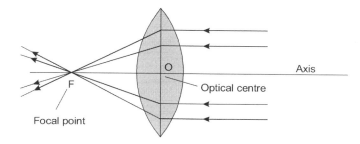

Figure 1.5   Light rays passing through a convex lens

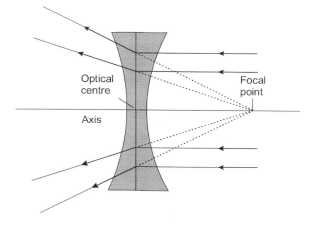

Figure 1.6   Light rays passing through a concave lens

In a convex lens, the converging rays of light meet at a point, and thereafter, diverge. The point of convergence is the principal focus (focal point) of the lens.

In a concave lens, such a convergence does not take place. But, if the paths of the divergent rays are tracked back, they will appear to meet at a point, the virtual focus.

The convergence and divergence of light rays caused by a lens is due to the change in the direction of the light rays and is termed refraction. It is this refraction that makes it possible for lenses to produce images.

The images formed by a lens may be a real image or a virtual image. The characteristics of real and virtual images are given in Table 1.2.

Table 1.2   Characteristics of real and virtual images

Real image	Virtual image
Real image is formed if the object is situated beyond the principal focus of the lens.	Virtual image is formed if the object is situated between the principal focus and the surface of the lens.
Real image can be caught on a screen placed at the plane of its formation.	Virtual image cannot be caught on a screen.
Real image is inverted when compared to the object.	Virtual image is not inverted.

The distance of the object from the focal point of the lens decides the distance at which the image is formed and the size of the image. The nearer the object is to the focal point, the greater will be the distance from the lens where the image is formed and the greater will be the size of the image.

Microscopes are constructed with these optical principles in mind.

DISPERSION OF LIGHT

Natural light consists of light rays of different wavelengths, ranging from 390 nm to 760 nm (the visible part of the spectrum) (Figures 1.7 and 1.8). The component wavelengths undergo different degrees of refraction when the light enters from one medium to another medium of a different optical density.

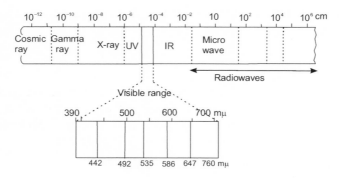

The visible spectrum of radiant energy lies between 380 and 760 mμ

Figure 1.7   The electromagnetic spectrum

Examples

1. Formation of normal spectrum of VIBGYOR when light passes through a glass prism.
2. Formation of rainbow

Red wavelengths deviate very little, while violet wavelengths deviate greatly. The difference between the refraction index of red wavelength and that of violet wavelength is the dispersion index.

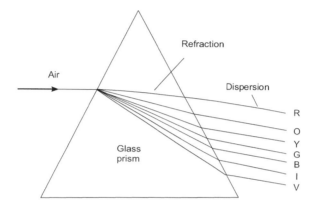

Figure 1.8   Refraction and dispersion of light, and formation of normal spectrum

For example,

    The red light refraction index of diamond = 2.41

    The violet light refraction index of diamond = 2.47

    Therefore, the dispersion index of diamond is 0.06.

    Very high degree of diffraction and dispersion occur in glass and normal daylight.

ABERRATIONS OF LENSES

The beam of light entering into a lens undergoes refraction at the same time while it undergoes dispersion. This leads to distortion of the shapes and colour in the images made by the simple lenses. This property of forming distorted images is called aberrations of lenses.

    Aberrations are of two types.

1. Spherical aberrations
2. Chromatic aberrations

Spherical Aberration

Spherical aberration is caused by the refraction of light. The light rays entering different parts of a lens get refracted at different degrees (Figure 1.9). For example, light rays entering the lens very near its centre, deviate very little (<), and therefore, travel to great distance on the other side to make the image.

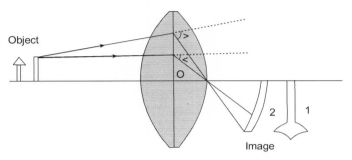

1. Front view; 2. Side view
> Greater degree of deviation from its normal path
< Less degree of deviation from its normal path

Figure 1.9   Spherical aberration

Light rays entering the lens, near its periphery, deviate greatly, and therefore, travel to very short distance on the other side to make the image.

Because of this property, images of different parts of the object are formed at different distances on the other side of the lens, resulting in a distorted overall image.

Since lens is a part of a sphere, the image obtained is also curved. So this type of aberration is called spherical aberration.

Chromatic Aberration (Chrome = Colour)

Light rays entering a lens undergo dispersion at the same time when they undergo refraction. The different wavelengths disperse (separate) at different rates and hence, deviate at different degrees, travelling to different distances on the other side of the lens to form separate images (Figure 1.10).

For example, red wavelength is deviated very little, and therefore travels to greater distance on the other side, and forms a red image. On the other hand, blue wavelength is deviated greatly and hence travel to short distances on the other side of the lens to form blue images.

Therefore, the frontal image of the object presents a central white zone comprising all the wavelengths, a blue halo around the central white zone and red halo outer to that.

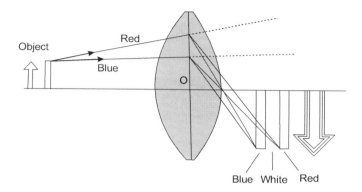

Figure 1.10   Chromatic aberration

The formation of different images of different colours by the lens because of the property of light dispersion, is called chromatic aberration.

THEORETICAL BASIS AND CORRECTION OF ABERRATIONS

The images obtained in a microscope should be free from aberrations. Therefore, microscopes are to be designed and constructed incorporating arrangements that correct the aberrations which are the inherent properties of the lens systems.

Correction of Spherical Aberration

Theoretically, spherical aberration is corrected with ease. This is because spherical aberration depends on the distance between the centre of the lens and its periphery.

Correction of spherical aberration is possible by any of the following three methods.

1. The easiest method is to place a diaphragm in front of the lens so that only the centre of the lens is used (Figure 1.11).

2. Use of Coddington lens effectively corrects the spherical aberration. Coddington lens is obtained by grinding a lens on each end of a cylindrical piece of glass. In fact, Coddington lens is nothing but the central part of a biconvex lens in which the peripheral parts are removed.

3. Spherical aberration can also be corrected by using a meniscus lens. A lens with one surface convex and the other concave is called meniscus lens. In such a lens, the one surface compensates for the effect of the other surface.

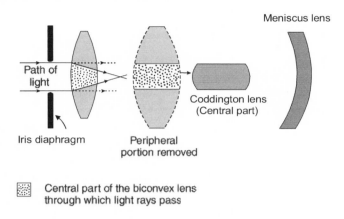

Figure 1.11   Correcting spherical aberration

The aforesaid devices are used in different combinations in the objective lens systems of compound microscopes to correct the spherical aberrations.

Correction of Chromatic Aberration

This is much more difficult than correcting the spherical aberration. Correction of chromatic aberration is attempted using the fact that the relation between the index of refraction and that of dispersion, differs in different kinds of glasses.

A combination of lenses, consisting of a biconvex lens and a biconcave lens, is used for correcting the chromatic aberration. If, in such a combination, the biconvex lens is made of a glass with high refraction index and low dispersion, it deviates the light rays to a high degree and separates the different wavelengths to a very low degree.

Moreover this image will be relatively free of spherical aberration, since the thick edge of the concave lens balances the thick centre of the convex lens (Figure 1.12). And, if the concave lens on the right side has a very low refraction index, the light rays are deviated to a very low degree. Similarly if this concave lens has a high dispersion index, it brings together the different wavelengths and corrects the chromatic aberration. Thus in such a lens combination, the effect of one lens is corrected by the action of the other.

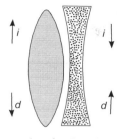

i—refraction; *d*—dispersion

Figure 1.12 Correction of chromatic aberration

However, the abovesaid is a theoretical dream. Glasses of very high refraction index and very low dispersion or vice versa do not exist. In fact double lenses are designed involving as many as six kinds of glasses, each having its own optical property, to achieve the aforesaid effect.

Approaches Generally Followed in Correction of Aberrations (Distortions) of Images

The following are some of the approaches generally followed in correction of distortion of images caused by curved surfaces of the lenses:

- ☉ A direct improvement in the distortion can be obtained by using two or more simple lenses.

- ☉ *Use of Huygenian telescope* Two planoconvex lenses are spaced a focal length apart in this magnifier. This arrangement reduces/corrects chromatic aberration as well as spherical aberration to a great extent.

- ☉ *Use of Coddington lens* This combines two lens elements into a single thick element, with a groove cut in the centre of the element to select the portion of the imaging light with the lowest aberrations. However, the magnifier has a very short working distance.

- ☉ *Use of special types of magnifiers* Special types of magnifiers such as Steinheil magnifier, Hastings magnifier, etc. use three or more elements to achieve better correction of the two kinds of aberrations.

In general, the better approach is the use of aspheric surfaces and fewer elements. Plastic-moulded lenses offer aspheric surfaces. Fresnel lens is an example for this. It is nothing but a form of thin sheet with the lens curvature placed in a series of concentric grooves on the surface of the sheet. This combines the options of a normal simple magnifier and the advantages of the aspheric form of lens though the presence of many symmetrical grooves reducing the quality of the image by light scattering.

IMAGES

In common usage, an image (from Latin *imago*) or picture is an artefact, usually two-dimensional, that has a similar appearance to some subject—usually a physical object or a person.

Images may be two-dimensional, e.g. a photograph, screen display, or three-dimensional, e.g. a statue. Images in the olden days were rendered manually as line drawings, paintings, etc. With the advent of imaging devices they may be *captured* by optical devices such as cameras, mirrors, lenses, telescopes, microscopes, etc. Natural objects and phenomena, such as the human **eye** or water surfaces respectively also do capture images of objects! Only we do not realize them as imaging devices and take them for granted.

Size of the image (magnification), clarity (resolution), contrast and sharpness are the quality criteria to be considered while we use artificial imaging devices such as cameras, microscopes, etc. The image obtained should be a true representation of the object.

The imaging devices employ lenses or lens combinations to create images on scales different from the actual dimensions (size) of the object. These lenses have their own inherent problems, which are introduced into the images obtained through them. While imaging macroscopic objects, at least the image can be compared with the actual object for its authenticity. This is not possible in case of microscopic objects imaged through magnifying devices such as lenses (simple microscopes) or compound microscopes (both light and electron microscopes). **Conrad Beck** succinctly pointed out the importance of a sound knowledge of the optical principles involved in producing images especially with high magnifying power.

"The appearances seen with high magnifying power under conditions which do not resemble those of ordinary vision require careful interpretation. This can only be accomplished by means of a knowledge of how the magnified images are produced." (Conrad Beck, 1938)

Intricacies of Seeing (Viewing) Objects on a Magnified Scale (Purpose of Imaging through a Microscope)

Eye is the sense organ concerned with seeing (imaging). For the human eye, seeing objects, in more and more detail, depends on the availability of light and its quality. No light means no seeing! (*See* How things are seen? in the earlier section of this chapter.)

Everyone knows the uses and properties of lens, the magnifying glass. A skillfully manufactured magnifying glass makes it possible to see some details, which are not easily visible to a naked eye, by magnifying the object to be studied or read. How a piece of glass results in magnification was studied by scientists centuries ago and explained by physical laws. (*See* the section on lenses of this chapter.)

The human eye is a marvellous but, at the same time, a restricted organ. If we cannot see fine details, we can just magnify a subject through a glass or by a microscope or something like that. The art and science of making even minutest things visible is, in reality, a large domain of the applied sciences of which a microscopist makes profitable use.

In using different viewing systems the question that is first to be addressed is: "How much can the image of the object be magnified?" Or in other words what is the possible upper limit of the magnification process. And it is true, that we cannot magnify things endlessly to see more details without compromising or losing information. There must be an equation describing this, and there is, of course, a mathematical outcome for it. We may express such an equilibrium with a scientific term, i.e., the **resolution**.

Since the phenomenon of resolution is a mathematical equation, it would be clear that we gain something at the expense of something else. This fact is explained by an intelligent author with the aid of the following example: If a puzzle consists of 100 pieces, looking at some of the pieces of the puzzle one may readily guess what the whole image is. If it consists of 1000 pieces, it would be rather difficult to find out what the whole image could be. And, what will be situation if it consists of 1,000,000 pieces and one looks at a few of them to decipher the whole image? The human mind loses its analytical power at high resolution!

A microscopist knows that with the light microscope he/she can achieve a maximum of magnification of about 1000×. Intelligent minds solved this limitation by using electron bundles instead of visible light. So, this ingenious technique opened a new era for morphologists making it possible to see more and more with an extreme power of resolution which may be expressed by the distance between two visible points to human eye. Nowadays, the distance of a few nanometres is indeed achievable on a molecular scale, and we can see details using such high-power magnifications.

Resolving power line from human eye to electron microscope through light microscope (including phase contrast and fluorescence microscopes)

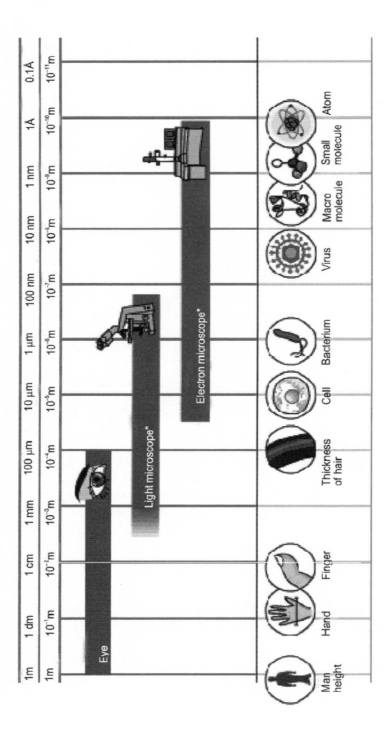

Figure 1.13 Resolving power line through various imaging devices

illustrated in Figure 1.13 shows what can be seen (imaged) with different kinds of microscopes. The human eye is capable of distinguishing objects down to a fraction of millimetre. With the use of light and electron microscopes it is possible to see (image) down to an angstrom and study everything from different cells and bacteria to single molecules or even atoms.

Image Quality

The two words, magnification and resolution are well-known terms for microscopists and morphologists. The magnified images obtained through microscopes should be clear and sharp bringing out more details than can be seen with the naked eye or lower scales of magnification. The following are the major criteria to be considered in imaging objects through microscopes (capturing images of objects using microscopes):

- ⊙ Magnification (Size)
- ⊙ Resolution (Clarity)
- ⊙ Contrast
- ⊙ Sharpness

Magnification   The ratio of the size of the focused image produced by a lens, to the actual size of an object.

Resolution   Generally, resolution is the ability to distinguish details in an image. Resolution is always limited by items such as wavelength, numerical aperture (NA), optical defects such as chromatic and spherical aberration, and overall image contrast. Two-point resolution, the conventional perspective, means distinguishing the space between two minuscule objects that are close together. This is a common criterion for examples such as observing intricate cellular detail in a tissue sample. In some cases, single-point resolution is appropriate when imaging isolated objects. Individual isolated points, smaller than those predicted by a two-point resolution definition, can be distinctly imaged. This criterion can apply to fibre samples having disperse, isolated particles and fibres.

Contrast   The difference between the brightness of various details in the object, and the difference as compared with the background.

Sharpness   As applied to an image, sharpness implies distinct, realistic image detail and contrast. With a sharp image of sufficient magnification, minimal effort is required to examine and interpret the image.

Figures 1.14 and 1.15 bring out the importance of the aforesaid criteria of image quality.

The images obtained from a light compound microscope and documented photographically (Figure 1.14), represent increases in the scale of magnification (40×, 100×, 400×) without sacrificing resolution. These images are also sharp.

| 40X | 100X | 400X |

Figure 1.14   Photomicrograph images of leaf of *Elodea* at magnifications of 40×, 100× and 400× respectively.

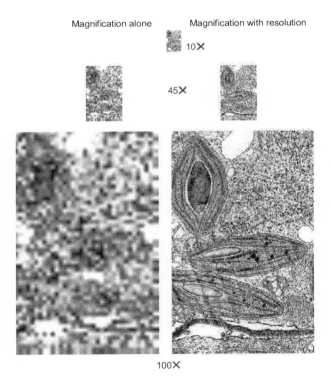

Magnification alone   Magnification with resolution

10X

45X

100X

Figure 1.15   Magnification versus resolution: images of microsection depicting the effects of magnification with resolution on the quality of image as compared to the effect of magnification alone.

The photomicrographs illustrated in Figure 1.15 show the images being magnified not sacrificing resolution as compared to the magnification sacrificing resolution (empty magnification). Note that the images on the right side representing increased scale of magnification with resolution are clear and sharp.

This background information on images, imaging mechanisms and quality criteria of images form the basis for the discussion on magnification, resolution, contrast and sharpness in the following pages:

MAGNIFICATION

MAGNIFICATION—THE CONCEPT

A simple microscope or magnifying glass (lens) produces an image of the object upon which the microscope or magnifying glass is focused. Simple magnifier lenses are biconvex, meaning that they are thicker at the centre than at the periphery as illustrated with the magnifier in Figure 1.16. The image is perceived by the eye as if it were at a distance of 10 inches or 25 centimetres (the **reference**, or **traditional** or **conventional viewing distance**).

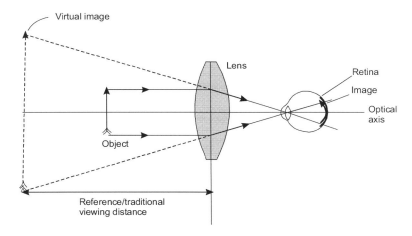

Figure 1.16 Magnification with a simple lens

Since the image appears to be on the same side of the lens as the object, it cannot be projected onto a screen. Such images are termed **virtual images** and they appear upright, not inverted. Figure 1.16 presents an illustration of how a simple magnifying lens operates. The object (an arrow) is being viewed with a simple biconvex lens. Light reflected from the object enters the lens in straight lines as illustrated in the figure. This light is refracted and focused by the lens to produce a virtual image on the retina. The image of the arrow is magnified because we perceive the actual size of the object to be at infinity because our eyes trace the light rays back in straight lines to the virtual image.

When one looks into a microscope, one is not looking at the specimen, but at the image of the specimen. The image appears to be "floating" in space about 10 millimetres below the top of the observation tube (at the level of the fixed diaphragm of the eyepiece (*see* Figure 1.28)) where the eyepiece is inserted. The image one observes is not tangible; it cannot be grasped. It is a "map" or representation of the specimen in various colours and/or shades of gray from black to white. The expectation is that the image will be an accurate representation of the specimen; accurate as to detail, shape and colour/intensity.

In such an attempt of microscopy (viewing through a microscope) there are two possible implications:

- ⊙ That it may well be possible (and is) to produce highly accurate images.
- ⊙ Conversely, it may be (and often is) all too easy to degrade an image through improper technique or poor equipment.

In order to understand how the microscope's lenses function, let us recall some of the basic principles of lens action in image formation by reviewing several of the following different imaging scenarios using a simple biconvex lens.

Imaging Scenario 1

Light from an object that is very farther away from the 2F of a convex lens (the "object" under observation is the arrow illustrated in Figure 1.17) will be brought to a focus at the focal point behind the lens. The **focal point** (F) of the lens is a fixed point for each lens. The vertical plane in which the focal point lies is the **focal plane**. The distance from the centre of the convex lens to the focal plane is known as the **focal distance**. For an idealized symmetrical thin convex lens, this distance is the same on either side of the lens.

(We are all familiar with the idea of a "burning glass" which can focus the essentially parallel rays from the sun to burn a hole on a piece of paper. Heat generated is acute when the paper/hand is held at the focal point!)

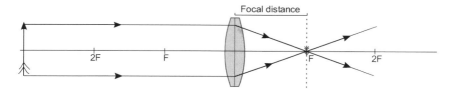

Figure 1.17   Imaging scenario 1: Object farther away from 2F; image—real, very small, inverted, on 'F' on the other side of lens

Imaging Scenario 2

The object is now moved closer to the front of the lens near 2F (Figure 1.18). Now, the image is found further behind the lens. It is larger than the one described above, but is still smaller than the object. The image is inverted, and is a real image. This is the case for ordinary portrait photography.

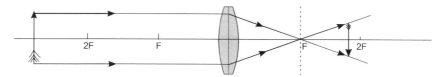

Figure 1.18   Imaging scenario 2: Object nearer 2F; image—real, small, inverted, between 'F' and '2F' on the other side of lens

Imaging Scenario 3

The object is now brought to 2F in front of the lens. The image obtained is now two focal lengths (2F) behind the lens as illustrated in Figure 1.19. It is the same size as the object; it is real and inverted.

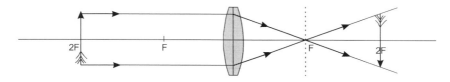

Figure 1.19   Imaging scenario 3: Object at 2F; image—real, as big as object, inverted, at '2F' on the other side

Imaging Scenario 4

The object is now situated between F and 2F in front of the lens (shown in Figure 1.20). Now the image is still further away from the back of the lens (beyond 2F). This time, the image is magnified and is larger than the object; it is still inverted and it is real.

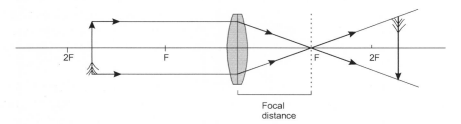

Focal
distance

Figure 1.20   Imaging scenario 4: Object in between F and 2F; image—real, larger
than object, inverted beyond 2F on the other side of lens

This case describes the functioning of all finite tube length objectives used in microscopy. Such finite tube length objectives project a real, inverted, and magnified image into the body tube of the microscope. This image comes into focus at the plane of the fixed diaphragm in the eyepiece. The distance from the back focal plane of the objective (not necessarily its back lens) to the plane of the fixed diaphragm of the eyepiece is known as the **optical tube length** of the objective.

Imaging Scenario 5

In this case, the object is situated at the front focal plane of the convex lens. The image is located on the **same** side of the lens as the object, and it appears upright (*see* Figure 1.21). The image is a virtual image and appears as if it were 10 inches from the eye, similar to the functioning of a simple magnifying glass; the magnification factor depends on the curvature of the lens.

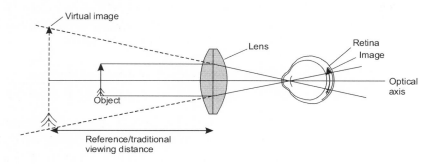

Figure 1.21   Imaging scenario 5: Object in between F and optic centre; image—
virtual, larger than object, erect and on the same side as object

The imaging scenario 5 listed above describes the functioning of the observation eyepiece of the microscope. The "object" examined by the eyepiece is the "magnified, inverted, real image" projected by the objective. When the human eye is placed above the eyepiece, the lens and cornea of the eye "look" at this secondarily magnified virtual image and see this virtual image as if it were 10 inches from the eye, near the base of the microscope!

This case also describes the functioning of the now widely used infinity-corrected objectives. For such objectives, the object or specimen is positioned at exactly the front focal plane of the objective. Light from such a lens emerges in parallel rays from every azimuth. In order to bring such rays to focus, the microscope body or the binocular observation head must incorporate a **tube lens** in the light path, between the objective and the eyepiece, designed to bring the image formed by the objective to focus at the plane of the fixed diaphragm of the eyepiece. The magnification of an infinity-corrected objective equals the focal length of the tube lens (for **Olympus** equipment this is 180 mm, **Nikon** uses a focal length of 200 mm; other manufacturers use other focal lengths) divided by the focal length of the objective lens in use. For example, a 10× infinity-corrected objective, in the Olympus series, would have a focal length of 18 mm (180 mm/10) (*also see* the section on Objective lens system).

Note Students are advised to refer to "The working of an optical light microscope " given in Chapter 2 at the end of the description of compound microscope to relate these basic principles of magnification with the working of the compound microscope.

EXPRESSION OF MAGNIFICATION

Optical instruments used for magnifying objects are those equipment by means of which the size of the retinal image of an object can be increased. The ratio of the magnified image to that formed on the retina of an unaided normal eye is termed as the magnification of that instrument.

$$\text{Magnification} = \frac{\text{Size of the retinal image seen with the instrument}}{\text{Size of the retinal image seen with the unaided normal eye}}$$

Magnification of a microscope can also be expressed as a linear magnification which is the ratio of the size of the final image to that of the object. The magnification of most microscopes lies between ×25 at the lower end and ×1500 at the upper end.

The reason why the upper limit in magnification of a microscope is set at about ×1500 is that, at that level we can conveniently see all the details that we can hope to make out. Further magnification merely results in a larger image which may not be informative. It is like trying to make out more detail in the photograph in newsprint using a magnifying glass.

In light microscopes, it is the wavelength of light which limits the amount of detail. In the printed picture it is the number of dots per square inch.

Our aim in using microscope is to see more details than we can make out with our naked eyes. Magnification is only a means to this end, not the end in itself.

OTHER ASPECTS OF MAGNIFICATION

Range of Useful Magnification

The **range of useful magnification** for an objective/eyepiece combination is defined by the numerical aperture of the system. There is a minimum magnification necessary for the detail present in an image to be resolved, and this value is usually rather arbitrarily set as 500 times the numerical aperture (500 × NA). At the other end of the spectrum, the maximum useful magnification of an image is usually set at 1000 times the numerical aperture (1000 × NA).

Useful magnification (total) = 500 to 1000 × NA (objective)

Magnification higher than this value will yield no further useful information or finer resolution of image detail, and will usually lead to image degradation.

Given that the highest practically achievable NA is about 1.40 it follows that ×1400 is the highest useful magnification obtainable before passing into what is generally called "empty magnification"—giving enlargement of the image but revealing no more detail.

Exceeding the limit of useful magnification causes the image to suffer from the phenomenon of "**empty magnification**", where increasing magnification through the eyepiece or intermediate tube lens only causes the image to become more magnified with no corresponding increase in resolution of details.

Table 1.3 lists the common objective/eyepiece combinations that lie in the range of useful magnification.

Table 1.3 Range of useful magnification (500–1000 × NA of objective)

Objective	NA	Eyepieces			
		10×	12.5×	15×	20×
2.5×	0.08	–	–	–	+
4×	0.12	–	–	+	+
10×	0.35	–	+	+	+
25×	0.55	+	+	+	+
40×	0.70	+	+	+	+
60×	0.95	+	+	+	–
100×	1.40	+	+	–	–

+ = Good combination

Magnification as Related to Microscope and Human Eye

Microscope observations are also affected by the following sensitivity attributes of the observer's eyes to:

1. intensity of illumination
2. colour temperature of illumination
3. age of the observer
4. presence of floaters in the eye
5. whether the eye is rested or fatigued

In microscopy, for visual observation, the image of the specimen (fine structure) must be viewed at an angle slightly larger than the resolving power of the human eye. With a microscope having good illumination, the distance between the resolved points in the specimen viewed at the reference visual distance of 250 mm is about 0.15 mm. This corresponds to a visual acuity angle of about 2 minutes of arc. This limiting angle is determined by the separation distance of visual elements in the retina (rods and cones) which are spaced about 5 microns apart.

Infinite Magnification

When an observer views an image through a correctly adjusted microscope, the lens of the observer's eye is totally relaxed as though viewing a distant horizon—the eye is focused for infinity. The focus mechanisms of the microscope bring to the relaxed eyes of the observer a sharp image of the object in the field of view.

Any image arriving at the eye from infinity must be infinitely magnified. This would imply that all optical devices producing an aerial image have the same infinite magnification in spite of our experience that some images are definitely more magnified than others.

This anomaly was resolved in the 19th century by deciding that 10 inches (250 mm) was a suitable close viewing distance for most people to see the finest detail of which the eye is capable. The magnifications could then be calculated assuming that the image in the eyepiece of a microscope was actually located in space at a plane ten inches from the eyes of the observer. At that distance (or any distance short of infinity) all features of the image would have calculable dimensions, and would therefore be comparable to other images measured in the same plane.

The actual magnification is determined by using an object of known size, and then measuring the size of its image when projected 250 mm from the exit pupil of the instrument—in the case of microscope, 250 mm from the Ramsden disc of the eyepiece.

Conversely, the size of any feature of the object can be determined by measuring the size of that feature's image, and dividing by the magnification. (*Refer* Micrometry in Chapter 3.) This standard is still in use today in that the magnifying power of simple lenses and lens systems is determined by dividing their focal length into 250 mm. For example, a hand magnifier with a focal length of 25 mm is a ten-power magnifier.

For many years in the 1800s, English microscope manufacturers produced, in observance of this standard, microscopes having tube length (between objective and eyepiece) of ten inches. But these proved unwieldy in use.

In the 20th century, infinity-corrected objectives were developed and the accepted standard for microscope objectives was (and is/became) an optical tube length of 160 mm. In other words, a microscope objective produced an image of the stated magnification only when it projected its image a distance of 160 mm measured from its back focal plane. This was also the conjugate distance required for spherical correction of the magnified image.

According to these criteria, a microscope objective having a focal length of 16 mm is a ten-power objective (160 divided by 16), a forty-power objective has a focal length of 4 mm and so on.

Any objective would of course produce larger or smaller magnifications with greater or lesser projection distances, but only at an optical tube length of 160 mm provided the objective was corrected both for spherical and chromatic aberration delivering the magnification engraved on it.

So with regard to magnification, there is a close relationship between NA (as a measure of the amount of detail in the image), and the visual acuity of the person using the microscope.

While such is the magnification of the image that arrives at the plane of the eyepiece diaphragm in a properly set up microscope, what magnification should an eyepiece have?

Enough extra magnification for an observer of good/normal vision to see all the detail in the image.

Thumb Rule for Recommended Magnification of Microscope

Based upon long experience, it has been said that the microscope should have a total magnification of around a thousand times the NA of the objective for a person of good vision to see all the detail the image has to offer. People of better-than-average vision could see the detail at lower magnification; people with less acute vision would require more.

According to this thumb rule, a good quality ×40 objective of 0.65 NA could use a ×15 eyepiece and still look sharp (at ×600) whereas, a ×100 oil-immersion objective of 1.30 NA would not be revealing all of its detail with ×10 eyepieces (at ×1000) (*see* Table 1.3).

For the person of average eyesight using an expertly set up microscope of the highest correction, specimens of high contrast would probably still look good at ×2000—which could be seen as the outer limit of useful magnification in the light microscope.

The foregoing observations apply only to the visual use of the microscope. Different criteria apply to the recording of microscope images on film of various formats, and in video and other CCD cameras.

Choice of Eyepiece/Objective Combinations to Ensure Optimal Magnification

In practice, magnifications deviating considerably from the useful magnification range are often employed. (*See also* Table 1.3 under Range of useful magnification in this section.)

For example, very low magnifications (1× through 4×) are often used to topographically map a specimen where a wide field of view desirable in order to quickly note all available specimen features.

In many cases, a 2.5× objective may be combined with a widefield eyepiece at 10× magnification to reveal an area having a diameter of 8 mm or greater.

At high magnifications, the limit of useful magnification is sometimes exceeded in order to view the image more comfortably. This is often the case when small particles or organisms are observed and counted at very high numerical apertures and magnifications. Sharpness in the specimen details is then sacrificed, which usually does not interfere with quantitative analysis of the image.

An objective cannot show its full efficiency if it is not used with a condenser of an NA large enough to fill the back of the objective with light.

Depth of focus (also known as sharpness or penetration) is another important factor which is often not clearly understood. It depends on the NA and the magnification, and is inversely proportional to both. **The higher the NA and the higher the magnification, the less the depth of focus.** It is beyond the power of the optician to change these conditions. Every effort aiming at an increase of the depth of focus, for example, by inserting diaphragms above the back lens must necessarily decrease the effective diameter of the back lens and thus decrease the NA, thereby lowering the efficiency of the objective.

RESOLUTION AND RESOLVING POWER

RESOLUTION—THE PHENOMENON

Resolution (R) is the action or process of separating or reducing something into its constituent parts. Resolution of sunlight into its spectral colours when passed through a prism is a good example. Resolution is indicated by sharpness of an image on a film/paper/computer screen/disc/tape or other medium. Resolution also denotes the amount of detail that can be seen.

Resolution is a measure of clarity and is defined by resolving distance (separation distance) or the minimum distance observable between two closely placed lines or points or objects.

Resolving distance is the smallest distance between two points that allows the observer to see these points as distinctly separate.

Resolving power is the efficiency with which an instrument or technique can separate or distinguish the component parts of something. Resolving power of a lens or a microscope is its ability to reveal two very closely placed lines or dots or objects as actually separate and distinct objects. In other words, resolving power is the smallest/shortest distance at which we can see that two objects are present rather than one.

The terms resolution and resolving power are often used interchangeably in literature. Some authors go to the extent of treating resolution synonymous with resolving power.

In the viewing systems such as microscopes, it is resolution that is more important, not magnification. However much magnified, a blur is still a blur. In optics and optical instruments such as microscopes, resolution is usually expressed in terms of the minimum distance observable between two objects. The smaller the distance that can be seen between two objects, the better the resolution. In other words, **the resolving distance and resolution are inversely related.**

Of course, the resolvable detail must be magnified to a sufficient amount in order to be seen. That is the importance of understanding the relationship between magnification and resolution.

Finally it can be said that "Resolution is directly related to the useful magnification of the microscope and the perception limit of specimen detail".

The resolution of an image focused by a lens or captured by a film is measured using a standardized target. A lens that produces a sharp image is said to have good resolution while a lens that produces a fuzzy image is said to have poor resolving power.

In case of a digital image, the resolution is expressed as number of dots per inch. Most laser printers have a resolution of 300 dots per square inch area (dpi). Image-setters have resolutions from 1,000 to over 3,600 dpi. Higher resolution improves image sharpness.

Some prefer to describe/define resolution as a measure of the ability of a lens or optical **system** to form separate and distinct images of two objects with small angular separation.

MATHEMATICAL EXPRESSION OF RESOLUTION AND RESOLVING POWER

Resolution for a diffraction-limited optical microscope is described as the minimum detectable distance between two closely spaced specimen points. It is mathematically expressed as:

$$R = \lambda / 2n \cdot \sin \alpha$$

where,

R is the separation distance (resolution),

λ is the illumination wavelength,

n is the imaging medium refraction index, and

α is one-half of the objective angular aperture (semi-angle of the cone of light falling on the objective lens).

In examining the equation, it becomes apparent that resolution is directly proportional to the illumination wavelength. The human eye responds to the wavelength region between 400 and 700 nanometres, which represents the visible light spectrum that is utilized for a majority of microscope observations. Resolution is also dependent on the refraction index of the imaging medium and the angular aperture (AA) of the lens of the observer's eyes in case of normal unaided viewing and AA of the objective lens system while viewing through a microscope.

Objectives are designed to image specimens either with air or a medium of higher refraction index between the front lens and the specimen. The field of view is often quite limited, and the front lens element of the objective is placed close to the specimen with which it must lie in optical contact.

Taking into account the two factors namely wavelength of the light used (λ) and the semi-angle (α) of the cone of light subtended by the object at the objective, the resolving power (δ) can be expressed by the following equation:

$$\text{Resolving power } (\delta) = \frac{\lambda}{\sin \alpha}$$

where,

λ = wavelength of light used and

α = semi-angle of the cone of light falling on the lens (one-half of the objective angular aperture (AA_{obj})).

In order to be more precise, a constant, 0.5 is also introduced in the equation. Incorporating these two factors, the equation becomes,

$$\delta = \frac{0.5\lambda}{n \sin \alpha}$$

The quantity is termed numerical aperture (NA) of the objective.

Therefore, a clear idea of angular aperture and numerical aperture is essential for proper understanding of the phenomenon of resolution.

Resolution is also affected by another factor namely refraction index (n) of the medium in which the lens operates. The refraction index of the medium through which light travels plays a role in resolution. A gain in resolution by a factor of approximately 1.5 is attained when immersion oil is substituted for air as the imaging medium. Therefore, the refraction index (n) of the medium between the object and the objective is also to be incorporated in the above equation.

In most microscopic observations, the medium is air ($n = 1$) and therefore, the equation remains the same. But when water or oil is introduced in between the object and the objective, the resolving distance is reduced by $1/n$. For example when oil is used, the relationship becomes

$$\frac{1}{1.5} = 0.61$$

Resolving power of a microscope is also given by the following relationship:

$$\delta = h' \frac{0.61\lambda}{n' \sin u'}$$

where,

h' = the smallest distance between two points resolved,

λ = wavelength of the light used,

n' = refraction index of the medium between the object and objective (usually air, with a refraction index = 1),

u' = angle which the marginal rays form with the axis (semi-angle of the cone), and

$n' \cdot \sin u'$ = NA (numerical aperture).

When u' is 90°, sin u' (sin 90°) will be equal to unity and if $n' = 1$ (in case of air), NA will be unity. Since maximum limit of u' is 90°, NA cannot be more than 1, if air is the medium.

However, if the space between the object and the objective is occupied by oil (immersion oil) having higher refraction index, the value of NA can increase. Therefore, the resolving power of the microscope will depend upon the wavelength of light used and the numerical aperture of the objective. Thus the distance resolved will decrease, with an increase in NA and a decrease in wavelength.

The relationship between numerical aperture (NA), wavelength of light used and resolution is indicated by the several equations that have been derived to express these relationships mathematically:

$$\text{Resolution (R)} = \lambda / 2NA \qquad\qquad (1)$$
$$\text{Resolution (R)} = 0.61\lambda / NA \qquad\qquad (2)$$
$$\text{Resolution (R)} = 1.22\lambda / (NA_{(obj)} + NA_{(cond)}) \quad (3)$$

where,

R = Resolution

λ = Imaging wavelength

NA = Numerical aperture

NA$_{(obj)}$ = NA of the objective

NA$_{(cond)}$ = NA of the condenser

When a microscope is in perfect alignment and has its objectives appropriately matched with the substage condenser, we can substitute the NA of the objective into equations (1) and (2), with the added result that equation (3) reduces to equation (2).

Note Equations (1) and (2) differ by the multiplication factor, which is 0.5 for equation (1) and 0.61 for equation (2). These equations are arrived on the basis of a number of factors and should not be considered as absolute values for any one physical law.

In some instances, the resolution may exceed the limits placed by any one these three equations. Other factors such as low specimen contrast and improper illumination may serve to lower resolution and, more often than not, the real-world maximum value of r (about 0.25 mm using a mid-spectrum wavelength of 550 nm) and a NA of 1.35 to 1.40 are not realized.

Magnification does not figure as a factor in any of these equations, because only NA and wavelength of the illuminating light determine specimen resolution

FACTORS GOVERNING/LIMITING RESOLUTION

The following factors governing or limiting resolution and their interaction are to be kept in mind:

⊙ Wavelength of the light illuminating the specimen is the most important limiting factor to resolution. Shorter wavelengths (r) yield higher resolution and vice versa.

⊙ Blue light (360 nm to 420 nm) permits greater resolution than does red light (650 nm to 800 nm).

⊙ The greatest resolving power in optical microscopy is realized with near-ultraviolet light which is the shortest effective imaging wavelength.

⊙ Near ultraviolet light is followed by blue, then green and finally red light, in the ability to resolve specimen detail.

⊙ The visible light spectrum is centred at about 550 nm, the dominant wavelength being green light.

- ⊙ Refraction index of the medium through which the light rays pass is another factor limiting resolution.

- ⊙ Refraction index of glass is 1.52 compared to that of air which is 1.00.

- ⊙ Light rays passing through a glass slide, using high dry-lens, will pass through air and be bent before reaching the objective lens. **Less bending will occur with water than with air and even less with oil.**

- ⊙ The angle of the greatest divergence of light rays that the objective lens can collect is called **angular aperture (AA)**. The maximal AA will not be realized with air. With an oil-immersion lens the space between the glass slide and the lens is replaced with oil that has a refraction index very close to that of glass. This increases the AA of the objective.

- ⊙ These factors are combined in the **numerical aperture (NA)** of the lens.

- ⊙ The NA value is also important in these considerations. Higher NA produces higher resolution.

RESOLVING POWER OF MICROSCOPE

The most important attribute of a microscope is resolution and not magnification. The best image is not the largest. It is the clearest. A simple black dot, the size of a pinhead is just as understandable as a simple dot an inch in diameter. What is expected of a microscope is, whether the pinhead-sized dot is a simple dot or whether its smallness conceals a pattern. The ability of the microscope to reveal this pattern is known as resolution.

Resolving power, also sometimes referred to as resolution power, of a microscope is the most important feature of the optical system. Obtaining maximum resolution depends upon the design of the objective. Three critical design characteristics of the objective set the ultimate resolution limit of lenses or lens systems or the microscope. These include the wavelength of light used to illuminate the specimen, the angular aperture of the light cone captured by the objective, and the refraction index in the object space between the objective front lens and the specimen.

An objective lens capable of utilizing a larger angular cone of light coming from the specimen will have a higher resolving power than a lens limited to a smaller cone of light (*see* Figure 1.27a, b and c).

Resolution is a somewhat subjective value in optical microscopy because at higher magnification, an image may appear unsharp but still be resolved to the maximum ability of the objective.

Resolution was explained by Ernst Abbe by what is known as the diffraction theory of resolution. An object becomes visible in a microscope as a result of an interaction between it (object) and the light waves used to illuminate it. This interaction which comes as a disturbance or deviation of the waves as they pass through the object is called diffraction. Light waves which do not interact with the object will not be diffracted.

According to Abbe, the details in the final image arise as a result of interference between the diffracted and undiffracted light, which in some parts of the image will arrive in phase with each other and tend to reinforce, while in others they will arrive out of phase and tend to cancel each other. This results in a pattern of light and dark areas which is the image of the object.

He also pointed out that for ideal resolution of a structure it is necessary that all the diffracted rays be included within the angular cone of the objective and re-united perfectly in the image. A large angular aperture is therefore essential for high resolution (resolving power).

Numerical aperture, as pointed out earlier, determines the resolving power of an objective, but the total resolution of a microscope system is also dependent upon the numerical aperture of the substage condenser. The higher the numerical aperture of the total system, the better will be the resolution.

Numerical aperture (NA) and magnification are the two main design criteria that specify the performance of the microscope. NA is the most important in that it defines the limit of detail, which can be resolved by the lens. Magnification determines at what degree of enlargement that detail is presented to the eye.

Magnification is how much an image is enlarged under a microscope. An image being seen at a magnification of $100\times$ means that its linear dimensions are 100 times those of the object giving rise to the image. The compound microscope has two separate lens systems, the objective and the ocular. The objective which is nearer to the specimen magnifies the specimen to a certain amount, and the ocular further magnifies this image. Thus, the image seen by the eye has a magnification equal to the product of the objective and ocular lens systems.

FACTORS THAT DETERMINE RESOLUTION IN OPTICAL LIGHT MICROSCOPES

- ⊙ Wavelength of light used to image a specimen (illumination wavelength)
- ⊙ Angular aperture of the objective lens (AA_{obj})
- ⊙ Correct alignment of the microscope optical system*
- ⊙ The refraction index in the object space between the objective front lens and the specimen
- ⊙ Objective numerical aperture ($NA_{(obj)}$)
- ⊙ Type of specimen (contrast)
- ⊙ Coherence of illumination
- ⊙ Degree of aberration correction
- ⊙ The contrast enhancing methodology applied in the optical system itself and in the specimen (staining)

(*Correct alignment of the microscope optical system is of paramount importance to ensure maximum resolution. The substage condenser must be matched to the objective with respect to NA and adjustment of the aperture iris diaphragm for accurate light cone formation and specimen illumination).

METHODS OF INCREASING THE RESOLVING POWER OF A LENS SYSTEM

Having known that the resolving power of the light microscope depends upon the factors namely, wavelength of the light illuminating the specimen, numerical aperture (NA) of the objective in use and refraction index of the media in the light path, it was soon possible to increase resolving power of the microscope by adopting any one of the following methods:

1. By using short wavelengths
2. By using immersion oil in the light path
3. By using inclined light

NA is the lens specification which takes these factors into account, and is effectively an index of the objective's ability to resolve fine detail. This is in turn dependent upon the refraction indices of the media in the light path.

Increasing the Resolution Using Short Wavelengths

Use of blue or blue-green light in a light microscope effectively increases the resolution. The blue and green filters supplied along with the microscopes serve this purpose.

Use of UV rays enhances the resolution greatly. The image thus formed can be caught on a fluorescent screen and observed or can be photographed for observation. UV rays do not penetrate glass. Therefore, with glass lenses, 365-nm wavelength is the shortest wavelength that can be used.

However, with a quartz lens system, short wavelength of 275 nm can be used to give nearly double the resolution obtained in visual microscopy using white light.

(By the same logic, an electron microscope gives greater resolving power because the wavelength of electrons is several orders shorter than that of white light.)

Increasing the Resolution Using Immersion Objectives

The frequency of monochromatic light is constant. But, the wavelength varies inversely with the refraction index of the medium traversed by the light. Short wavelengths are deviated more than the longer wavelengths, when they pass from one medium to another medium of a different refraction index. This principle forms the basis for the functioning of the immersion objectives.

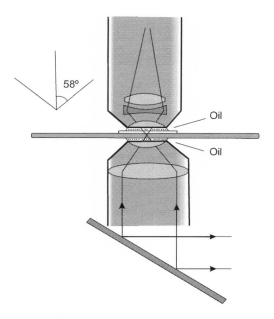

Figure 1.22   Increasing the resolution using immersion oil

The wavelength of light passing through the object can be shortened by surrounding the object with a medium of a refraction index higher than that of air (Figure 1.22).

The objective lens system separates more effectively the light rays entering into it through a medium of refraction index higher than that of air. Because of this, the structural details that are beyond the resolution limit of the lens system are separated and a clear image is formed. In other words, the numerical aperture of the lens (NA) increases resulting in higher resolution.

While using immersion objective lens system, both the upper and the lower surfaces of the microslide are to be covered with the medium of higher refraction index.

The refraction indices (i), of the various media that can be used for immersion purposes and their positive effect on the NA and AA of the objectives are tabulated in Table 1.4.

Table 1.4   Refraction indices of different media and the numerical aperture and angular aperture they yield

Medium	Refraction index (i)	Numerical aperture (NA)	Angular aperture (AA)
Air (dry objective)	1.0	0.95	143°
Water immersion	1.33	1.25	140°
Glycerin	1.46	1.25	116°
Oil	1.515	1.40	134°
α-Bromonaphthalene	1.658	1.60	150°

Increasing the Resolution Using Inclined Light

According to Abbe, the direct ray and one of the refracted rays should be sufficient to resolve a grating. In those cases where only the direct rays would enter the objective, resolution will not be possible (Figure 1.23).

When oblique illumination is used, both direct and deviated rays enter the objective lens. Hence, a better resolution is possible. Proper degrees of obliquity will nearly double the resolving power of an objective.

If the oblique illumination is unilateral, the structural details of the different parts of the object will not be resolved equally. Hence, light is generally made to converge on to the object from different directions by using a condenser.

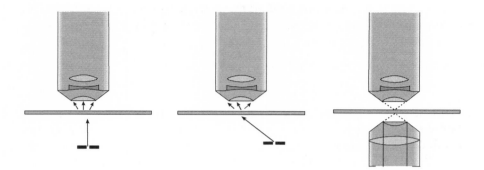

Figure 1.23   Direct, inclined and converged light rays

ANGULAR APERTURE (AA) OF LENS

Angular aperture (AA) of a lens is the angle of the pencil ray of light that converges onto the surface of a lens system. A larger angular aperture is a prerequisite for obtaining a clear image with a high resolution.

The angular aperture of a lens is also defined as the apparent angle of the lens aperture as seen from the focal point. The angular aperture is approximately equal to twice the numerical aperture of the lens.

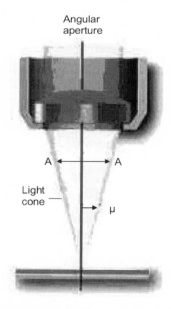

Figure 1.24   Angular aperture (AA) and semi-angle of the cone (μ, also designated as α)

The light rays that fall on the object mounted on a glass microslide, resemble the cone at the tip of a pencil (pencil of rays) (Figure 1.24).

The angle α is one-half the angular aperture (A) and is related to the numerical aperture through the following equation:

$$\text{Numerical aperture (NA)} = n \cdot \sin \alpha$$

where n is the refraction index of the imaging medium between the front lens of the objective and the specimen cover glass, a value that ranges from 1.00 for air to 1.51 for specialized immersion oils. Many authors substitute the variable μ for α in the numerical aperture equation.

If the pencil of rays is acute, it does not diverge much, after it passes through the object. As it does not diverge, the different parts of the object do not resolve properly. On the contrary, if the pencil of rays falling on the object has wide angle, it diverges very widely after passing through the object. Because of this, the different parts of the object resolve better and a clear image is obtained (*see* also Figure 1.28).

The angular aperture of a lens depends upon two factors:

1. Wavelength of the light used   Under normal conditions natural daylight is used in light microscopes. The natural daylight is in reality the "resultant light"—a combination of deviated and undeviated rays. The wavelength of natural light is generally expressed as midway between the two ends of the visible spectrum, i.e., 550 nm in the 390 nm to 700 nm spectrum (Figure 1.25). Use of monochromatic light may alter the angular aperture of the lens system. This is also achieved by use of colour filters placed in the path of light before it enters the lens system.

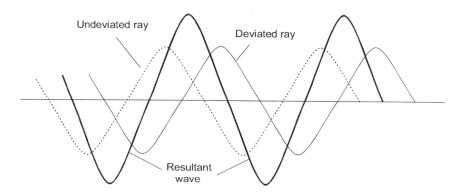

Figure 1.25   Natural light or "resultant light"—a combination of deviated and undeviated rays

2. *The medium in which the lens is operating* In routine microscopic works, the objective lens system works in air. Therefore, under normal conditions, the objective lens system is said to operate in airy medium (dry lens system).

By placing a few drops of a fluid with a refraction index higher than that of air, such as water, glycerine, oil, etc. in the space between the surface of the coverslip and objective lens, it is possible to change the medium in which the lens system operates. This alters the angle of the pencil cone of light falling on the lens of the objective. The relationship between the angle of the pencil cone of light falling on the objective lens and the medium in which the lens is operating is called numerical aperture (NA) of the lens.

Perhaps the most important factor in determining the resolution of an objective is the angular aperture mentioned earlier. The angular aperture has a practical upper limit of about 72 degrees (with a sine value of 0.95). When combined with refraction index (n), the product ($n \cdot \sin \alpha$) is known as the numerical aperture (abbreviated NA), and provides a convenient indicator of the resolution for any particular objective. It is in this way that the numerical aperture (NA) becomes an important factor of the objective, determining its resolving power!

NUMERICAL APERTURE (NA)

Numerical aperture (also termed object-side aperture) is a value (often symbolized by the abbreviation NA) originally defined by Abbe for microscope objectives and condensers.

The numerical aperture of a microscope objective is a measure of its ability to gather light and resolve fine specimen detail at a fixed object distance. Image-forming light waves pass through the specimen and enter the objective in an inverted cone as illustrated in Figure 1.24. A longitudinal slice of this cone of light reveals the angular aperture, a value that is determined by the focal length of the objective.

The light-gathering ability of a microscope objective is quantitatively expressed in terms of the **numerical aperture,** which is a measure of the number of highly diffracted image-forming light rays captured by the objective. Higher values of numerical aperture allow increasingly oblique rays to enter the objective front lens, producing a more highly resolved image.

The value for the numerical aperture is given by the equation,

$$\text{Numerical aperture (NA)} = n \cdot \sin \alpha$$

where *n* is the refraction index of the imaging medium between the front lens of the objective and the specimen cover glass, a value that ranges from 1.00 for air to 1.51 for specialized immersion oils and α is the half angle subtended by rays entering the objective lens.

Numerical aperture determines the resolving power of an objective—the higher the numerical aperture of the system, the better the resolution.

The relationship between the angle of divergence of the pencil cone of light falling on the lens and the refraction index of the medium in which the lens is operating is called numerical aperture (NA), which can be calculated as follows:

$$NA = n' \times \sin \alpha$$

where,

> $n' =$ the refraction index of the medium in which the lens is operating and

> $\alpha =$ semi-angle of divergence of the pencil cone of light that falls on the object.

For example, if the angle of divergence of the pencil cone of light falling on the object is 64° (Figure 1.26), then the numerical aperture (NA) of the lens in air as medium will be,

$$NA = 1 \times \sin 32$$
$$= 0.62$$

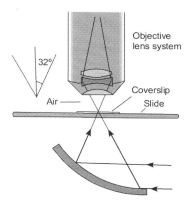

Figure 1.26 Numerical aperture of an objective lens when a condenser is not used

A condenser placed under the stage of the microscope (a substage condenser) helps in increasing the angular divergence to 96° (Figure 1.27).

Now, the numerical aperture of the lens will be,

$$NA = 1 \times \sin 48$$
$$= 0.8$$

Thus, use of a substage condenser increases the numerical aperture and thus also the resolution of the lens.

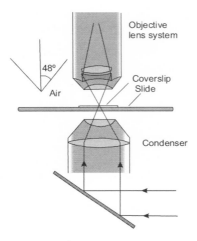

Figure 1.27   Numerical aperture of the objective lens increased by use of a substage condenser

Since the refraction index of air (*i*) is 1.0 and since the value of sin is never more than unity, the numerical aperture of a lens operating in air is always less than 1.0.

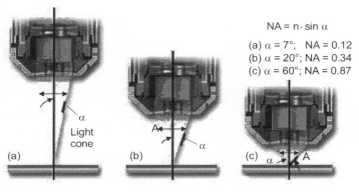

NA = n · sin α

(a) α = 7°;   NA = 0.12
(b) α = 20°; NA = 0.34
(c) α = 60°; NA = 0.87

Low numerical aperture
Low value for a low resolution

High numercial aperture
High value for a high resolution

Figure 1.28   Numerical aperture of objectives of different powers

In practice, it is difficult to achieve NA values above 0.95 with dry objectives. Figure 1.28 illustrates a series of light cones derived from objectives of varying focal length and NA. As the light cones grow larger, the angular aperture (α) increases from 7° to 60°, with a resulting increase in the NA from 0.12 to 0.87, nearing the limit when using air as the imaging medium.

Higher NAs can be obtained by increasing the imaging medium refraction index (n) between the specimen and the objective front lens.

Oil-immersion objectives allow imaging in an alternative media such as water (refraction index = 1.33), glycerin (r = 1.47), and immersion oil (r = 1.51).

The NA of an objective is also dependent, to a certain degree, upon the amount of correction for optical aberration.

Highly corrected objectives tend to have much larger numerical apertures for the respective magnification. (Table 1.5). For example in a series of typical 10× objectives, the NA-increments correspond to enhanced correction for chromatic and spherical aberration: plan achromat, NA = 0.25; plan fluorite, NA = 0.30; and plan apochromat, NA = 0.45.

Table 1.5 Numerical aperture versus optical correction

Magnification	Plan achromat (NA)	Plan fluorite (NA)	Plan apochromat (NA)
0.5×	0.025	N/a	N/a
1×	0.04	N/a	N/a
2×	0.06	N/a	0.10
4×	0.10	0.13	0.20
10×	0.25	0.30	0.45
20×	0.40	0.50	0.75
40×	0.65	0.75	0.95
40× (oil)	N/a	1.30	1.00
60× (oil)	N/a	N/a	1.40
100× (oil)	1.25	1.30	1.40
150×	N/a	N/a	0.90

A majority of the objectives in the range of 60× and 100× (and higher) are designed for use with immersion oil. The highest theoretical NA obtainable with common immersion oils is 1.51. In practice, however, most oil-immersion objectives have a maximum NA of 1.4 with the most common NA ranging from 1.0 to 1.35.

Numerical aperture determines the resolving power of an objective, but the total resolution of the entire microscope is also dependent upon NA of the substage condenser. The higher the NA of the total system, the better the resolution.

RESOLVING POWER OF OBJECTIVE AND SIZE OF THE AIRY DIFFRACTION PATTERN

The resolving power of an objective determines the size of the airy diffraction pattern formed, and the radius of the central disc is determined by the combined numerical apertures of the objective and condenser. When the condenser and objective have equivalent numerical apertures, the airy pattern radius from the central peak to the first minimum is given by the equation

$$r_{(Airy)} = 1.22\ \lambda/2NA$$

where,

$r_{(Airy)}$ = radius of the airy diffraction pattern formed at the microscope intermediate pane.

λ = wavelength of the illuminating light

NA = numerical aperture of objective (and condenser)

RESOLUTION AND NUMERICAL APERTURE

Similarly, the relationship between the resolution and the numerical aperture of a lens is also very simple.

$$\text{Resolution (R)} = 2 \times \frac{NA}{\lambda}$$

where, R is the separation distance in mm or inches (resolution), λ is the illumination wavelength, NA is the numerical aperture (NA= $n \cdot \sin \alpha$; n is the imaging medium refraction index, and α is one-half of the objective angular aperture).

Some prefer to give resolution as number of lines per inch and wavelength as mm. In that case, this relationship becomes,

$$r = \frac{2.54 \times NA}{\lambda}$$

As mentioned earlier in the section on Mathematical expression of revolution and resolving power, NA cannot be more than 1, in dry objectives.

Numerical aperture can be increased by using immersion oil and short wavelengths, in an attempt to increase resolution.

Based on the above principle, it is known that an unaided human eye can resolve 0.25 mm to 0.1 mm. Lines closer than this will not be resolved.

A compound microscope normally resolves up to 2750 Å or 0.275 μ (μ = 1/1000 mm; Å = 10^{-7} mm). Since the wavelength of light used in electron microscope is very low, the resolution reaches as low as 10 Å. In other words, while human eye resolves up to 100 μ, the light microscope resolves up to 0.001 μ.

DIFFERENT EQUATIONS FOR NA FOUND IN LITERATURE

In existing literature numerical aperture (NA) is given by the following expressions:

$$\text{Numerical aperture (NA)} = n \times \sin (\mu) \text{ or}$$
$$NA = n \cdot \sin (\alpha) \text{ or}$$
$$NA = N (\sin a)$$

where,

n (also denoted as N by some) = refraction index of the medium between the objective front lens and the specimen (cover glass)

θ or α or a = one-half angular aperture (AA) of the objective

Note Many authors use the variable μ to designate the one-half angular aperture while others employ the more common symbol α and some others use θ.

Similarly some authors use the designation 'n' to denote the refraction index of the medium between the objective front lens and the specimen (cover glass) while others use 'N'.

AIRY DISCS AND UPPER LIMIT OF RESOLUTION

When light rays from the various points of a specimen pass through the objective and an image is created, the various points in the specimen appear as small patterns in the image. These are known as **airy patterns**. This phenomenon is caused by diffraction of light as it passes through the minute spaces and parts in the specimen and circular back aperture of the objective.

The central maximum of the airy patterns is often referred to as an **airy disc**, which is defined as the region enclosed by the first minimum of the airy pattern and contains 84 per cent of the luminous energy. These airy discs consist of small concentric light and dark circles as illustrated in Figure 1.29. This figure shows airy discs and their intensity distributions as a function of separation distance.

Airy discs

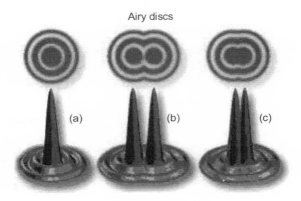

Intensity distributions

Figure 1.29   Airy discs and intensity distribution (a) Unresolvable point (b) Two different points at resolvable distance (c) Two points at the limit of resolvable distance (Rayleigh criterion)

Airy discs consist of small, concentric light and dark circles. The smaller the airy discs projected by an objective in forming the image, the more detail of the specimen is discernible. Objective lenses of higher numerical aperture are capable of producing smaller airy discs, and therefore can distinguish finer detail in the specimen.

The limit at which two airy discs can be resolved into separate entities is often called the Rayleigh criterion. This is when the first diffraction minimum of the image of one source point coincides with the maximum of another. This is also the upper limit of resolution.

The aperture of the objective, the wavelength of light and the refraction index of the medium between the point (object) and the lens govern the diameter of the airy disc.

The diameter of the airy disc is always equal to 1.2/NA. This is also the theoretical limit of resolution, i.e., two adjacent points will be seen as two separate points, only if they are separated from each other at least by this distance.

Figure 1.30 illustrates the effect of numerical aperture on the size of airy discs imaged with a series of hypothetical objectives of the same focal length, but differing numerical apertures. With small numerical apertures, the airy disc size is large (Figure 1.30a). As the numerical aperture and light cone angle of an objective increases however, the size of the airy disc decreases as illustrated in Figure 1.30b and Figure 1.30c.

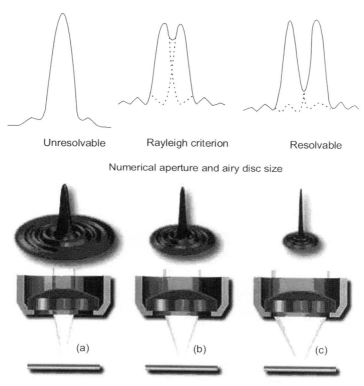

Unresolvable   Rayleigh criterion   Resolvable

Numerical aperture and airy disc size

(a)   (b)   (c)

Figure 1.30   Numerical aperture and airy disc size

The resulting image at the eyepiece diaphragm level is actually a mosaic of airy discs which we perceive as light and dark. Where two discs are too close together so that their central spots overlap considerably, the two details represented by these overlapping discs are not resolved or separated and thus appear as one, as illustrated in Figure 1.30.

CONTRAST AND RESOLUTION OF IMAGES

The main task in microscopy of objects that do not show colour (for example, diatoms) is to find a good balance between contrast and resolution. Unfortunately, one cannot always have both these in ordinary microscopy (also called "bright-field" microscopy) because the objects are seen against a bright background. Contrast is at the expense of resolution. This is why phase contrast and interference-contrast have come into use. Contrast and resolution have often been confused, but since computer images have become familiar to all, an explanation has become easier.

Contrast is the difference between the brightness of various details in the object, and the difference as compared with the background. A typical black-and-white computer image will consist of pixels in 256 shades of gray, ranging from intense white to intense black. The "gray-value" of the pixels will thus lie between 0 and 255. If the values in the image range from 30 to 50 only, contrast will be very low (soft image), if the values range from 30 to 200, the image will be very contrasty. If the background has a uniform pixel value of 50 and the image pixel values range from 70 to 120, contrast between object and background will be poor; if the background pixels have a value of 50 and the image pixel values range from 120 to 180, the object stands out clearly from the background. The figures given are arbitrary, it's the principle that counts and for colour the situation is similar.

Resolution is the finest detail actually visible in the image (the resolving power is the highest resolution possible with the lenses in question). This is roughly comparable to pixel size: the smaller the pixels, the finer the detail visible in a computer image. The maximum resolving power (think of it as "optimal pixel size") for a 40×/NA 0.65 objective is about 0.5 μm, for a 100×/NA 1.25 objective it is about 0.25 μ. Whether that value is really attained depends on the expertise of the microscopist. It is just like when you scan a picture for the computer: if you do this at 100 dpi (dots per inch) quality will be much poorer than at 600 dpi, for instance.

Why is that in optical microscope details smaller than about 0.2 μm (0.0002 mm) cannot be resolved?

The resolving power in an optical microscope is dependent on the following factors:

- ⊙ Wavelength of light illuminating the object
- ⊙ Refraction index of the medium through which the illuminating light rays pass
- ⊙ Angular aperture of the objective lens (the acceptance angle of the light from the specimen at the objective lens)

Ernst Abbe determined that the limitations imposed by these factors on resolving power (RP) could be predicted by the following equation:

$$RP = 0.612\lambda / n \cdot \sin \alpha$$

where,

0.612 = Abbe's constant derived from factors such as the coherence of light and visibility

λ = wavelength of the illumination (approximately 0.5 μm for white light)

n = refraction index of the medium between the object and lens (1.0 for air and about 1.5 for immersion oils)

α = half of the lens acceptance angle at the objective lens (α cannot be larger than 90° with a practical maximum being about 75°. The maximum value for sin α is therefore about 0.96)

$n \cdot \sin \alpha$ = is equivalent to the NA of the lens and is a measure of the resolving capability of a lens

Substituting the approximate maximum values for these factors in Abbe's equation,

RP = 0.612 × 0.50 / 1.50 × 0.96 μm

RP = 0.30 / 1.44 μm

RP = 0.2 μm

Therefore, it is not possible to resolve details in the optical microscope any smaller than about 0.2 μm (0.0002 mm).

Note The same basic principles apply in the case of electron microscope. As the wavelength of an electron beam is many thousands of times shorter than the wavelength of visible light, the RP of electron microscopes is correspondingly better.

The difficulties in the construction of electron lens systems of these instruments limit the improvement of the RP to a factor of about 2000. That is the reason why the RP of modern electron microscopes is not able to exceed 0.1 nm.

CONDENSERS

Condenser is a cylindrical boxlike arrangement containing two or more lenses for use in light microscope to concentrate the light precisely onto the object under observation. It is housed beneath the stage in the path of light. Hence it is referred to as substage condenser.

The substage condenser gathers light from the microscope light source and concentrates it into a cone of light that illuminates the specimen with uniform intensity over the entire field of view. It is critical that the condenser light cone be properly adjusted to optimize the intensity and angle of light entering the objective front lens. Each time an objective is changed, a corresponding adjustment must be performed on the substage condenser to provide the proper light cone for the numerical aperture of the new objective.

STRUCTURAL DESCRIPTION OF A SUBSTAGE CONDENSER

Most condensers have a twin lens assembly. The upper lens can be unscrewed and separated. It is a planoconvex lens with its plane side facing upwards, having a small diameter that defines the circular path of light. There is another lens of larger diameter within the body of the condenser. It is a single biconvex lens in Abbe types of condensers and a twin lens system of one biconcave and one biconvex lens pasted together in case of achromatic condensers. For routine microscopic work involving low-power observation, the lower lens of the condenser itself is sufficient and for higher magnification, both the lenses are to be used (Figure 1.31).

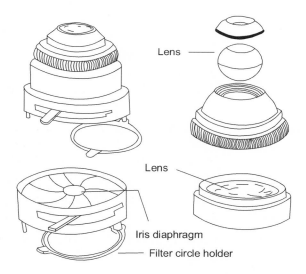

Figure 1.31   Parts of a substage condenser with iris diaphragm

Aperture adjustment and proper focusing of the condenser are of critical importance in realizing the full potential of the objective. Specifically, appropriate use of the adjustable aperture iris diaphragm (incorporated into the condenser or just below it) is most important in securing correct illumination, contrast, and depth of field. The opening and closing of this iris diaphragm controls the angle of illuminating rays (and thus the aperture) which pass through the condenser, through the specimen and then into the objective.

An iris diaphragm is present at the base of the condenser below the larger lens. The diaphragm helps in varying the diameter of the path of light as required. The iris diaphragm is exactly like the iris of our eye. Hence it is called iris diaphragm. There is a small pinlike knob to operate the iris.

The functions of iris diaphragm are as follows:

1. The primary function is to control numerical aperture.

2. By controlling the NA, iris diaphragm increases resolution. For example, when opened to required width, the NA is enhanced, resulting in enhanced resolution. The structural details of the object under observation are seen very clearly.

3. On the other hand if the iris diaphragm is closed more than necessary, structural details of the object observed are lost. Moreover, artefacts are formed.

    Similarly, if the iris diaphragm is opened more than needed, the NA of the pencil cone of light falling on the object (1.3) is increased, exceeding that of the objective lens (0.93). This results in a glare, which obscures the image.

4. There is a circular ringlike holder to hold filters. By placing filters of desired colour (blue or green), light of desired wavelength can be obtained.

5. Less expensive microscopes have fixed substage condensers. More expensive microscopes have movable substage condensers. Such movable condensers can be moved up and down vertically.

Engravings found on the condenser housing include its type (achromatic, aplanatic, etc.), the numerical aperture, and a graded scale that indicates the approximate adjustment (size) of the aperture diaphragm.

The main purpose of using a condenser is to enhance the following attributes of a light microscope:

1. Numerical aperture (NA)
2. Working distance of the lens
3. Focal point

TYPES OF CONDENSERS

Various types of condensers are recognized based on purpose of use (e.g. bright-field, dark-field, phase contrast, etc.), and also according to their degree of optical correction.

As one can understand, the lenses used in the condenser also introduce spherical and chromatic aberrations which defeat the main purposes of using a condenser! Therefore, it is imperative to make corrections for these aberrations. Accordingly condensers corrected for spherical aberrations are called aplanatic condensers and those corrected for chromatic aberrations are called achromatic condensers. The achromatic condensers are corrected in red and blue wavelength regions.

There are four basic types of condensers with respect to correction of optical aberrations, as listed hereunder:

Condenser type	Aberrations corrected	
	Spherical	Chromatic
Abbe	−	−
Aplanatic	+	−
Achromatic	−	+
Aplanatic-Achromatic	+	+

Abbe Type Condenser

Abbe type condenser is a simple two-lens condenser and is capable of passing bright light (Figure 1.32). This is the simplest and is not corrected for spherical or chromatic aberrations.

An Abbe condenser normally can have a numerical aperture (NA) of 1.25 (up to 1.4 in high-end models with three or more internal lens elements).

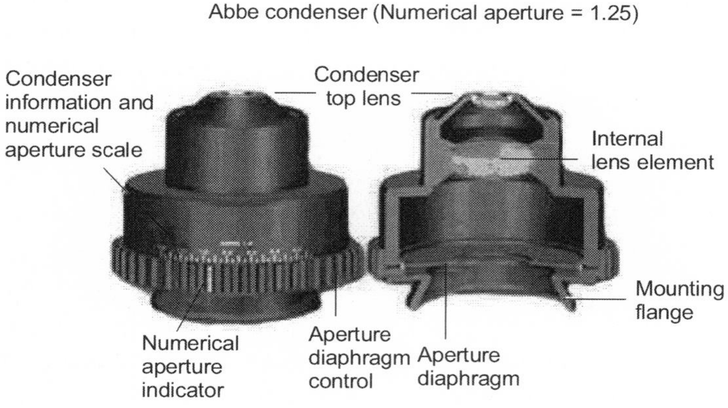

Abbe condenser (Numerical aperture = 1.25)

Figure 1.32   Abbe type condenser

In its simplest form, Abbe condenser has two optical lens elements that produce an image of the illuminated field diaphragm that is not sharp and is surrounded by blue and red halos.

The optical pathway of an Abbe condenser is shown in Figure 1.33. Light from the microscope illumination source passes through the condenser aperture diaphragm, located at the base of the condenser. The internal lens elements concentrate this light, and project it through the specimen in parallel bundles from every azimuth. The size and numerical aperture of the light cone is determined by adjustment of the aperture diaphragm. After passing through the specimen (on the microscope slide), the light diverges into an inverted cone with the proper angle to fill the front lens of the objective.

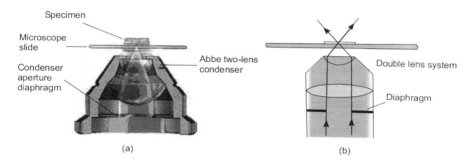

Figure 1.33   Optical pathway of Abbe condenser

Abbe condenser is suited mainly for routine observation with objectives of modest numerical aperture and magnification as no optical correction is made.

The primary advantages of the Abbe condenser are the wide cone of illumination that the condenser is capable of producing as well as its ability to work with long working distance objectives. Most microscopes are supplied by the manufacturer with an Abbe condenser as the default and these condensers are real workhorses for routine laboratory use.

Aplanatic Condenser

Aplanatic condensers are corrected for spherical aberration (green wavelengths*) but not for chromatic aberration (Figure 1.34). This condenser features five lens elements and is capable of focusing light in a single plane. Aplanatic condensers are capable of producing excellent black-and-white photomicrographs when used with green light* generated by either a laser source or by use of an interference filter with tungsten–halogen illumination.

(* Correction for spherical aberration by default takes care of green wavelengths.)

Aplanatic condenser (Numerical aperture = 1.40)

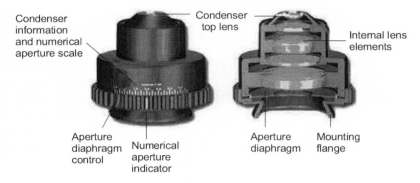

Figure 1.34   Aplanatic condenser

Achromatic Condenser

Notwithstanding its nomenclature achromatic condenser is described as having a lens system in which both the spherical aberration and chromatic aberration have been rectified. This type of condenser consists of a biconcave lens along with a biconvex lens. The aberration effect of one lens corrects that of the other.

Achromatic condenser is ideal for microscopic observations that require accuracy.

Achromatic condenser (Numerical aperture = 0.95)

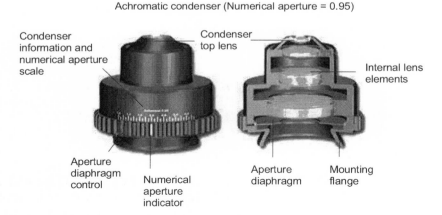

Figure 1.35   Achromatic condenser

The achromatic condenser illustrated in Figure 1.35 contains four lens elements and has a numerical aperture of 0.95, the highest attainable without requiring immersion oil. This condenser is useful for both routine and critical laboratory analysis with "dry" objectives and also for black-and-white or colour photomicrography.

Achromatic-Aplanatic Condenser

The highest level of correction for optical aberration is incorporated in the aplanatic-achromatic condenser. This condenser is well corrected for both chromatic and spherical aberrations and is the condenser of choice for use in critical colour photomicrography with white light. A typical aplanatic-achromatic condenser is illustrated in Figure 1.36 (numerical aperture = 1.35). This condenser features eight internal lens elements cemented into two doublets and four single lenses.

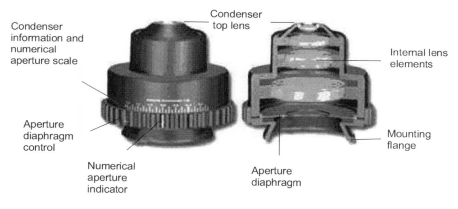

Figure 1.36   Achromatic-aplanatic condenser

VALUE ADDITION TO CONDENSERS

The types of condensers described in the previous pages are the basic types designed for optic corrections. However, in practical use certain changes and added improvisations are made to serve specific purposes. The following is an account of such value additions available.

Flip-Top Lens (Swing-Out Top Lens) Condenser

In practical use, a broad range of light cones must be produced to match objective numerical apertures. Use of a single condenser with the entire range of objectives (2× to 100×) will not be able to give the expected results. For example, with low-power objectives in the range 2× to 5×, the illumination cone will have a diameter between 6–10 mm, while the high-power objectives (60× to 100×) need a highly focused light cone only about 0.2–0.4 mm in diameter. With a fixed focal length, it is difficult to achieve this wide range of illumination cones with a single condenser.

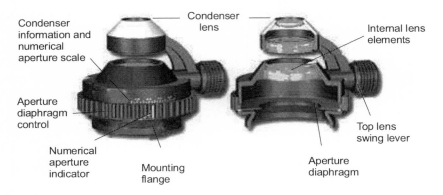

Figure 1.37   Swing-top lens condenser

In practice, this problem can be solved in several ways. For low-power objectives (below 10×), it may be necessary to unscrew the top lens of the condenser in order to fill the field of view with light as mentioned elsewhere in this chapter.

Some condensers are produced with a flip-top upper lens to accomplish this more readily, as illustrated in Figure 1.37. Many manufacturers now produce a condenser which flips over completely when used with low-power objectives. Flip-top condensers are manufactured in a variety of configurations with numerical apertures ranging from 0.65 to 1.35. Those condensers that have a numerical aperture value of 0.95 or less are intended for use with "dry" objectives. However, flip-top condensers that have a numerical aperture greater than 0.95 are intended for use with oil-immersion objectives and they must have a drop of oil placed between the bottom of the microscope slide and the condenser top lens when examining critical samples.

Some manufacturers may incorporate auxiliary correction lenses in the light path for securing proper illumination with objectives less than 10×. When the condenser is used without its top lens, the aperture iris diaphragm is opened wide and the field diaphragm, now visible at the back of the objective, serves as if it were the aperture diaphragm.

Immersion Condenser

Use of immersion condensers increases the numerical aperture greatly. The immersion condensers are specially built so that the lens system is waterproofed as it is to be used with a few drops of immersion oil on the front lens.

Movable and Fixed Condensers

In less expensive microscopes, the condenser is a fixed substage arrangement. However, correct positioning of the condenser in relation to the cone of illumination and focus is critical to quantitative microscopy and optimum photomicrography. Therefore in microscope models meant for higher levels of use, the condenser height is controlled by a rack-and-pinion gear system that allows the condenser focus to be adjusted for proper illumination of the specimen. These are called movable condensers (Figure 1.38).

Figure 1.38   Vertically movable condenser

POINTS/TIPS ON OPTIMAL USE OF CONDENSERS

⊙ Care must be taken to guarantee that the condenser aperture is opened to the correct position with respect to objective numerical aperture. When the condenser aperture diaphragm is opened too wide, stray light generated by refraction of oblique light rays from the specimen can cause glare and lower the overall contrast. On the other hand, when the aperture is made too small, the illumination cone is insufficient to provide adequate resolution and the image is distorted due to refraction and diffraction from the specimen.

⊙   A critical factor in choosing substage condensers is the numerical aperture performance that will be necessary to provide an illumination cone adequate for the objectives. The condenser numerical aperture should be equal to or slightly less than that of the highest objective numerical aperture. Therefore, if the highest magnification objective is an oil-immersion objective with a numerical aperture of 1.40, then the substage condenser should also have an equivalent numerical aperture to maintain the highest system resolution. In this case, immersion oil would have to be applied between the condenser top lens and the underside of the microscope slide to achieve the intended numerical aperture (1.40) and resolution. Failure to use oil will restrict the highest numerical aperture of the system to 1.0, the highest obtainable with air as the imaging medium.

⊙   As mentioned earlier, condensers with numerical apertures above 0.95 perform best when a drop of oil is applied to their upper lens in contact with the under surface of the specimen slide. This ensures that oblique light rays emanating from the condenser are not reflected from underneath the slide, but are directed into the specimen. In practice, this can become tedious and is not commonly done in routine microscopy, but is essential when working at high resolutions and for accurate photomicrography using high-power (and numerical aperture) objectives.

⊙   Another important consideration is the thickness of the microscope slide, which is as crucial to the condenser as coverslip thickness is to the objective. Most commercial producers offer slides that range in thickness between 0.95 and 1.20 mm with the most common being very close to 1.0 mm. A microscope slide of thickness 1.20 mm is too thick to be used with most high numerical aperture condensers that tend to have a very short working distance. While this does not greatly matter for routine specimen observation, the results can be devastating with precision photomicrography. It is recommended that microscope slides be chosen that have a thickness of 1.0 ± 0.05 mm, and that they be thoroughly cleaned prior to use.

⊙   When the objective is changed, for example from a 10× to 20×, the aperture diaphragm of the condenser must also be adjusted to provide a new light cone that matches the numerical aperture of the new objective. This is done by turning the knurled knob on the condensers illustrated in Figure 1.32.

⊙   There is a small yellow arrow or index mark located on this knob that indicates the relative size of the aperture when compared to the linear gradation on the condenser housing. Many manufacturers will synchronize this gradation to correspond to the approximate numerical aperture of the condenser. For example, if the microscopist has selected a 10× objective of numerical aperture 0.25, then the arrow would be placed next the value 0.18–0.20 (about 80 per cent of the objective numerical aperture) on the gradation inscribed on the condenser housing.

⊙ In addition to the common bright-field condensers discussed above, there are a wide variety of specialized models suited to many different applications. Table 1.6 lists a number of different condenser configurations and the intended applications.

Table 1.6 Substage condenser applications

Condenser type	Bright-field	Dark-field	Phase contrast	DIC	Polarizing
Achromat-aplanat (NA=1.3)	(10×~100×)				
Achromat Swing-out (NA=0.90)	(4× ~100×)				
Low-power (NA=0.20)	(1× ~ 10×)				
Phase contrast Abbe (NA=1.25)		(up to NA=0.65)	(10× ~100×)		
Phase contrast Achromat (NA=0.85)		(up to NA=0.70)	(4× ~100×)		
DIC Universal Achromat/ Aplanat		(up to NA=0.70)	(10×, 100×)	(20×, 40×, 100×)	
Dark field, dry (NA= 0.80~0.95)		(4× ~40×)			
Dark field, oil (NA = 1.20~1.43)		(4× ~100×)			
Stain-free Achromat Swing- out (NA = 0.90)					(4× ~100×)

Note From the data in Table 1.6, it is obvious that substage condensers have a great deal of interchangeability among different applications. For instance, the DIC universal achromat/aplanat condenser is useful for bright-field, dark-field, and phase contrast, in addition to the primary DIC application. Other condensers have similar interchangeability.

ILLUMINATING SYSTEMS OF A MICROSCOPE

In light microscopes, the clarity of the magnified images largely depends upon focusing either white light or monochromatic light on the object viewed to optimal intensity. The quality of the magnified image also depends on the combined effect of the transparency of the object and the refraction index of the different parts of the object. However, the internal structural details of thick opaque objects cannot be seen; their outline alone can be seen. This is the reason why very thin sections of the object are needed for microscopic examination of their internal structure. The different parts of such sections may have varying degrees of transparency depending on the types of cells present. Accordingly, the light rays passing through different parts of the section (object) are deviated to varying degrees. Because of this, the image of the section is obtained as a combination of bright and dark regions.

ILLUMINATING SYSTEMS SUITABLE FOR VARIOUS MICROSCOPY NEEDS

Proper illumination of the object is a prerequisite for visual light microscopy. Natural daylight is used to illuminate the object in most microscopes. Artificial illumination involving electric bulbs of different kinds is also in use in expensive microscopes. All microscopes are provided with reflectors that can be rotated in all planes.

For routine microscopic observations, natural daylight can be reflected using a reflection mirror. The reflector used in the light microscope is a circular glass mirror, plane on one side and concave on the other side (Figure 1.39). If there is no condenser in the microscope, the concave side is to be used. Only then the light will be focused on the object. If there is a condenser, only the plane side is to be used. The light rays reflected by the plane mirror will travel in parallel lines and the condenser converges these light rays on the object.

In microscopes fitted with a movable condenser, the reflector is also fixed to the movable condenser unit, so that it also moves vertically up and down along with the condenser.

Where daylight is not available, artificial light is used. Incandescent electric bulb, tungsten filament bulb, flat filament bulb, tungsten arc lamp or fluorescent tube lamp or carbon arc lamp may serve as sources of the artificial light. The light source is fitted in a safe housing. It should have an additional condenser and diaphragm. There can be some cooling arrangement to prevent heating when a powerful source of light is used.

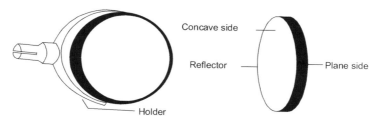

Figure 1.39   Reflection mirror

Cooling cells containing dilute $FeSO_4$ or $CuSO_4$ or water can be used to reduce heat radiation from the light source. However, these solutions absorb long wavelength.

Axial Reflected Light

Axial reflected light helps in differentiating the darker and brighter regions very clearly. In other words it gives a greater contrast between dark and bright regions.

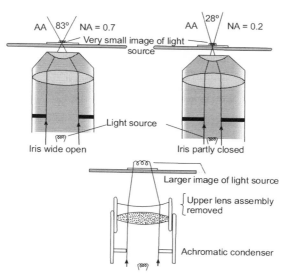

Figure 1.40   Use of condenser and iris diaphragm to control illumination

A condenser has to be used for this. Using the plane side of the reflector, the light is to be reflected onto the condenser. The iris diaphragm is to be closed to a minimal diameter. By this, a very thin beam of light parallel to the axis of the microscope is allowed to pass through the microscope (Figure 1.40).

The same effect can be achieved by lowering the condenser, if it is movable. The main axis of the condenser should be in line with the main axis of the microscope. Though axial reflected illumination gives a greater contrast between bright and dark regions, resolution decreases because of this.

Condensed Reflected Light

Condensed reflected light is obtained by moving the condenser up or down until the focusing point of the condenser coincides with the plane of the object exactly. The amount of light condensed can be controlled by lowering the condenser and by closing the iris diaphragm.

For most microscopic examinations, the diaphragm aperture need not be closed beyond two-thirds of its diameter. This can be done looking through the drawtube after removing the ocular lens system.

Uniformly condensed reflected light is required for all microscopic observations requiring magnifications greater than 100×.

Inclined or Unilaterally Reflected Light

Under normal circumstances, light focused through a condenser falls on the object uniformly on all sides. But inclined reflected light is required for certain types of observation. This is achieved in the following steps.

1. Close the diaphragm almost fully, allowing only a thin beam of light.
2. Move the condenser to focus the light exactly on the plane of the object.

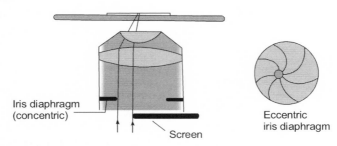

Iris diaphragm (concentric)

Screen

Eccentric iris diaphragm

Figure 1.41   Inclined or unilaterally reflected light and eccentric diaphragm

3. Now open the diaphragm fully.

4. Using a thin sheet (screen), close the opening of the condenser from one side. This gives inclined or unilaterally reflected light (Figure 1.41).

5. Eccentric diaphragm assemblies available also give this effect.

Circular Ringlike Light

Use of an opaque screen with a circular transparent ring like path for light results in a hollow cone of light which gives a circular ringlike field. The same can be achieved by placing an opaque circular dotlike disc exactly in the centre of the window on the lower side of the condenser (Figure 1.42).

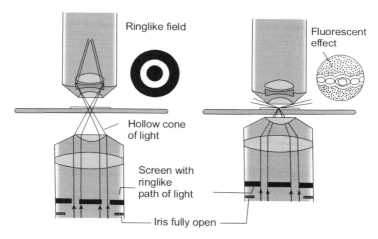

Figure 1.42   Effect of circular ringlike light

If only the angular aperture (AA) of the objective lens system is wide enough to include all the rays of this hollow cone of light, a circular ringlike bright field of vision is obtained.

A dark field can be obtained by raising the condenser until brighter part of the hollow cone of light goes out of the objective lens system. The object present at the tip of the cone of light makes a fluorescent image in this dark field.

ILLUMINATING SYSTEMS INVOLVING ADDITIONAL CONDENSERS

Additional condensers are used for very accurate microscopic observations. There are two approaches to illuminating the object by the use of additional condenser, namely critical illumination and Kohler illumination.

Critical Illumination

For very accurate microscopic observations and photomicrography, the illuminating system is to be decided carefully.

Artificial light-source-housing, with an additional condenser is used for this purpose. This additional condenser has a planoconvex lens with its plane side facing the light source (bulb). This helps in arranging the light rays to travel parallel to each other and fall on the reflector.

The parallel light rays falling on the reflector are converged on the substage condenser, which in turn condenses the light precisely at the plane of the object. This kind of illumination is called critical illumination (Figure 1.43).

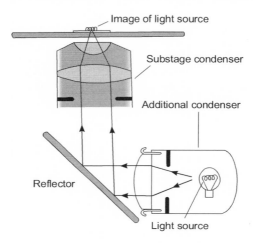

Figure 1.43   Critical illumination

Kohler Illumination

Lenses are designed theoretically to work at their best when they are used to examine a self-luminous object. This theoretical objective is closely approximated if an image of a self-luminous object is superimposed on the transparent object actually being examined. In the yesteryears, this was possible as the microscopist of that time used only oil lamps with broad wicks, the flames of which would fill the field of vision. In the present time of electric bulbs, this is achieved by Kohler illumination.

This approach averages the non-uniformities in the light source so that a clear image is obtained (Figure 1.44). It involves production of two images. The first image (a) is that of the source of light (the filament of the bulb), which is made to fall exactly on the plane of the substage iris diaphragm (1). The second image (b) is that of the iris of the field condenser (additional condenser), which is made to fall on the object by the substage condenser.

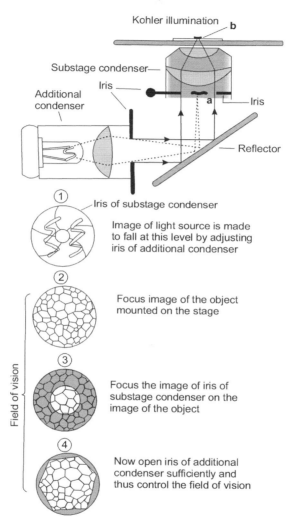

Figure 1.44   Kohler illumination (a) Image of the filament of the bulb (b) Image of the iris of the additional condenser

The image of the field iris can be centred in the field of vision by adjusting the mirror. With the microsection in focus (2), open the field iris until it delimits the field.

Now remove the eyepiece and look down through the drawtube. Close the substage iris (which has been wide open till now) until it cuts off 1/10 or 1/5 of the fields (3), (4). With these adjustments, the objective will be working at a desirable 80–90% of its maximum aperture.

By shuffling the neutral density filters, the desired intensity of illumination is obtained.

With Kohler illumination, the illuminated portion of the field of vision is under better control. However, all the steps are to be repeated with every change of objective as well as slide.

Note   In conventional optical microscopy, the quality of image formation from the condenser is not of importance. The condenser is mainly intended to provide uniform illumination. However, in special kinds of applications such as phase contrast imaging, the quality of the light source image is also important.

LENS SYSTEMS USED IN MICROSCOPES

OBJECTIVE LENS SYSTEMS

The lens system of the microscope that operates very near the micro section/microslide and forms the primary image (I_1) of the object is called objective lens system.

Microscope objectives are perhaps the most important components of an optical microscope because they are responsible for primary image formation and play a central role in determining the quality of images that the microscope is capable of producing. Objectives are also instrumental in determining the magnification of a particular specimen and the resolution under which fine specimen detail can be observed in the microscope.

The objective is the most difficult component of an optical microscope, to design and assemble. The three critical design characteristics of the objective that set the ultimate resolution limit of the microscope are

1. Wavelength of the light used to illuminate the specimen
2. The angular aperture (AA) of the light cone captured by the objective, and
3. The refraction index of the medium in which the front lens of the objective works.

Similarly, the following three attributes define the optics of the objective:

1. Focal length
2. Numerical aperture
3. Field of view

STRUCTURAL DESCRIPTION OF AN OBJECTIVE

The objective lens system is a hollow cylinder fitted with lenses at its distal end. The lens at the distal end is a planoconvex lens with plane side towards the microslide. Inner to this distal lens, in line with its median axis, is a double lens system. This consists of two or more lenses or groups of lenses made of different materials.

A very simple early version of objective is shown in Figure 1.45. It contains a single lens element and a doublet. In the doublet, one lens is made of glass and the other is made of quartz. One is biconcave and the other is biconvex. The double lens system is intended to correct the aberrations.

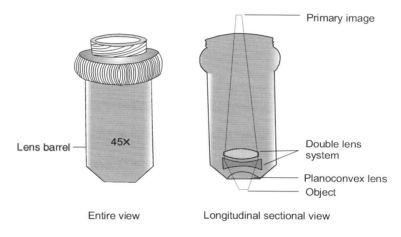

Entire view   Longitudinal sectional view

Figure 1.45   Objective lens system

The numerical aperture and complexity of construction increase as the magnification of the objective increases. Low-power objectives (2× to 5×) are simple two elements or doublet lenses.

In objectives with 10× power, the required NA increases to 0.25, necessitating use of a more complex type of lens. Most 10× objectives use a separated pair of doublets, sharing the refractive power.

The objective lens system produces the primary image on the other side of the lenses above the ocular tube.

The magnification of the primary image is called primary magnification, which is engraved on the objective lens system. The primary magnification may vary from a minimum of 3.5× or 4× to a higher level of 45× or even 90× or 100×, in case of oil-immersion objectives.

Primary magnification is expressed in two ways. In the older system, the equivalent focal length of the objective system is denoted in inches (e.g. 1/2", 2/3", 1/6", and so on). The magnification of the simple lens obtained at a distance of 10" is the equivalent focal length. The lens with an equivalent focal length of 1" will give a magnification of 10 times at a distance of 10" (10×). Likewise, a 1/2" lens will give 20 times magnification at the same distance (20×).

Table 1.7 gives the different equivalent foci and the magnifications caused by them.

Table 1.7 Equivalent foci and their magnification

Equivalent focus	Magnification at a distance of 10"
1"	10× (1/1 × 10)
1/2"	20× (2/1 × 10)
2/3"	15× (3/2 × 10)
1/6"	60× (6/1 × 10)

If the magnification is engraved as equivalent focus value (EF) we can mentally convert this value with ease into magnification, e.g. EF 1/6 = 6/1×10 = 60×.

In the recent years, manufacturers have resorted to marking the magnification as such. For example 10×, 15×, 20×, 40×, 80×, 100×, 120×, etc.

Focal length (FL) of objective is inversely proportional to the magnification and in majority of modern microscopes, equals the tube length (usually 160 mm*) divided by the magnification.

For example,

Focal length of a 10× objective = 160/10 = 16

Focal length of a 45× objective = 160/45 = 3.6

The angular field of view of the objective is related to the field of view of ocular lens system. The field of view of the eyepiece (ocular) is usually (customarily) set to be of a standard size of about 20 mm in diameter. The field of view of the objective is then set to range from 10 mm (for 2× objectives) to 0.2 mm for (100× objectives). As a result, the angular field of view is a total of 7° for all objectives.

Wavelength requirements and the tube length of the microscope are further attributes defining objectives that have been corrected for aberration.

(*Objective lens systems of microscopes are generally constructed with this finite distance of 160 mm tube length in mind.)

There is a wealth of information inscribed on the objective barrel. Each objective has inscribed on it the following information:

- ⊙ Magnification (e.g. 10×, 20×, 40×, etc.).

- ⊙ The tube length for which the objective was designed to give its finest images (usually 160 millimetres or the Greek infinity symbol).

- ⊙ Thickness of cover glass protecting the specimen, which was assumed to have a constant value by the designer in correcting for spherical aberration (usually 0.17 millimetres).

- ⊙ If the objective is designed to operate with a drop of oil between it and the specimen, the objective will be engraved OIL or OEL or HI (homogeneous immersion).

- ⊙ In cases where these latter designations for oil are not engraved on the objective, the objective is meant to be used dry, with air between the lowest part of the objective and the specimen.

- ⊙ Objectives also always carry the engraving for the numerical aperture (NA) value. This may vary from 0.04 for low-power objectives to 1.3 or 1.4 for high-power oil-immersion apochromatic objectives.

- ⊙ More highly corrected objectives have inscriptions such as apochromat or apo, plan, FL, fluor, etc. If the objective carries no designation of higher correction, one can usually assume it is an achromatic objective.

- ⊙ Older objectives often have the focal length (lens-to-image distance) engraved on the barrel, which is a measure of the magnification. In modern microscopes, the objective is designed for a particular optical tube length, so including both the focal length and magnification on the barrel becomes somewhat redundant.

- ⊙ The maximum useful field number (field diameter). Unfortunately the maximum useful field number is not engraved on most brands of objectives.

CORRECTIVE ARRANGEMENTS IN OBJECTIVE LENS SYSTEM

As one can understand the optics used in the objective imposes certain constraints which are to be corrected. In addition to the optics, the thickness of the cover glass used imposes additional problems. Therefore, the following constraints are to be corrected in the objective lens system.

1. Optical aberrations (spherical aberration and chromatic aberration)
2. Field curvature
3. Effect of variation in cover glass thickness
4. Infinite light space path

1. Correction for Optical Aberration

Objective lens systems have their inherent problems of optical aberrations (spherical and chromatic) which are to be corrected. Ordinary crown glass of low refraction index (r) and flint glass of high refraction index can be used to obtain correction for the spherical aberration and chromatic aberration. Even in these the correction of spherical aberration is readily achieved. But residual chromatic aberration is obtained when normal optical glasses are used for the lens elements. For most optical applications this is not important. But, in case of critical high-magnification objectives, say of powers $>25\times$, this aberration is visible as a chromatic blur. The only method of correcting this residual aberration is through the use of special optical glasses whose light dispersion properties vary from those of normal glasses. There are only a few such glasses or crystalline materials that are useful for this purpose. Objectives designed using these special glasses are called apochromats.

Field curvature of image is another major problem to be tackled in constructing objectives for high-end uses. Traditional microscope objectives do not produce a flat image surface. The intrinsic field curvature of image is generally of little importance in the visual use of the microscope because the eye has a reasonable accommodative capability when examining the image. Field curvature, however, is a problem for video or photographic systems. Special objectives with flat field lenses have been developed for these purposes.

The following three major classes of objectives are known based on the correction of optical aberrations:

1. Achromatic objectives (Achromats)
2. Semi-apochromatic objectives (Fluorites)
3. Apochromatic objectives (Apochromats)

The corrections of various optical aberrations in the different types of objectives are presented in Table 1.8.

Table 1.8   Objective types and corrections of optical aberrations

Objective type	Spherical aberration	Chromatic aberration	Field curvature
Achromat	1 colour	2 colours	No
Plan achromat	1 colour	2 colours	Yes
Fluorite	2–3 colours	2–3 colours	No
Plan fluorite	3–4 colours	2–4 colours	Yes
Plan apochromat	3–4 colours	4–5 colours	Yes

Achromatic objective lens system   Chromatic aberration can be corrected by using a composite lens system consisting of two lenses made of two different types of materials. Such a composite lens system helps in focusing (converging) all the different wavelengths at the same point on the other side of the lens, thus rectifying the chromatic aberrations. Such objectives are called achromatic objective lens systems.

The least expensive (and most common) objectives, employed on a majority of laboratory microscopes, are the achromatic objectives (Figure 1.46a). This contains a single planoconvex front lens and two lens doublets.

Very accurate achromatic objective lens systems are not possible. These objectives are corrected for axial chromatic aberration in two wavelengths (blue and red; about 486 and 656 nanometres, respectively), which are brought into a single common focal point. Furthermore, achromatic objectives are also corrected for spherical aberration in the green region, i.e., 546 nanometres.

Though the images obtained in this objective are bright without any halo, faint blue or red halo appear around the images when the focus is disturbed even very slightly. For routine microscopic work this is not a serious problem. If green or blue background (field) is created, this halo disappears. That is why green and blue filter discs are supplied along with microscopes. Achromatic objectives yield their best results with light passed through a green filter (often called interference filter) and using black-and-white film when these objectives are employed for photomicrography.

The limited correction of achromatic objectives can lead to substantial artefacts when specimens are examined and imaged with colour microscopy and photomicrography. If the specimen is focused in the green region of the spectrum, images will have a reddish magenta halo (often termed residual colour).

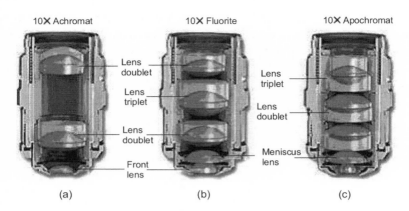

Figure 1.46   Various types of corrected objectives

Semi-apochromatic objectives (semi-apochromats or fluorites)   The **semi-apochromats** (also called fluorites) represent the next higher level of correction and cost (Figure 1.46b). This is named after the mineral fluorite, which was originally used in their construction. The front lens is coupled with a meniscus lens. There is a lens triplet positioned in between the two lens doublets in this type of objective.

Apochromatic objective lens systems   Objective lens systems that are capable of separating the colours very effectively are called apochromatic objective lens systems. They represent the highest level of correction (and expense) found in objective lens systems. These contain composite lens system consisting of fluorite lens and optical glass lenses. Traditionally, apochromats are corrected chromatically for three colours (red, green, and blue), almost eliminating chromatic aberration, and are corrected spherically for either two or three wavelengths (*see* Table 1.8).

A typical apochromat contains two internal lens doublets and a front lens element. It contains multiple lens groups and single elements. Although similar in construction to fluorite objectives, the lenses of apochromats have different curvatures and thickness, and are arranged in a configuration that is unique to apochromat objectives (Figure 1.46c).

Figure 1.47 gives a comparison of the lens elements in a series of apochromatic objectives ranging from 10× to 100× in magnification. The lower power apochromat objectives (10× and 20×) have a longer working distance and the overall objective length is shorter than in higher power (40× and 100×) apochromat objectives.

Apochromatic objectives are the best choice for colour photomicrography in white light. Because of their high level of correction, apochromat objectives usually have, for a given magnification, higher numerical apertures than do achromats or fluorites. Many of the newer high-performance fluorite and apochromat objectives are corrected for four (dark blue, blue, green and red) or more colours chromatically and four colours spherically.

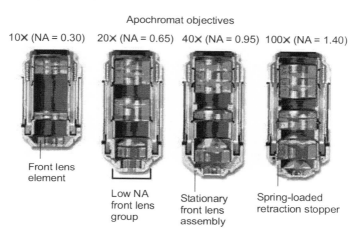

Apochromat objectives

10X (NA = 0.30)   20X (NA = 0.65)   40X (NA = 0.95) 100X (NA = 1.40)

Front lens
element

Low NA
front lens
group

Stationary
front lens
assembly

Spring-loaded
retraction stopper

Figure 1.47   Apochromat objectives of various powers

Note   As apochromatic objective lens systems separate the wavelengths too much, true to their name, it is necessary to combine all these wavelengths by using a compensating eyepiece (ocular) to obtain a white light. If ordinary eyepieces are used in combination with apochromatic objectives, very poor image is obtained. Apochromatic objective lens systems normally have magnifications higher than 20×, higher NA and very short working distances. These are very ideal for microscopic observations of higher research level and for purposes of photomicrography. (*Also see* Note under Correction for field curvature.)

2. Correction for Field Curvature

All three types of objectives namely, achromats, semi-apochromats and apochromats, suffer from pronounced field curvature and project images that are curved rather than flat. This artefact becomes much pronounced with increasing magnification. This inherent condition arises from curved lens surfaces.

Uncorrected field curvature is the most severe optical aberration in fluorite (semi-apochromat) and apochromat objectives, and it was tolerated as an unavoidable artefact for many years. During routine use, the viewfield would have to be continuously refocused between the centre and the edges to capture all specimen details.

To overcome this problem, optical designers have produced flat-field corrected objectives, which yield images that are in common focus throughout the view field. Objectives that have flat-field correction and low distortion are called plan achromats, plan fluorites, or plan apochromats, depending upon their degree of residual aberration. Such correction, although expensive, is quite valuable in digital imaging and conventional photomicrography. The introduction of flat-field (plan) correction to objectives perfected their use for photomicrography and video microscopy, and today these corrections are standard in both general use and high-performance objectives.

Figure 1.48 illustrates correction of a simple achromat for field curvature. The uncorrected achromat on the left (Figure 1.48a) contains two lens doublets, in addition to a simple thin-lens front element. In contrast, the corrected plan achromat on the right (Figure 1.48b) contains three lens doublets, a central lens triplet group, and a meniscus lens positioned behind the hemispherical front lens. Plan correction, in this instance, has led to the addition of six lens elements bundled into more sophisticated lens groupings, which dramatically increases the optical complexity of the objective. The significant increase in lens elements for plan correction also occurs with fluorite and apochromat objectives, frequently resulting in an extremely tight fit of lens elements within the internal objective sleeve.

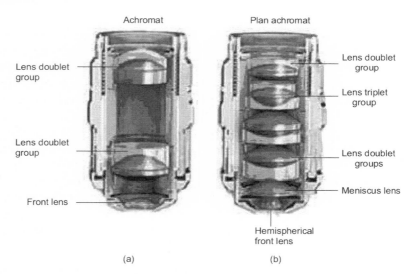

Figure 1.48   Correction of an achromat objective for field curvature

In general, plan objectives corrected for field curvature sacrifice a considerable amount of free working distance, and many of the high-magnification versions have a concave front lens, which can be extremely difficult to clean and maintain.

Note Older objectives generally have lower numerical apertures, and are subject to an aberration termed chromatic difference of magnification that requires correction by the use of specially designed compensating oculars or eyepieces. This type of correction was prevalent during the reign of fixed tube length microscopes, but is not necessary with modern infinity-corrected objectives and microscopes. In recent years, modern microscope objectives have their correction for chromatic difference of magnification either built into the objectives themselves (Olympus and Nikon) or corrected in the tube lens (Leica and Zeiss). (*Also see* Note under Apochromatic objective lens system.)

3. Correction/Compensation for Variations in Cover Glass

In most biological and petrography applications, a cover glass is utilized in mounting the specimen, both to protect the integrity of the specimen and to provide a clear window for observation. The cover glass acts to converge the light cones originating from each point in the specimen, but also introduces chromatic and spherical aberration (and consequent loss of contrast) that must be corrected by the objective. The degree to which light rays are converged is determined by the refraction index, dispersion, and thickness of the cover glass.

The standard thickness for cover glasses is 0.17 millimetres, which is designated as a number 1½ cover glass. Unfortunately, not all 1½ cover glasses are manufactured to this close tolerance (they range from 0.16 to 0.19 millimetres) and many specimens have media between them and the cover glass. Although the refraction index should be relatively constant within a batch of cover glasses, the thickness can vary between 0.13 and 0.22 millimetres. The effect of cover glass thickness variation is negligible for dry objectives having numerical apertures less than 0.4, but such deviation becomes significant at numerical apertures exceeding 0.65, where fluctuations as small as 0.01 millimetre can introduce spherical aberration. This poses problems with high-power apochromats, which must use very short working distances in air and contain sensitive corrections for spherical aberration that tends to make it difficult to obtain sharp images.

The aqueous solvent or excess mounting medium that lies between the specimen and cover glass in wet or thickly mounted preparations is another concern. These factors add to the effective variations in refraction index and thickness of the coverslip and are very difficult for the microscopist to control.

The imaging medium between the objective front lens and the specimen coverslip is also very important with respect to correction for spherical aberration and coma in the design of lens elements for objectives. Lower power objectives have relatively low numerical apertures and are designed to be used **dry** with only air as the imaging medium between the objective front lens and the cover glass. The maximum theoretical numerical aperture obtainable with air is 1.0. However in practice it is virtually impossible to produce a dry objective with a numerical aperture above 0.95.

Compensation for cover glass thickness can be accomplished by,

1. Use of specialized correction collars
2. Adjusting the mechanical tube length of the microscope

i. *Use of correction collars*   The correction collar changes the spacing between critical elements inside the objective barrel. The correction collar is utilized to adjust for the subtle differences in cover glass thickness to ensure the optimum objective performance.

Many high-performance apochromat dry objectives are fitted with correction collars, which allow adjustment to correct for spherical aberration by correcting for variations in cover glass thickness (Figure 1.49).

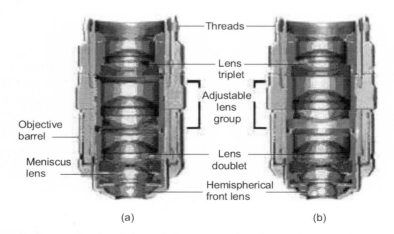

(a)   (b)

Figure 1.49   Objectives with correction collar (a) Collar adjusted for cover glass thickness 0.20 mm (b) Collar adjusted for cover glass thickness 0.13 mm

Optical correction for spherical aberration is produced by rotating the collar, which causes two of the lens element groups in the objective to move either closer together (as in Figure 1.49a) or farther apart (Figure 1.49b). A majority of the correction collar objectives designed for upright transmitted light microscopy have an adjustment range for cover glass thickness variations between 0.10 and 0.23 millimetres. Many of the specialized phase contrast objectives designed for observing tissue culture specimens with an inverted microscope have an even broader compensation range of 0 to 2 millimetres. This allows specimens to be viewed through the bottom of most culture vessels, which often have dramatic thickness fluctuations in this size range. Uncovered specimens, such as blood smears, can also be observed with correction collar objectives when the adjustment is set to 0 to account for the lack of a cover glass.

Proper utilization of objective lenses with correction collars demands that the microscopist is experienced and alert enough to reset the collar using appropriate image criteria. In most cases, focus may shift and the image may wander during adjustment of the correction collar. The steps listed below may be followed to make small incremental adjustments to an objective's correction collar while observing changes in the image of the specimen:

⊙ Position the correction collar so that the indicator mark on the objective barrel coincides with the 0.17 millimetre scale mark engraved on the collar housing.

⊙ Place a specimen on the stage and focus the microscope on a small specimen feature.

⊙ Rotate the correction collar very slightly and re-focus the objective to determine if the image has improved or degraded. Due to the fact that most specimen preparations suffer from cover glass/media sandwiches that are too thick, start the rotation experiment by trying larger compensation values (0.18–0.23) first.

⊙ Repeat the previous step to determine if the image is improving or degrading as the correction collar is turned in a single direction.

⊙ If the image has degraded, follow the same steps and rotate the correction collar in the opposite direction (toward lower values) to find the position offering optimum resolution and contrast.

ii. *Adjusting the mechanical tube length of microscope (correction for infinity)* The **mechanical tube length** of an optical microscope is defined as the distance from the nosepiece opening, where the objective is mounted, to the top edge of the observation

tubes where the eyepieces (oculars) are inserted. Figure 1.50 illustrates the optical path (the dark line) defining the mechanical tube length for a typical transmitted light microscope.

For many years, almost all prominent microscope manufacturers designed their objectives for a **finite tube length**. The designer proceeded under the assumption that the specimen, at focus, was placed at a distance a "little" further than the front focal plane of the objective. The objective then projects a magnified image of the specimen which converges (is brought into focus) at the level of the eyepiece diaphragm, located ten millimetres below the top edge of the opening of the microscope observation tube where the eyepieces are inserted (Figures 1.50 and 1.51).

Figure 1.50   Mechanical tube length

The Royal Microscopical Society (RMS) suggested a mechanical tube length of 160 mm for finite-corrected transmitted light microscopes. Accordingly the tube length has been standardized to 160 millimetres for finite-corrected transmitted light microscopes. Objectives designed for a 160-millimetre finite tube length microscope bear the inscription "**160**" (mm) on the barrel (as outlined in structural description of objectives).

The positioning of the ocular and objectives is reversed in metallographs, which are essentially inverted reflected light microscopes. Note that in both the examples depicted in Figures 1.50 and 1.51, the "tube" is not a straight line and the light waves are transmitted from the objectives to the eyepieces (oculars) with mirrored beam splitters.

This is the case with most modern microscopes, especially those equipped with trinocular heads for photomicrography.

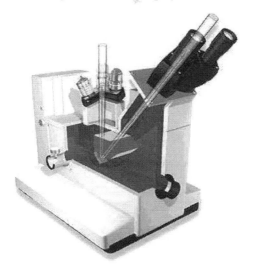

Figure 1.51   Mechanical tube length in inverted reflected light microscope

Caution

Microscopists who attempt to insert objectives designed for one mechanical tube length into a microscope designed for a different tube length should note the following points.

⊙ Some older microscopes have mechanical tube lengths that deviate from the 160-millimetre standard (finite tube length microscope system). Microscopes produced by Leitz instruments continued to be manufactured with a 170-millimetre tube length long after the RMS standard had been incorporated by other manufacturers.

⊙ When objectives and tube lengths are mismatched, image quality often suffers due to the introduction of spherical aberrations because the optical tube length is changed. The optical tube length is defined as the distance between the objective rear focal plane and the intermediate or primary image at the fixed diaphragm of the eyepiece. When this tube length is altered to deviate from design specifications, spherical aberrations are introduced into the microscope and images suffer from deterioration in optical quality. Under circumstances where an objective designed for a 170-millimetre tube length is used in a microscope with a 160-millimetre tube length, corrections designed into the objective will cause it to under-compensate for aberrations. The opposite is true when 160-millimetre objectives are used in a 170-millimetre tube length microscope.

⊙ With a finite tube length microscope system, whenever an accessory such as a polarizing intermediate piece, a DIC Wollaston prism, or a fluorescence illuminator, is placed in the light path between the back of the objective and the eyepiece, the mechanical tube length becomes greater than 160 millimetres. Aberrations may then be introduced when the specimen is refocused. As a result, each such accessory in a finite system must contain optical elements to bring the tube length ostensibly back to 160 millimetres. Often such devices result in an undesirable increase in magnification and lower the overall intensity of the image. There is also the danger of producing "ghost images", the result of converging rays passing through the beam splitter of a reflected light accessory.

⊙ The intermediate image in an infinity-corrected system appears at the reference focal length (formerly, the optical tube length) behind the tube lens in the optical pathway. This length varies between 160 and 250 millimetres, depending upon design constraints imposed by the manufacturer. The magnification of an infinity-corrected objective is calculated by dividing the reference focal length by the focal length of the objective lens.

4. Infinity-Corrected Objectives

Several design problems are inherent with high-power objectives of finite design. With increasing magnification, numerical aperture increases and focal length decreases. This results in reduction in working distance. In high-power objectives, the working distance is greatly reduced as the focal length is very low. The need to use additional lens elements for obtaining higher magnifications further shortens the working distance to, say, only 10 to 20% of the focal length. For example, a 40× objective with focal length of 4 mm will have a working distance of <0.4 mm. This is a problem leading to breakage of slides while focusing.

To alleviate this problem, a negative lens is used in between the object/specimen and ocular. This has an additional effect of providing some field flattening as well. This advanced new optical system allows microscopes to support complex optical component clusters in the optical pathway between the objective and the lens tube. This is especially useful for techniques such as confocal, polarized, DIC, and epifluorescence microscopy where specialized lens systems must be employed for optimum results.

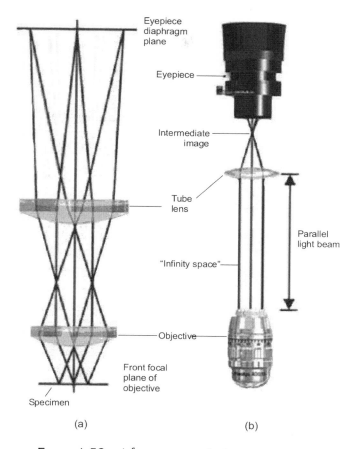

Figure 1.52   Infinity-corrected objective system

As we have seen from the discussion above, the body tubes in modern microscopes contain a complex assembly of lenses, mirrors, and beam splitters that transmit light from the objective into the eyepieces. Almost all microscope manufacturers are now designing their microscopes to support **infinity-corrected objectives**. Such objectives project an image of the specimen to infinity (the common description is not quite accurately stated as emerging parallel rays). To make viewing of the image possible, the body tube of the microscope, or in reflected light microscopy the vertical illuminator itself, must contain a tube lens. This lens has, as its main function, the formation of the image at the plane of the eyepiece diaphragm, the so-called intermediate image plane. The eye lens of the eyepiece "looks at" this real, inverted, magnified image and magnifies that image in the usual second stage magnification of the compound microscope.

In modern infinity-corrected systems, the tube lens is a multi-element optic (to prevent introduction of coma or astigmatism even with increased "infinity light path space") built into and sealed in the observation tube. In this design, as many as two intermediate accessories can be accommodated, with no additional optics to correct the image, in the "infinity space" (Figure 1.52) between the objective and the tube lens. Ghost images are eliminated as discussed above. Accessories are much easier to design; and unwanted extra magnification factors are avoided. The light paths illustrated in the figure are diagrammatic representations of an infinity-corrected microscope system. Figure 1.52a shows the focal points at the front focal plane of the objective and the eyepiece diaphragm plane and Figure 1.52b illustrates the "infinity space" between the objective and tube lens where intermediate attachments are placed into the light path.

Figure 1.53 schematically indicates how additional optical components can be inserted into the light path of infinity-corrected systems.

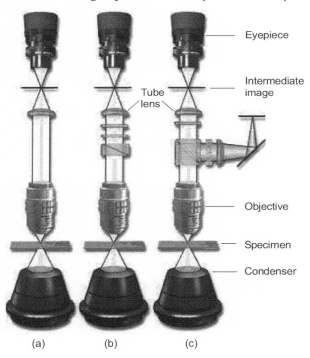

(a)	(b)	(c)

Figure 1.53   Different types of additional optical components introduced in the light path of infinity-corrected microscopic system for different applications

Figure 1.53a is a diagrammatic representation of an infinity-corrected system showing a specimen on a microslide being illuminated by a substage condenser. The image-forming light rays pass through the objective and form a parallel light beam that is focused by the tube lens into the eyepiece. Accessories such as a Wollaston prism and several polarizers can be inserted into the parallel light beam without further optical correction in the pathway as shown in Figure 1.53b. Figure 1.53c illustrates the insertion of a beam splitter into the parallel light beam. This beam splitter diverts light to the external accessory positioned on the right of the parallel beam.

Infinity-corrected objectives come in a wide range of magnifications, from $1.5\times$ to $200\times$, and in various qualities of chromatic and spherical correction—from simple achromats to plan achromats and precision plan apochromats. Most, but not all, are designed to be used dry, that is with air in the space between the objective and the specimen. The bright-field series have the customary microscope thread for screwing into the nosepiece (Figure 1.54). The objectives which are used for bright-field/ dark-field observation usually have wider diameter threads as shown in Figure 1.55, and require a nosepiece with wider openings for attaching such objectives (these objectives are called **Neo**, **BF/DF**, or **B/D** objectives).

Infinity-corrected objectives

(a)   (b)   (c)

Figure 1.54   Different types of infinity-corrected objectives

Infinity-corrected objectives are inscribed with an infinity mark (∞). The magnification yielded by the objective is the quotient of the focal length of the tube lens divided by the focal length of the objective. For example, in the Olympus microscope system with the tube lens having a focal length of 180 millimetres, a 9-millimetre-focal-length objective will project a $20\times$ magnified image onto the plane of the eyepiece diaphragm. With a tube lens of 180 millimetres, it is possible to design objectives with a magnification as low as $1.25\times$ while still maintaining the parfocalizing distance of 45 millimetres.

LONG WORKING DISTANCE (LWD) OBJECTIVES

Some reflected light objectives are designed to focus at a longer working distance from the specimen than is usual; such objectives are labelled on the barrel of the objective as **LWD** (long working distance) or **ULWD** (ultra-long working distance). The manufacturer usually designates the objective series to be used for reflected light Nomarski differential interference contrast studies; e.g. in the case of Olympus, the appropriate series is the **MS Plan** series for brightfield objectives and the **Neo S Plan** in the bright-field/dark-field series. Such objectives are sometimes labelled **NIC** on the objective barrel or designated as strain-reduced.

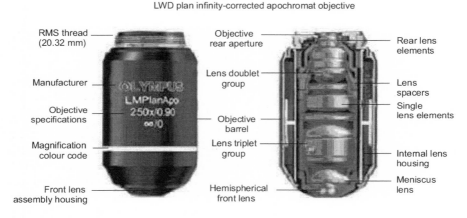

LWD plan infinity-corrected apochromat objective

Figure 1.55   Long working distance (infinity-corrected) apochromat

The long working distance plan infinity-corrected apochromatic shown in Figure 1.55 contains 14 optical elements that are cemented together into three groups of lens doublets, a lens triplet group, and three individual internal single-element lenses. The objective also has a hemispherical front lens and a meniscus second lens, which work synchronously to assist in capturing light rays at high numerical aperture with a minimum of spherical aberration. Internal lens elements are carefully oriented and tightly packed into a tubular brass housing that is encapsulated by the objective barrel. Specific objective parameters such as numerical aperture, magnification, optical tube length, degree of aberration correction, and other important characteristics are imprinted or engraved on the external portion of the barrel. Although the objective featured in Figure 1.55 is designed to operate utilizing air as the imaging medium between the objective front lens and specimen, other objectives have front lens elements that allow them to be immersed in water, glycerin, or a specialized hydrocarbon-based oil.

IMMERSION OBJECTIVES/OIL-IMMERSION OBJECTIVES

The highest power in microscope objectives is obtained by the use of a liquid medium excluding air in between the object and the lower lens element of the objective. The lower lens element operates/works immersed in some liquid and hence the objective is called immersion objective. A drop of oil is placed on the slide and the objective is lowered until the lower lens element contacts the drop of oil. Thus a region of oil is captured between the slide and objective which becomes the medium in which the objective lens element operates and the light rays diffracted by the object (the deviated and non-deviated, i.e., rays coming out of the object), pass through.

The oil used should have a refraction index,

- ⊙ matching that of glass in the first lens component of the objective, and
- ⊙ greater than that of air.

Thus the oil captured between the slide and objective acts as an additional lens and increases the NA and thus permits higher magnification.

The objective numerical aperture is dramatically increased by designing the objective to be used with an immersion medium, such as oil, glycerin, or water. By using an immersion medium with a refraction index similar to that of the glass coverslip, image degradation due to thickness variations of the cover glass are practically eliminated whereby rays of wide obliquity no longer undergo refraction and are more readily grasped by the objective. Typical immersion oils have a refraction index of 1.51 and a dispersion similar to that of glass coverslips. Light rays passing through the specimen encounter a homogeneous medium between the coverslip and immersion oil and are not refracted as they enter the lens, but only as they leave its upper surface. It follows that if the specimen is placed at the aplanatic point (at the focal point and in the centre of the field) of the first objective lens, imaging by this portion of the lens system is totally free of spherical aberration.

The general design of a practical oil-immersion objective includes a hemispherical front lens element (a small optical surface shaped like a hemisphere but with a bounding curvature exceeding 180°). It acts as an aplanatic coupler between the slide and the rest of the microscope objective. The hyper-hemispheric first lens is followed by a positive meniscus lens and a doublet lens group.

The aplanatic refractions that occur at the first two lens elements in a typical apochromatic oil-immersion objective are presented in Figure 1.56. The specimen is sandwiched between the microscope slide and cover glass at point **P**, the aplanatic point of the hemispherical lens element. Light rays refracted at the rear of the hemispherical lens appear to proceed from point **P₁**, which is also the centre of curvature for the first surface of the meniscus lens. The refracted light rays enter the meniscus lens along the radius of its first surface and experience no refraction at that surface. At the rear surface of the meniscus lens, light rays are refracted aplanatically, so they appear to diverge from point **P₂**. Refraction of the light rays at the surfaces of subsequent lens groups in the objective complete the convergence of light rays originating from point **P**, thus forming the intermediate image.

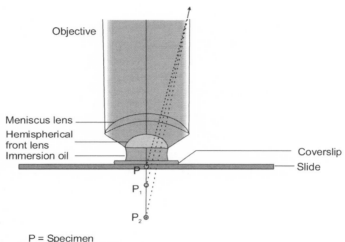

P = Specimen
P₁, P₂ = Specimen conjugate points

Figure 1.56   Aplanatic refractions occurring in oil-immersion objective

Properly designed oil-immersion objective lenses also correct for chromatic defects that are introduced by the first two lens elements, while introducing a minimum amount of spherical aberration. The fact that the light cone is partially converged before entering the first lens element aids in the control of spherical aberration. It should be noted that employing an oil-immersion objective without the application oil between the coverslip and first lens element results in defective images. This due to refraction that occurs at the surface of the front lens, which introduces spherical aberration that cannot be corrected by subsequent lens components within the objective.

Objectives that use water and/or glycerin as an imaging medium are also available for applications with living cells in culture or sections of tissue immersed in physiological saline solution. Plan apochromat water immersion lenses are equipped with correction collars and numerical apertures up to 1.2, slightly less than their oil-immersion counterparts. These objectives allow microscopists to focus through up to 200 microns of aqueous media and still retain excellent optical correction.

Since the focusing length is greatly reduced, the lens elements of the immersion objective are spring loaded to avoid breaking of the slide.

Note The advantages of oil-immersion objectives are severely compromised if the wrong immersion fluid is utilized. Microscope manufacturers produce objectives with tight tolerances to refraction index and dispersion, which require matching values in the liquid placed between the cover glass and objective front lens. It is advisable to employ only the oil intended by the objective manufacturer, and to not mix immersion oils between manufacturers to avoid unpleasant artefacts such as crystallization or phase separation.

PARFOCALITY AND PARCENTRICITY

Parfocality and parcentricity are phenomena of convenience and safety offered by objectives that are manufactured in sets.

Objectives are always manufactured as matched sets of various magnifications. In a set of matched objectives all the objectives of various magnifications are usually designed to project an image to approximately the same plane in the body tube when mounted on the nosepiece. Thus, changing objectives by rotating the nosepiece usually requires only minimal use of the fine adjustment knob to re-establish sharp focus. Such a set of objectives is described as being parfocal, a useful convenience and safety feature.

Matched sets of objectives are also designed to be parcentric, so that a specimen centred in the field of view for one objective remains centred when the nosepiece is rotated to bring another objective into use.

For many years, objective lenses designed for biological applications from most manufacturers all conformed to an international standard of parfocal distance. Thus, a majority of objectives had a parfocal distance of 45 millimetres and were considered interchangeable. With the migration to infinity-corrected tube lengths, a new set of design criteria emerged to correct for aberrations in the objective and tube lenses. Coupled to an increased demand for greater flexibility to accommodate the need for ever-greater working distances with higher numerical apertures and field sizes, interchangeability between objective lenses from different manufacturers disappeared. This transition is exemplified by the modern Nikon CFI-60 optical system that features "Chrome Free" objectives, tube lenses, and eyepieces. Each component in the CFI-60 system is separately corrected without one being utilized to achieve correction for another. The tube length is set to infinity (parallel light path) using a tube lens, and the parfocal distance has been increased to 60 millimetres. Even the objective mounting thread size has been altered from 20.32 to 25 millimetres to meet new requirements of the optical system.

Note Avoid interchanging objectives between microscopes.

FIELD DIAMETER (FIELD-OF-VIEW NUMBER/FIELD NUMBER)

The field diameter in an optical microscope is expressed by the **field-of-view number** or simply **field number**, which is the diameter of the view field expressed in millimetres and measured at the intermediate image plane. The field diameter in the object (specimen) plane becomes the field number divided by the magnification of the objective.

Although the field number is often limited by the magnification and diameter of the ocular (eyepiece) field diaphragm, there is clearly a limit that is also imposed by the design of the objective.

In early microscope objectives, the maximum usable field diameter was limited to about 18 millimetres (or considerably less for high magnification eyepieces). Modern plan apochromats and other specialized flat-field objectives often have a usable field that can range between 22 and 28 millimetres or more when combined with wide-field eyepieces.

Unfortunately, the maximum useful field number is not generally engraved on the objective barrel and is also not commonly listed in microscope catalogues.

Working Distance and Depth of Focus of an Objective

The clearance distance between the closest surface of the cover glass and the objective front lens is termed the **working distance**. In situations where the specimen is designed to be imaged without a cover glass, the working distance is measured at the actual surface of the specimen. The working distance of an objective is related to the numerical aperture (NA) and magnification. Therefore, it is not related to the focal point.

Generally, working distance decreases in a series of matched objectives as the magnification and numerical aperture increase (*see* Table 1.9). Objectives intended to view specimens with air as the imaging medium should have working distances as long as possible, provided that numerical aperture requirements are satisfied. Immersion objectives, on the other hand, should have shallower working distances in order to contain the immersion liquid between the front lens and the specimen.

Many objectives designed with close working distances have a spring-loaded **retraction stopper** that allows the front lens assembly to be retracted by pushing it into the objective body and twisting to lock it into place. Such an accessory is convenient when the objective is rotated in the nosepiece so it will not drag immersion oil across the surface of a clean slide. Twisting the retraction stopper in the opposite direction releases the lens assembly for use.

The large NA of most microscope objectives severely restricts the focusing requirements of the objective. The highest possible resolution that can be obtained with an objective depends on the depth of focus (the accurate location of focal plane in a direction along the axis of the microscope optics). Table 1.9 provides the resolving power and depth of focus of visual microscopes.

Table 1.9   Maximum resolving power and depth of focus

Objective focal length (mm)	Numerical aperture (NA)	Maximum useful magnification in compound microscope	Maximum resolution on object (mm)	Object depth of focus (mm)
32	0.10	100×	0.0025	0.025
16	0.25	250×	0.001	0.0038
8	0.50	500×	0.0005	0.00086
4	0.95	1000×	0.00026	0.00024
3	1.38	1500×	0.00018	0.00010
		(Oil immersion)		

Resolution depends on NA of the objective lens system. The NA increases when the angle of the pencil cone of light entering into the objective is increased. The NA can further be increased by bringing the objective lens system very close to the coverslip, i.e., by decreasing the working distance. That is the reason why objective lens systems of very high NA have very short working systems. In other words, such objectives work very close to the coverslip.

While using objective lens systems of low power, the working distance is not of any consequence. However, in case of objectives of higher powers, there are chances for breakage of slides, as they work very close to the slides (Figure 1.57).

The objective systems of most student microscopes have a NA of 0.85. As the thickness of the slide along with the microsection and coverslip is to be discounted, these objectives cannot work beyond 0.6 mm. This is the reason why students using high-power objectives tend to focus further beyond this limit of 0.6 mm resulting in breakage of slides.

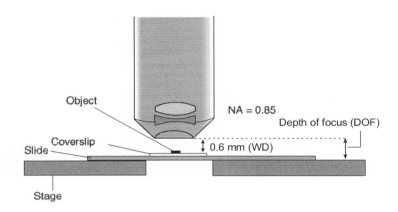

Figure 1.57   Working distance and depth of focus

The working distance decreases because of higher magnification also. Working distance of the objective system plays a major role, in selecting a suitable objective for specific use.

It is to be noted that dry objectives of all powers have a numerical aperture value of less than 1.0 and only objectives designed for liquid immersion media have a numerical aperture that exceeds this value.

In some applications, a long free working distance is indispensable, and special objectives are designed for such use despite the difficulty involved in achieving large numerical apertures and the necessary degree of optical correction.

Depth of Field

Depth of field is treated as synonymous with working distance by some. However, there is a subtle difference between the two.

The axial range, through which an objective can be focused without any appreciable change in image sharpness, is referred to as the objective depth of field. This value varies radically from low to high numerical aperture objectives, usually decreasing with increasing numerical aperture (Figure 1.58).

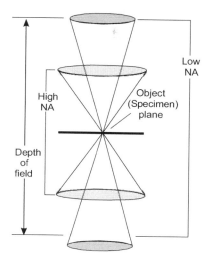

Figure 1.58   Ranges of depth of field

CONCLUSION

Construction techniques and materials used to manufacture objectives have greatly improved over the course of the past 100 years. Today, objectives are designed with the assistance of computer-aided design (CAD) systems using advanced rare-element glass formulations of uniform composition and quality having highly specific refraction indices. Many of the microscope objectives being produced today offer remarkably low degrees of aberration and other imperfections, provided the appropriate objective is selected and it is utilized properly.

Nevertheless, the microscopist needs to be aware that objectives are not made to be perfect from every standpoint, but are designed to meet a certain set of specifications depending on intended use, constraints on physical dimensions, and price ranges. Therefore, objectives are made with different degrees of correction for chromatic and spherical aberration, field size and flatness, transmission wavelengths, freedom from fluorescence, birefringence, and other factors contributing to background noise. In addition, they are designed to be used under certain circumscribed conditions, such as with specific tube lengths and tube lenses, type and thickness of immersion media and coverslips, wavelength ranges, field sizes, ocular types, and special condensers. The ultimate goal of the optical microscope is to provide useful magnification that allows minute specimens to be observed in great detail, thus exposing a hidden world of invisible objects that would otherwise remain unseen.

In conclusion, it must be mentioned that the development of high-quality microscope objectives was ushered by Ernst Abbe, who first developed apochromatic objectives and compensating oculars during the late 1880s in collaboration with Carl Zeiss and Otto Schott. The next major advance in objective design occurred when Hans Boegehold (Zeiss) constructed the first plan achromat and plan apochromat objectives in the late 1930s. More recently, the development of "Chrome Free" (CF) optics by Zenji Wahimoto (Nikon) and Horst Riesenberg (Zeiss) has led to a new revolution in microscope objective design.

OCULAR LENS SYSTEMS (OCULARS/EYEPIECES)

An **ocular lens system** also called **eyepiece,** is a type of lens system that is attached to a variety of optical devices such as **telescopes** and **microscopes.** It is so named because it is usually the lens system that is closest to the eye when someone looks through the device. In a microscope the objective lens system collects light focused by the mirror and brings it to focus creating an image. The eyepiece is placed at the focal point of the objective to magnify this image. The amount of magnification depends on the **focal length** of the eyepiece.

Oculars work in combination with microscope objectives to further magnify the intermediate image so that specimen details can be observed. Best results in microscopy require that objectives be used in combination with eyepieces that are appropriate to the correction and type of objective.

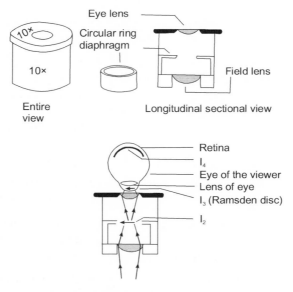

Figure 1.59   Ocular lens system

Figure 1.59 shows a typical 10× ocular its anatomy and the optical path. The basic anatomy of a typical Ramsden type ocular and Huygenian type ocular is illustrated in Figure 1.60.

An ocular consists of planoconvex "lens elements" in a housing, with a "barrel" on one end. The barrel is shaped to fit in a special opening* of the instrument to which it attached. The plane sides of both the lenses are towards our eyes.

(*Microscopes have standard barrel diameters measured in millimetres: 23.2 mm and 30 mm, slightly smaller than telescope barrels.)

The lower lens of the ocular is called field lens (FL). The FL captures the primary image (I_1) created by the objective and forms the secondary image (I_2) on the other side.

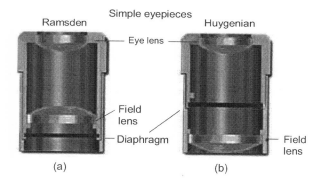

Figure 1.60   Anatomy of simple oculars (a) Ramsden type ocular (b) Huygenian type ocular

The upper lens of the ocular is called eye lens (EL). This eye lens captures the secondary image and forms the tertiary image (I_3) about a millimetre above its plane surface. The tertiary image can be caught on a screen held just above the ocular. This tertiary image is also called Ramsden disc. This is caught by the lens in our eye and seen as the final image (I_4) in the retina.

The ocular has an annular diaphragm at the focal plane of FL, which defines the limits of the field of view. When micrometric scales or cross hairs or micrographs are used they are placed on this diaphragm.

The diameter of this annular diaphragm is equal to the diameter of the objective lens. Because of this arrangement, the field of vision obtained in the microscope appears equally bright on all sides.

The magnifying power of the eyepiece generally does not exceed 10×. The field of vision is then about 40°. The parallel rays originating at all points in the field defined by the diaphragm form a circular area at the upper focal point/exit pupil of the eye lens. This area is actually the image of the aperture of the objective. This circular area is called eye point (EP). The pupil of the eye must be placed at this plane to receive light from all parts of the field. The distance from the exit pupil to the last element of the eyepiece (eye lens of the ocular) is called eye relief. In most cases an eye relief of about 1 cm is desirable. Too short an eye relief makes viewing difficult for observers who wear corrective eye glasses.

The focal length of the ocular and the position of the upper focal equivalent determine the height of the eye point above the ocular.

The diameter of the eye point depends on the NA of the objective and the magnification of the microscope. In general, the height of the eye point above the ocular is inversely related to the magnification. The height of the eye point is a very important feature of the microscope. This is to be borne in mind when camera lucida is used. When the viewer uses corrective optical glasses, it becomes difficult to place the pupil exactly at the plane of the eye point (EP). Therefore, it is advisable to remove correction glasses at the time of microscopic observation. Viewers with contact lenses will not experience any difficulty in placing their pupil at the plane of eye point.

Functions of the ocular are as follows:

- ⊙ It creates the secondary virtual image from the primary virtual image created by the objective.
- ⊙ The lenses of our eye receive this secondary image.
- ⊙ The ocular magnifies the primary image created by the objective.
- ⊙ It also creates the image of the microscales placed in the ocular.

TYPES OF OCULARS (EYEPIECES)

There are two major types of eyepieces that are grouped according to lens and diaphragm arrangement:

- ⊙ Positive ocular that have a diaphragm below the lenses of the eyepiece (Ramsden ocular)
- ⊙ The negative oculars with an internal diaphragm (Huygenian ocular)

Positive Type of Oculars

In this type of oculars, all the lenses of the ocular are above the virtual primary image (I_1) created by the objective. There are two types of positive oculars namely 1. **simple positive ocular** and 2. **compensative positive ocular**.

1. *Simple positive oculars (also known as Ramsden ocular)* This eyepiece has an eye lens and field lens that are planoconvex. The eye lens has its flat side towards the observer's eye. But the field lens is mounted with the curved surface facing towards the eye lens. The front focal plane of this eyepiece lies just below the field lens, at the level of the eyepiece diaphragm, making this eyepiece readily adaptable for mounting reticles.

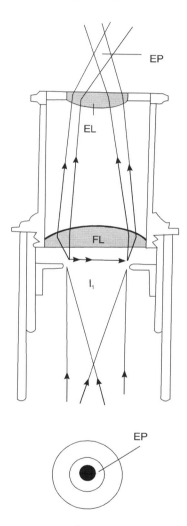

Figure 1.61 Longi-section view of a simple positive ocular (Ramsden ocular)

Figure 1.61 shows the longi-sectional view of a simple positive ocular. The eye point formed in this type of ocular is fairly larger when compared to the field of vision.

A modified version of the Ramsden ocular is known as Kellner ocular (Figure 1.62). In this improved version a doublet eye lens consisting of two lens elements cemented together replaces the singlet eye lens. This modification provides better correction besides yielding a higher eye point and a much larger field of view than obtained in the normal Ramsden ocular.

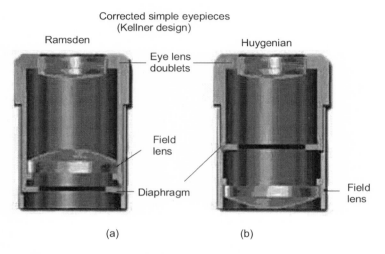

Figure 1.62   Corrected simple oculars (Kellner design) (a) corrected Ramsden ocular (b) corrected Huygenian ocular

2. *Compensative positive oculars*   The images formed by apochromatic and achromatic objectives suffer from excessive separation of colours. Therefore, when apochromats and achromats are used, the excessive separation of colours is to be compensated by the ocular. Simple oculars such as the Huygenian and Ramsden and their achromatized counterparts will not correct this situation. To remedy this, manufacturers produce **compensating eyepieces** that introduce an equal, but opposite, chromatic error in the lens elements. Compensating eyepieces may be either of the positive or negative type, and must be used at all magnifications with fluorite, apochromatic and all variations of plan objectives They can also be used to advantage with achromatic objectives of 40× and higher.

The field lens in a compensating positive ocular is a triplet element with two biconvex lenses cemented to a biconcave element in the middle. Only such compensating oculars can correct the excessive separation of colours caused by the apochromatic objectives.

The compensating positive ocular shown in Figure 1.63 has four parts. From above, the first part contains the eye lens (EL). The EL is a planoconvex lens with its plane side towards the eye. The EL converges the tertiary Image (I$_3$) on the pupil of the eye.

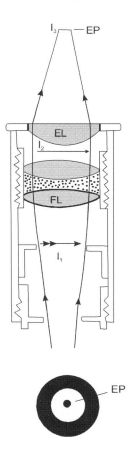

Figure 1.63 Longi-section of a compensative positive ocular

The second part contains the field lens (FL) which is a composite arrangement of three lenses. There is a middle biconcave lens, sandwiched by two biconvex lenses. The biconcave lens is made of one kind of material and the biconvex lenses are made of another kind of material. The field lens corrects the separation of the colours caused by the apochromatic objective.

The third part contains the annular diaphragm. This diaphragm is exactly in the plane of primary image (I$_1$) formed by the objective.

The opening of the fourth part determines of the diameter of the light path.

The eye point in this type of ocular is very narrow when compared to the field.

Compensating eyepieces play a crucial role in helping to eliminate residual chromatic aberrations inherent in the design of highly corrected objectives. Hence, it is preferable that the microscopist uses the compensating eyepieces designed by a particular manufacturer to accompany that manufacturer's higher-corrected objectives. Use of an incorrect eyepiece with an apochromatic objective designed for a finite (160 or 170 millimetre) tube length application results in dramatically increased contrast with red fringes on the outer diameters and blue fringes on the inner diameters of specimen detail. Additional problems arise from a limited flatness of the viewfield in simple eyepieces, even those corrected with eye lens doublets.

However, in the recent years, modern microscope objectives have their correction for chromatic difference of magnification either built into the objectives themselves (in Olympus- and Nikon-made objectives) or corrected in the tube lens (in Leica and Zeiss brands). (*See* Note at the end of Apochromatic objectives in the previous section.)

Negative or Huygenian Oculars

Negative eyepieces have the diaphragm in between the eye lens and field lens. Such a diaphragm is referred to as internal diaphragm.

In the simplest form of negative ocular, both lenses are planoconvex, with convex sides "facing" the specimen. Approximately midway between these lenses there is a fixed circular opening or internal diaphragm which, by its size, defines the circular field of view that is observed in looking into the microscope.

The two-element **Huygens** eyepiece was invented by Christian Huygens in the 17th century. This optical design is now considered obsolete. Their main use in optics is as an example of the simplest possible compound lens design. The simplest negative eyepiece design is often termed the **Huygenian** eyepiece illustrated in Figures 1.64 and 1.60b is found on most teaching and laboratory microscopes fitted with achromatic objectives.

Although the Huygenian eye and field lenses are not well corrected, their aberrations tend to cancel each other out. This consists of a simple eye lens and a field lens. Both are planoconvex lenses. In Huygenian ocular, the secondary image (I_2) is formed at the focal point of the field lens (in between the FL and EL).

The eye lens acts like a positive lens. The field lens converts the primary image formed by the objective. As a result the image I_2 obtained is reduced in size. This facilitates the EL to obtain greater field details.

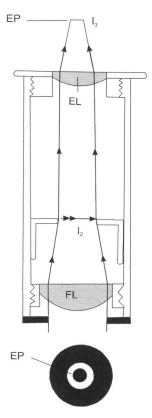

Figure 1.64   Longi-section of a Huygenian ocular

The annular diaphragm is placed exactly in the focal point of the eye lens near the field lens.

The field of vision obtained in Huygenian ocular is of medium diameter. The eye point obtained is larger than those obtained in other types of oculars.

Corrections have been attempted in Huygenian oculars also. More highly corrected negative eyepieces have two or three lens elements cemented and combined together to make the eye lens (Figure 1.62b). While these modified eyepieces perform better than their simple one-lens counterparts, they are still only useful with low-power achromat objectives. If an unknown eyepiece carries only the magnification inscribed on the housing, it is most likely to be a Huygenian eyepiece, best suited for use with achromatic objectives of $5\times$–$40\times$ magnification.

Huygens eyepieces suffer from the following setbacks:

⊙ Short eye relief

⊙ High image distortion (especially on short focus telescopes)

⊙ Chromatic aberration

⊙ Very narrow apparent field of view

Despite the setbacks, these eyepieces are inexpensive to make and so are often sold with the cheapest microscopes.

OTHER ADVANCED/IMPROVED TYPES OF OCULARS

Periplan Oculars

Periplan ocular illustrated in Figure 1.65 above represents a major advancement in eyepiece designing. This ocular contains seven lens elements that are cemented into a single doublet, a single triplet, and two individual lenses. Design improvements in periplan eyepieces have lead to better correction for residual lateral chromatic aberration, increased flatness of field, and a general overall better performance when used with higher power objectives.

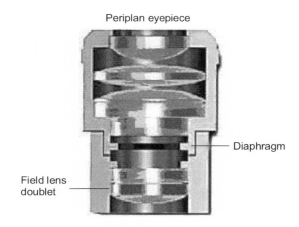

Figure 1.65   Periplan ocular

A TYPICAL MODERN OCULAR

Modern microscopes are provided with vastly improved *plan*-corrected objectives in which the primary image has much less curvature of field than the older objectives do. In addition, most modern microscopes feature much wider body tubes that have greatly increased the size of intermediate images. To address/match/suit these new features, manufacturers now produce wide-eyefield eyepieces (illustrated in Figure 1.66) that increase the viewable area of the specimen by as much as 40 percent. Because the strategies of eyepiece–objective correction techniques vary from manufacturer to manufacturer, it is very important (as stated above) to use only eyepieces recommended by a specific manufacturer for use with their objectives.

Figure 1.66   A typical modern ocular (aberration-free 10× ocular with dioptre adjustment)

INSCRIPTIONS FOUND ON OCULARS

Inscriptions found on the side of the eyepiece describe its particular characteristics and function. A typical modern ocular has the following inscriptions:

UW = an abbreviation for the *Ultra Wide* viewfield.

H indicates a high-eye point focal point that allows microscopists to wear glasses while viewing samples.

HE for **High Eye point.**

WF for **Wide-Field.**

UWF for **Ultra Wide-Field.**

SW and SWF for **Super Wide-Field.**

CF for eyepieces intended for use with **CF-corrected objectives.**

K, C, or **comp** indicate **Compensating eyepieces.**

Plan-Comp Eyepieces used with flat-field objectives are sometimes labelled.

10×, 20×, 3×,6× etc., (indicated on the housing) indicate the eyepiece magnification.

A/24 indicates the field number is 24, which refers to the diameter (in millimetres) of the fixed diaphragm in the eyepiece. These eyepieces also have a focus adjustment and a thumbscrew that allows their position to be fixed.

Manufacturers now often produce eyepieces having rubber eyecups that serve both to position the eyes the proper distance from the front lens, and to block room light from reflecting off the lens surface and interfering with the view.

TIPS ON CHOOSING AND USING OCULARS

It is wise to carefully choose the objective first, and then purchase an eyepiece that is designed to work in conjunction with the objective. When choosing eyepieces, it is relatively easy to differentiate between simple and more highly compensated eyepieces.

Simple eyepieces such as the Ramsden and Huygenian (and their more highly corrected counterparts) will appear to have a blue ring around the edge of the eyepiece diaphragm when viewed through the microscope or held up to a light source. In contrast, more highly corrected compensating eyepieces with have a yellow-red-orange ring around the diaphragm under the same circumstances.

Light rays emanating from the eyepiece intersect at the exit pupil or eye point, often referred to as the **Ramsden disc**, where the pupil of the microscopists eye should be placed in order for her to see the entire field of view (usually 8–10 mm from the eye lens). By increasing the magnification of the eyepiece, the eye point is drawn closer to the upper surface of the eye lens, making it much more difficult for the microscopist to use, especially if they are wearing eye glasses. To compensate for this, specially designed high eye point eyepieces have been manufactured that feature eye point distances approaching 20–25 mm above the surface of the eye lens. These improved eyepieces have larger diameter eye lenses that contain more optical elements and usually feature improved flatness of field. Such eyepieces are often designated with the inscription "H" somewhere on the eyepiece housing, either alone or in combination with other abbreviations, as discussed above. We should mention that high-eye point eyepieces are especially useful for microscopists who wear eye glasses to correct for near or farsightedness, but they do not correct for several other visual defects, such as astigmatism. Today, high eye point eyepieces are very popular, even with people who do not wear eye glasses, because the large eye clearance reduces fatigue and makes viewing images through the microscope much more pleasurable.

At one time, eyepieces were available in a wide spectrum of magnifications ranging from 6.3× to 25× and sometimes even higher for special applications. These eyepieces are very useful for observation and photomicrography with low-power objectives. Unfortunately, with higher power objectives, the problem of empty magnification becomes important when using very high magnification eyepieces and these should be avoided. Today most manufacturers restrict their eyepiece offerings to those in the 10× to 20× range. The diameter of the viewfield in an eyepiece is expressed as a "field-of-view number" or field number (**FN**), as discussed above.

RAMSDEN DISC

A **Ramsden disc**, in **optics**, is an archaic name for the exit **pupil** of an optical instrument. The exit pupil is the image of the instrument's aperture stop as formed by system elements which follow it (the "image space"). In a **telescope** or compound **microscope**, this image is the image of the objective element(s) as produced by the eyepiece. The size and shape of this disc is crucial to the instrument's performance, because the observer's eye can see light only if it passes through this tiny aperture.

To use an optical instrument, the entrance pupil of the viewer (the iris of the human eye, or the iris of a camera lens) must be placed at the same position and be of similar size to the Ramsden disc, to properly couple the two optical systems and avoid **vignetting**. The location of the exit pupil thus determines the **eye relief** of an eyepiece. Good eyepiece designs produce a Ramsden disc of diameter approximating the eye's pupil diameter, and located about 20 mm away from the last surface of the eyepiece for the viewer's comfort. Since the eye's pupil varies in diameter with viewing conditions (such as a larger pupil in the darkness versus a smaller pupil looking at a bright microscopic scene), the Ramsden disc formed by a well-designed eyepiece will vary in diameter depending on the application. The distance (eye relief) also varies, such as a rifle scope needing very long eye relief to prevent recoil from striking the observer.

The Ramsden disc can be visualized by focusing the instrument on a bright, nondescript field, and holding a white card up to the eyepiece. This projects a disc of light onto the card. By moving the card closer to or further away from the eyepiece, the disc of light will be minimized when the card is at the exit pupil, representing the Ramsden disc. A clear vial of milky fluid can also be used to visualize the light rays, which appear in the shape of an hourglass, converging and diverging as they exit the eyepiece, with the smallest cross-section (the waist of the hourglass shape) representing the Ramsden disc.

As a design characteristic, the Ramsden disc reveals several aspects of instrument performance. If the disc is much larger than the eye's iris, much of the light will be lost instead of entering the eye; if smaller, the view will be vignetted. If the disc is too close to the last surface of the eyepiece, the eye will have to be uncomfortably close for viewing; if too far away, the observer will have difficulty maintaining the eye's alignment with the disc.

VIGNETTING

In photography and optics, vignetting is a reduction in image brightness in the image **periphery** compared to the image centre.

Although vignetting is normally unintended and undesired, it is sometimes purposely introduced for creative effect, such as to draw attention to the centre of the frame. A photographer may deliberately choose a lens which is known to produce vignetting. It can also be produced with the use of special **filters** or **post-processing** procedures.

The following types of vignetting are commonly encountered, of which the first two are common to microscopy and photomicrography.

- ⊙ Mechanical vignetting
- ⊙ Optical vignetting
- ⊙ Natural vignetting
- ⊙ Pixel vignetting

Mechanical Vignetting

Mechanical vignetting occurs when light beams emanating from object points located off-axis are partially blocked by external objects such as thick or stacked filters, secondary lenses, and improper lens hoods. The corner darkening can be gradual or abrupt, depending on the lens **aperture**. Complete blackening is possible with mechanical vignetting.

Optical Vignetting

This type of vignetting is caused by the physical dimensions of a multiple element lens. Rear elements are shaded by elements in front of them, which reduces the effective lens opening for off-axis incident light. The result is a gradual decrease of the light intensity towards the image periphery. Optical vignetting is sensitive to the **aperture** and can be completely cured by stopping down the lens. Two or three stops are usually sufficient.

REVIEW QUESTIONS

Introduction

1. Define light.
2. Distinguish between amplitude and wavelength.
3. Describe the importance of deviated and undeviated rays in forming images.

Lens

1. Distinguish between real image and virtual image.
2. Describe the phenomenon of refraction with reference to convex and concave lenses.
3. Describe dispersion of light.
4. Distinguish between spherical aberration and chromatic aberration.
5. Explain the theoretical basis of correcting aberrations of images formed by lenses.
6. List the approaches followed in the correction of aberrations of images formed by lenses.

Images

1. Define "Image".
2. What are the attributes of an image?
3. Describe the intricacies of viewing objects on a magnified scale.
4. What are the limits of magnification obtainable in different viewing systems (imaging devices)?
5. Define the following attributes of image:
   i. Size of the image (Magnification)
   ii. Clarity of the image (Resolution)
   iii. Contrast (between the image and the background)
   iv. Sharpness
6. Explain the functioning of the objective and ocular lens systems of a light microscope from the image-forming scenarios of a simple biconvex lens.
7. Describe the expression of magnification in image formation.
8. Give an account of the range of useful magnification.
9. What are the attributes of the observer's eye that affect the image quality?

10. What is the thumb rule for recommended magnification of a microscope?

11. Explain the basis for choice of objective/ocular combination to obtain optimal magnification in a microscope.

Resolution and Resolving Power

1. Define resolution.

2. Define resolving distance.

3. Distinguish between resolution and resolving power.

4. Bring out the relationship between resolving distance and resolution.

5. Elucidate the mathematical expression of resolution.

6. Bring out the mathematical relationship of resolving power of a microscope.

7. List the factors that govern/limit resolution.

8. Write an essay on resolution and resolving power of a light microscope. Add a note on the factors that govern the resolving power of the microscope.

9. Describe the various methods of increasing the resolution of a lens system.

10. Define angular aperture (AA) of a lens.

11. Write an account of the factors that affect the angular aperture of a lens.

12. Define numerical aperture (NA) of a lens system.

13. Describe how using a condenser increases the numerical aperture of an objective lens system.

14. Bring out the relationship between the magnifying power and numerical aperture of the objective lens system.

15. Bring out the relationship between the resolving power of the objective and the size of the airy diffraction pattern.

16. Bring out the relationship between resolution and numerical aperture.

17. What is airy disc pattern? Bring out the relationship between airy discs and upper limit of resolution.

18. Bring out the relationship between contrast and resolution of images.

19. Why is it that in an optical microscope details smaller than about 0.2 μm (0.0002 mm) cannot be resolved?

Condensers

1. Give the structural description of a substage condenser.
2. Describe the structure and optical pathway of an Abbe type condenser.
3. Describe the structure of aplanatic condenser.
4. Describe the structure of achromatic condenser.
5. Describe the structure of aplanatic-achromatic condenser.
6. Describe the structure and use of a flip-top lens condenser.
7. List out the tips on optimal use of condensers.

Illuminating Systems of a Microscope

1. Describe the structure and use of a reflection mirror used in a light microscope.
2. Give a detailed account of the various types of reflected light used in light microscopy.
3. Distinguish between the effects of axial reflected light and condensed reflected light in light microscopy.
4. Distinguish between the effects of inclined reflected light and circular ringlike light used in light microscopy.
5. Describe critical illumination in light microscopy.
6. Describe Kohler illumination in light microscopy.

Objective Lens System

1. Describe the structure of a typical simple objective lens system.
2. What is primary magnification? Bring out the relationship between primary magnification and equivalent focus.
3. List out the information indicated by the inscriptions on the barrel of the objective lens system.
4. Describe corrective arrangements for optical aberrations in objective lens system.
5. Describe the corrective arrangements for field curvature in objective lens system.
6. Describe the corrective arrangements available in objective lens systems to compensate for the variations in the cover glass thickness.
7. Describe the principle of infinity-corrected objective lens systems.

8. Define:
    i. Achromatic objectives (Achromats)
    ii. Semi-apochromatic objective
    iii. Mechanical tube length of a microscope
    iv. Long working distance objectives (LWD objectives)
9. Give an account of infinity-corrected objectives
10. Give an account of oil-immersion objectives
11. Write notes on field diameter/field of view number/field number.
12. Distinguish between working distance and depth of focus of an objective.
13. Give an account of depth of field.

Ocular Lens System

1. Describe the structure of a simple ocular lens system.
2. Distinguish between positive and negative ocular lens systems.
3. Give an account of a simple positive ocular lens system.
4. Describe compensative positive ocular lens systems.
5. Describe negative or Huygenian ocular lens system.
6. Give an account of periplan ocular lens system.
7. Give an account of a typical modern aberration-free ocular.
8. List out the inscriptions found on oculars and the information elucidated by them.
9. Narrate the tips on choosing and using oculars.
10. Describe Ramsden disc.
11. Give an account of vignetting.

2

MICROSCOPES

INTRODUCTION

The microscope is perhaps the most widely used tool in biology. The invention of microscope in the 16th century is the single most important contribution ever made to the advancement of biology. Microscopes are extensions of our eyes enabling us to see very minute objects that cannot be seen with our naked eyes.

Ancient man used water-filled glass globes as magnifying devices. Later, lenses made of glass or other transparent materials were used as magnifying devices.

During the first century AD (year 100), glass was invented and the early man started looking through the glass and testing it. One of their samples was thick in the middle and thin at the edges and it was discovered that an object held below such a glass looked much larger. This was the accidental discovery/invention of lens. It was called a magnifying glass. It was also later discovered that fire could be started by focusing sun's rays with such "magnifying glasses". The word "lens" is derived from the Latin word *lentil,* as they resemble the shape of a lentil bean.

Until the turn of the 13th century, lenses were mainly produced to be worn as glasses. Only later, were various studies undertaken on lenses. Ancient Romans, Greeks and Indians had known lenses of glass and quartz.

In the 14th century itself spectacles and single lenses were used as magnifiers. Later it was Leonardo da Vinci (1452–1519), the Italian genius, who for the first time recommended that lenses can be used to study minute objects invisible to the naked eye. As mentioned in chapter 1, the magnifying glasses used during his period were called **Filimicroscopes** as they were used mainly to study insects (*fili* = insects).

HISTORY AND EVOLUTION OF MICROSCOPES

In the beginning, simple lenses were used as magnifiers. Hand lenses giving magnification of 2× to 10× were in use. Technically speaking, they are also microscopes.

It was in the year 1590, that two Dutch spectacle-makers by name Zacharias Jansen and his father Hans started experimenting with lenses. They had arranged several lenses together and made a very important discovery. They found that the object placed near the end of the "compound lens system" was greatly enlarged, much larger than any simple lens could. The compound microscope was thus invented.

Galileo succeeded in constructing a true telescope based on the above experiments. He used more than one lens and found that the images of distant objects can be had by placing them at suitable distances from each other in their axis. He found that the use of a second lens increased the magnification to the order of 50–100×. In the year 1610, Galileo invented a somewhat improved microscope by adding a focusing device. The modern compound microscope is based on this principle.

It was Robert Hooke (1635–1703) who first constructed and used a compound microscope that could be considered as a forerunner of the present day microscopes. The highest magnification that he could obtain in it was 200×. He also wrote a book entitled *Micrographia*. He is called the "English Father of Microscopy".

Antoni von Leeuwenhoek (1632–1723) was a contemporary of Robert Hooke. By profession, he was a linen merchant. Making lenses was his hobby. He was specialized in making small, single, biconvex, almost spherical lenses that could give magnification of about 300×. He made a total of 419 lenses, some mounted in gold and most in brass. To measure the size of the objects observed, he used grains of sand, seeds of millet or mustard or blood corpuscles for comparison. With his microscope, he was able to see yeasts, blood cells and many "tiny animalcules", that no man had ever seen before. He is called the "Father of Microscopy".

Campini, an Italian scientist found that the power of a lens can be increased by grinding it to a desired curvature. This discovery paved the way for the construction of more powerful magnifying devices.

The following is an account of some of the early microscopes.

Earliest Version of Compound Microscope

Jansen and Hans of Holland used multiple lenses and made the very important discovery that the object near the end of the lenses was greatly enlarged, much larger than any simple magnifying glass could. They constructed the earliest version of compound microscopes (Figure 2.1). Their device consisted of several hollow tubes that fit right one within the other. These tubes had lenses fitted in them. These lenses can be arranged exactly at the focal points by moving the tubes back and forth.

This helps in getting higher magnification. This microscope gave magnification to the order of 9×.

Figure 2.1   Jansen and Hans microscope

Robert Hooke's Microscope

This microscope may be considered as the forerunner of the present-day microscopes. Constructed by Robert Hooke (1635–1703), it consisted of a light source, a condenser and lenses fitted in movable tubes (Figure 2.2).

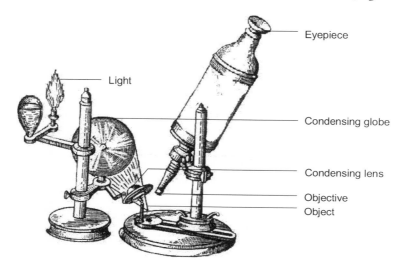

Figure 2.2   Robert Hooke's microscope

The flame burning at the nozzle of a fuel tank serves as a light source. A large lens called Bull's eye focuses the light on to a condenser, which in turn condenses the light on the object placed on the other side.

A tube fitted with lenses mounted on a stand helps in obtaining a magnified image of the object.

Leeuwenhoek's Microscope

In 1673, Antoni von Leeuwenhoek constructed a very simple microscope. It consisted of two flat metallic plates with a lens in between. The specimen holder could be moved back and forth using the screw. This microscope could give a magnification of up to 300× (Figure 2.3).

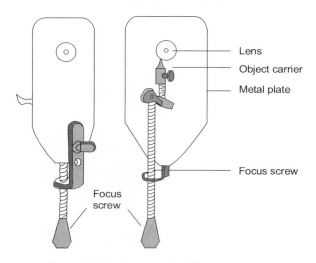

Figure 2.3 Leeuwenhoek's microscope

Binocular Microscope of Rhieta

Rhieta designed the binocular microscope in 1645. Binocular microscopes have two ocular lens systems. The eyes do not tire soon as both the eyes are used simultaneously.

Horizontal Microscope of Bonannes

Bonannes constructed a horizontal microscope in the year 1761. The path of light is horizontal in this microscope. It consisted of a reflector to direct light into the tube, a condenser and a diaphragm to control the light intensity. There was also a rack-and-pinion arrangement to adjust the focus.

Wilson's Screw Barrel Type Microscope

Wilson constructed a screw barrel type of microscope (Figure 2.4) in the year 1710. The ocular lens was provided with a number of grooves to fix additional lenses. The other end had a stage for mounting the object and a condenser. The object was mounted on a spring-loaded stage.

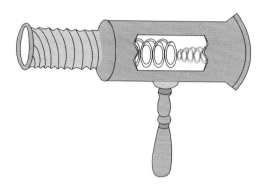

Figure 2.4   Wilson's screw barrel type microscope

The present-day compound microscope is the result of all these attempts and experimentation on the part of several innovators.

LIGHT MICROSCOPY

Light microscopy includes all magnifying facilities cum viewing systems that use visible light to illuminate the object to be examined. Light being the agent that creates the image, such systems are provided with a reflector which directs light on to the object, and a condenser that converges the light rays on the object. Some microscopes are provided with an artificial light source in case natural light fails. There is always a stage on which the object is mounted. The body is provided with rack-and-pinion arrangement to facilitate focusing.

The lens that is used in the viewing device may be a simple lens or a combination of lenses or a combination of more than one lens systems.

The following is an account of the various types of light microscopes, the simplest being the simple microscopes.

SIMPLE MICROSCOPES

The simple microscope consists of a simple, compound lens usually called a magnifier loupe. There are many mechanical forms in which a magnifier can be packaged to provide convenience in carrying or in use.

⊙ A lens supplied in a mount with a convenient handle is called a reading glass. A reading glass provided with a battery-operated illuminating bulb is called an illuminated magnifier or an illuminated loupe (Figure 2.5a). This is a very handy magnifier for reading very small prints in this computer age.

⊙ A pair of lenses of low to moderate magnifying power set in a spectacle frame is often used as a magnifying aid for persons with poor vision.

⊙ Lenses of higher magnification are frequently packaged in a cylindrical form that can be held in place immediately in front of the eye to serve as eye loupes, jeweller's loupes, stamp loupes (Figure 2.5b), etc.

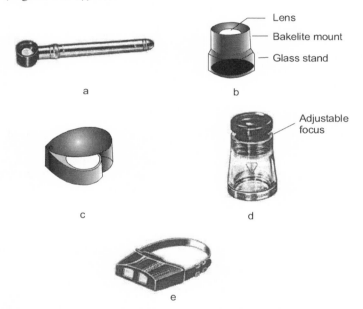

Figure 2.5   Different types of simple magnifiers (simple microscopes) (a) Illuminated loupe (b) Stamp loupe (c) Foldable field lens (d) Measuring and inspecting magnifier (e) Binocular loupe

⊙ Field lenses are widely used in the fields by biologists. A field lens consists of a simple lens mounted on a ring holder made of metal or bakelite, which can be folded into a protective cover. Several models are available, some with more than one lens (Figure 2.5c).

⊙ Measuring and inspecting magnifiers (Figure 2.5d) are available for a variety of uses. The lens mount is provided with a threaded arrangement so that the focus can be adjusted.

⊙ Binocular loupes with head band, also called head-band magnifiers are useful in field work in plant breeding exercises (Figure 2.5e).

Several types of magnifiers are available which can be used as simple microscopes. The choice of an optical design for a magnifier, depends on the required power and the intended application of the magnifier:

1. *For low powers of about 2–3 × (magnitude)*

⊙ A simple double convex lens is suitable.

⊙ The image can be improved, if the lens has specific nonspherical or aspheric surfaces. Plastic-moulded lenses offer aspheric surfaces.

⊙ Fresnel lens can be used. Fresnel lens is embossed in plastic. It is in the form of a thin sheet with the lens curvature placed in a series of concentric grooves on the surface of the sheet. It combines the options of normal simple lens and the advantages of the aspheric form of lens. However, the presence of many symmetrical grooves reduces the quality of the image by light scattering.

2. *For higher powers of 3–10 × (magnitude)*

⊙ A simple lens is replaced by a compound element made of several lenses mounted and sometimes cemented together.

⊙ Aspheric surfaces would be useful, but may prove to be more expensive to use in such compound magnifiers.

Basics of How to Use a Simple Magnifier

⊙ The simple magnifier permits the user to place his eye close to an object of interest.

⊙ The closer the object is to the eye, the longer the angle that it subtends at the eye. Thus the object appears larger.

⊙ However, if the object is brought too close to the eye, the latter can no longer form a clear image.

⊙ A magnifying lens placed in between the observer's eye and the object enables the formation of a virtual image located at a sufficient distance from the eye for the observer to focus on it.

⊙ To obtain the best possible image, the magnifier should be placed directly in front of the eye. The object is then brought towards the magnifier until a clear image is obtained.

⊙ The distance between the eye and the point/place/plane at which the object is to be held, to obtain the clearest image/highest magnification is called image distance.

⊙ The image distance is roughly 25 cm/10 inches for most people. With the age of a person, the nearest point of distinct vision recedes to longer distances (beyond 10 inches/25 cm). Thus a magnifier becomes a useful adjunct to vision for older people.

Magnifying Power and Field of View of a Simple Magnifier (Lens)

Magnifying power It is the extent to which the object being viewed appears enlarged.

$$\text{Magnifying power of a lens (approximately)} = \frac{\text{The least distance of distinct vision (25 cm)}}{\text{Focal length of the lens}}$$

e.g. Magnifying power of a lens
of focal length 5 cm $= 25/5$ cm
$= 5$ magnitudes written as $5\times$

Field of view In the case of simple magnifiers, field of view represents the size of the object that can be viewed. The field of view of the magnifier will be determined by the following parameters.

i. The extent to which the magnifying lens exceeds the working distance, and

ii. Distance of the lens from the eye.

Working diameter of the lens The diameter of the magnifying lens sufficient to fill or exceed the size of the eye of the pupil is called working diameter of the lens.

Thus magnifying power and field of vision are related by the geometry of the optical system.

Quality of the Image

The quality of the image obtained through a magnifying system, such as a lens or a combination of lenses, depends on the following:

⊙ The virtual image that is viewed will appear to be of substantially the same brightness as the original object, if the diameter of the magnifying lens is sufficient to fill or exceed the size of the pupil of the eye.

⊙ The distance of the lens from the eye.

⊙   The aberrations inherently present in the lens.

⊙   The manner in which the lens is used.

TYPES OF OPTICAL LIGHT MICROSCOPES

STUDENTS' DISSECTION MICROSCOPE

Students' dissection microscope is a very simple type of microscope meant for use in the observation of biological materials as such. This viewing instrument comes in handy for the following applications:

⊙   Observation of the gross external morphology of the biological object.

⊙   Low-power observation of sections of materials, with a view to make ground plan sketches.

⊙   Observation while dissecting the material mounted on the stage, facilitated by the longer working distance.

The dissection microscope is a very indispensable instrument for routine observation, at all levels of botanical investigations.

Structure/Construction of Dissection Microscope

The dissection microscope (Figure 2.6) is provided with a solid base. The base is either 'U' shaped or circular. There is a hollow, cylindrical metallic pillar at one end of the base. The focusing knob with the pinion wheel is fixed to the pillar on the back side.

On the front side is the rotatable clamp to which a circular planoconcave reflector is provided. The reflector can be rotated in its plane, along any axis for efficient illumination.

A vertically movable tube with a rack is fitted into the hollow of the pillar in such a way that it can be raised and lowered by rotating the focusing knob. A foldable arm with a circular eyepiece holder ring is screwed on to the upper end of the vertically movable tube. The foldable arm can be moved and folded to any angle, so that any area on the stage can be scanned.

The stage for mounting the object is provided at the upper end of the pillar. The stage is a thick metallic plate with a central circular window of about 8 cm diameter with a ledge cut in it, to hold a thick circular/rectangular glass plate. The glass plate facilitates larger viewing area.

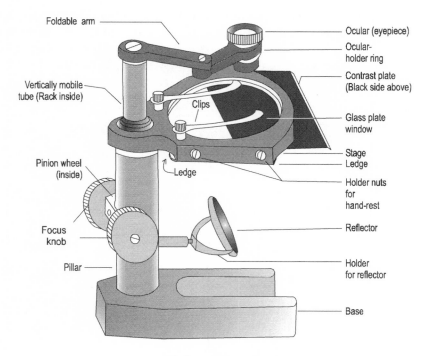

Figure 2.6   Dissection microscope

The underside of the metallic stage is provided with a ledge to hold a contrast plate. The contrast plate is a metallic sheet painted one side white and the other black. It is meant to provide the contrast needed for a clearer observation.

Two metallic clips are provided on the upper surface of the stage, one on either side. The clips serve to hold the slide or object under observation in place.

There is provision to fix hand-rests one on each side of the stage. The hand-rests are thick metallic sheets meant for resting the hand, while dissecting the objects under observation (Figure 2.7).

Figure 2.7   Hand-rest of dissection microscope

The ocular (eyepiece) supplied with the dissection microscope, is a simple double lens system. Both the lenses are biconvex and these are separated by a cylindrical sleeve (Figure 2.8) of appropriate length, to increase the magnifying efficiency. Two oculars of powers 10× and 15× are generally supplied with a dissection microscope.

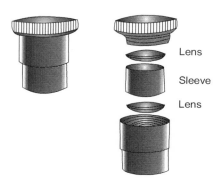

Figure 2.8   Ocular lens system of a dissection microscope

STEREOSCOPIC MICROSCOPE

Principle

The images obtained in ordinary microscopes are flat and two-dimensional. Stereoscopic microscopes have been designed to produce stereoscopic effect to the images obtained.

By using a matched pair of microscopes mounted side by side, usually with a small angle between the optical axes, the object is imaged independently to each eye retaining the stereoscopic effect, which permits discrimination of height on the object. This is the basic working principle of stereoscopic microscopes.

The stereoscopic effect can be exaggerated by proper choice of the design parameters for the microscope.

For practical reasons, the magnifying power of such instruments is usually in the range of 5–50 magnitudes.

Construction/Description of a Stereo-Binocular Dissection Microscope

The stereo-binocular dissection microscope is constructed on the same basic principle (Figure 2.9a and b) as that of a compound microscope. However, it differs from the latter in having a longer working distance.

The base is quite heavy and is 'U'shaped. The stage is fixed on to the pillar at the back of the base by a tube joint stabilized by a screw. The stage can be moved sideways to the right or left for the convenience of observing different parts of the object without changing the focus.

The handle is fitted on the pillar, above the stage and stabilized by a screw. The handle is foldable by a hinge joint so that the body tube can be moved in any angle to scan a larger area on the stage. The forearm of the handle is provided with a rack-and-pinion so that the body tube attached to it can be raised and lowered by rotating the focus knob. Thus the body tube can be moved along the frontal axis as well as side axes.

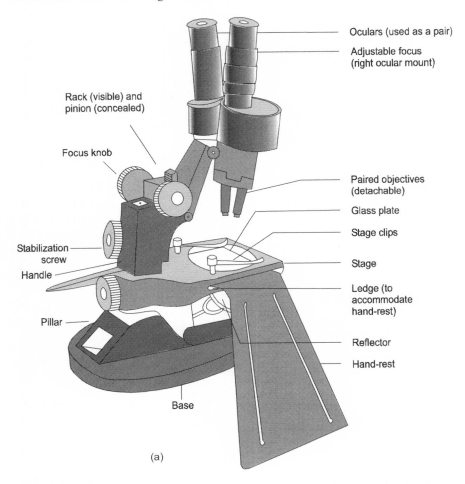

(a)

Figure 2.9   Stereo-binocular microscope (a) Drawing (b) Photograph of neopta stereo-binocular microscope (*Continues*)

(b)

Figure 2.9   Stereo-binocular microscope (a) Drawing (b) Photograph of neopta
stereo-binocular microscope

The optical system consists of paired sets of objectives and oculars with a small angle in between their optical axes. The mounts of the oculars can be moved apart from each other to suit/match the inter-pupillary distance of the observer. The mount of the right ocular is telescopic in nature so that the ocular can be raised or lowered to enhance the stereoscopic effect.

The stage is provided with a large, circular window on which is placed a thick glass plate. Stage clips are provided to hold the slide or specimen under observation.

The sides of the stage are provided with ledges to accommodate hand-rests which facilitates dissection of the object with ease.

Paired objectives of power 4×, 10×, 15×, etc., are supplied. Similarly paired oculars of power 5×, 10×, etc., are supplied.

Uses

⊙ Stereoscopic microscopes (SMs) are important in any work in which fine adjustment of tools or devices is to be made.

⊙ SMs are very useful for dissection of biological objects in biological labs.

⊙ SMs are employed in operation theatres of hospitals for microsurgical procedures.

⊙ In electronic manufacturing units, stereomicroscopes of moderate power, enable human workers as well as computer-controlled machines to bond lead to tiny integrated circuit chips.

COMPOUND MICROSCOPE

Construction and Optical Principles Involved in Light Microscopes

The compound light microscope (Figure 2.10) used by the students has the following parts.

1. Base
2. Stage and illuminating arrangement
3. Arm
4. Rack-and-pinion arrangement
5. Draw tube containing the ocular and objectives at the two ends

Base The base of the microscope is 'U' or 'V' shaped and is made of cast iron. It is quite heavy. The arm (handle) along with the stage is attached to the top of a pillar, which is at the distal joint of the base. The arm is fixed to the pillar through a hinge-joint, so that the microscope can be tilted to suit the convenience of the viewer. As the handle is tilted, the body tube, the stage and the illuminating arrangement are all tilted back as a single unit.

Stage and the illuminating arrangement The stage of the microscope is a square plate about ¼ of an inch in thickness, with a circular passage (window) cut in the centre to allow light to pass through. The specimen to be examined is to be generally mounted on a glass slide and placed on the stage, which is located below the objective.

There are two metallic clips to hold the microslides firm on the stage. In medical and research microscopes, the stage is provided with a mechanical stage device, which consists of a pair of knobs, featuring rack-and-pinion arrangement. This permits the glass slide to be moved across the stage in two directions namely, lateral and forward–backward, so that different areas of the specimen can be examined.

Detachable mechanical stages are also available which can be fitted to the conventional fixed stage of ordinary inexpensive models.

The mechanical stage, whether in-built or detachable, is always provided with "vernier readings" to help locating specific details or areas in the specimen.

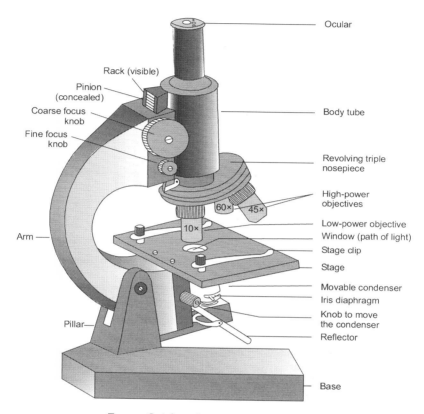

Figure 2.10 Compound microscope

The illuminating arrangement consists of a light source and a lens or lens system known as a condenser on the lower side of the stage. The condenser concentrates the light, providing bright, uniform illumination in the region of the object under observation. The condenser helps in increasing the angular aperture (AA) and also the magnification of the objective lens system.

There is an iris diaphragm in the condenser, which controls the light that passes through the condenser. This functions just like the iris of our eye and hence the name iris diaphragm providing a continuous variation in the diameter of the light path.

Natural daylight is generally used to illuminate the object. A mirror reflector, with one side plane and the other side convex, is used to direct the light along the axis of the microscope. The reflector is fixed lower to the condenser. The reflector can be rotated in any plane so that it can capture natural daylight from the side and reflect the same on to the slide mounted on the stage. The condenser, which is in the path of the light, helps in focusing the light on the material or section in the slide. Both the condenser and the reflector are fixed and immovable in most ordinary students' microscopes which are inexpensive. In more expensive models, the condenser and the reflector are provided as a vertically movable unit fitted with rack-and-pinion mechanism.

The plane side of the mirror is to be used when there is a condenser. The concave side of the mirror is to be used when there is no condenser.

Older models without a condenser lens assembly are provided with a disc diaphragm (Figure 2.11a and b) to delimit the path of light. This is a circular disc of metal attached to the underside of the stage by a central screw. It generally consists of five circular windows (holes) of different diameters progressing from the smallest to the largest (a little smaller than that of the circular window of the stage) along its periphery.

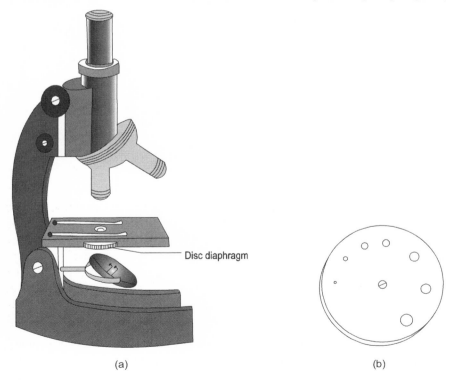

Disc diaphragm

(a)   (b)

Figure 2.11   (a) Compound microscope with disc diaphragm (without condenser)
(b) Disc diaphragm

By rotating the disc, any of these windows can be brought in line with the window of the stage, thus delimiting the path of light. Unlike the iris diaphragm, the disc diaphragm provides only discontinuous variation in the diameter of the light path.

In the absence of daylight, artificial illuminating systems (Figure 2.12) can be used in the place of the reflector.

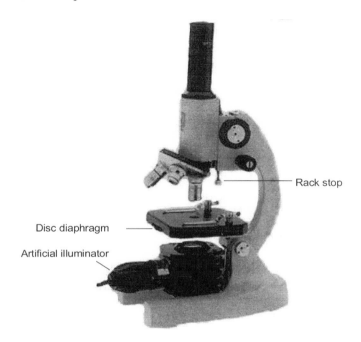

Figure 2.12 Compound microscope with disc diaphragm and artificial illuminator attachment

Arm (handle) of the microscope The arm of the microscope is that part which connects the tube to the base. Its lower end is connected to the base through a hinge joint at the top of the pillar. The body tube of the microscope is attached to the upper end of the curved handle through a rack-and-pinion arrangement. There are circular knobs on the sides of the upper end of the handle. These knobs help in focusing the microscope. The larger knob is called coarse focusing knob and the smaller one is called fine focusing knob.

Rack-and-pinion The movement of body tube while focusing has to be very accurate and stable even at smaller increments.

This is because, the depth of focus is high at lower power operations and very low at higher power operations. Therefore, at high-power operations, the need for accuracy is dire. In high-NA objectives, this depth of focus can be as small as one or two microns. Therefore, the mechanical components (rack-and-pinion) should provide stable motion at even smaller increments.

Rack-and-pinion arrangement (Figure 2.13) facilitates vertical movement of the body tube of the microscope.

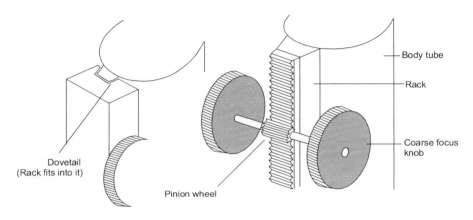

Figure 2.13   Rack-and-pinion

Rack is a vertical block of a hard metal with horizontal grooves (teeth) on its front surface. It is fixed with its flat side to the back of the body tube. Pinion is a horizontal metallic cylinder with horizontal teeth (grooves), that fit exactly in the teeth of the rack. The pinion is fixed horizontally on the upper end of the handle. Rotating the focusing knobs to which it is attached, the pinion is rotated which lifts or lowers the rack. The body tube attached to the rack is thus moved vertically up and down.

The larger coarse focusing knob helps in preliminary focusing. The smaller fine focusing knob helps in fine focusing.

Body tube   Body tube of the microscope is the path of light in the microscope. It separates the ocular and the objective and assures continuous alignment of the optics. It permits objectives and eyepieces (oculars) of different powers to be interchanged with the assurance that the quality of the image will be maintained.

The length of the body tube is standardized and by tradition (traditionally) it has been defined "from the end of the screw thread that attaches the objective to the tube to a specific location at the ocular end of the tube". A standard length of 160 mm has been accepted for most uses, and 250 mm for metallographic microscopes.

The body tube is a hollow metallic tube. A still narrower draw tube is screwed to the upper end of the body tube. The draw tube holds the ocular lens system at the upper end.

The draw tube to which the ocular is mounted is normally single and vertical in most student compound microscopes. These models are called vertical monocular microscopes. Medical microscopes intended for clinical use are provided with inclined monocular draw tubes. More expensive models have binocular heads which are always inclined (Figure 2.14).

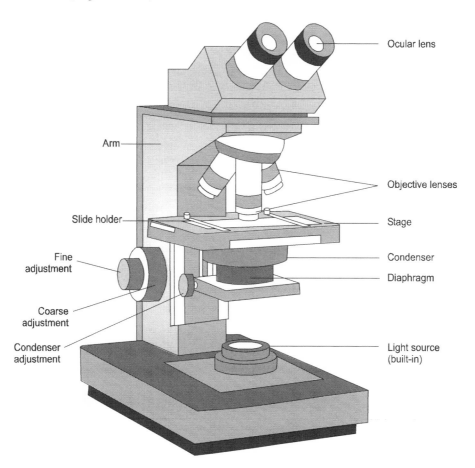

Figure 2.14   Inclined binocular microscope with fixed body and movable stage

Nosepiece   It is always desirable to be able to choose between objectives of several different magnifications in order to suit the magnification to the requirements of the object. Most microscopes are provided at the lower end of the body tube with a rotating nosepiece that carries several objectives in a turret. A central screw attaches the nosepiece, so that it can be rotated around its centre. There are equidistant holes in the nosepiece to which the objective lens systems can be screwed. Most microscopes are provided with a triple nosepiece to which three objectives such as 10×, 45×, and 60× or 100× (oil-immersion) can be screwed. By rotating the nosepiece, any one of the objectives can be brought to the path of light. More expensive models are provided with quadruple nosepiece and so on to suit the special requirements.

Some microscopes are equipped with readily interchangeable nosepieces carrying different objectives.

Microscope objectives have been designed to minimize aberrations at one of the distances—160 mm or 250 mm. Use of other distances will affect the aberration balance for high-magnification objectives. Therefore, focusing of the traditional microscopes requires moving the objective, body tube and the ocular as a rigid unit. The rack-and-pinion mechanism fitted to the entire body makes this possible.

In most microscopes, a rack stop screw (Figure 2.12) is provided to check the downward movement of the body tube. This helps to avert breaking of the slide.

Optical Systems and the Optic Principle of the Light Microscope

The optical system of the microscope consists of objectives and ocular lens systems. These work in consonance to create an image at eye point, just above the eye lens of the ocular. This image is captured by our eye and the object is viewed.

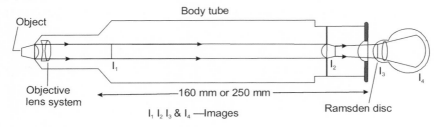

Figure 2.15   Optic principle of light compound microscope

Objectives are lens systems consisting of more than one lens fixed in a hollow tube. The objective operates very near the object and forms a larger primary image (I_1), within the body tube. There are two types of objectives namely, achromatic objectives and apochromatic objectives.

The magnification obtainable in the objective is carved as $10\times$, $45\times$, $60\times$, $100\times$ and so on.

The ocular is also a hollow tubular arrangement consisting of two or more lenses. The lower lens of the ocular is called field lens (FL). It receives the primary image and forms the secondary image (I_2).

The upper lens is called eye lens (EL). This receives the secondary image and forms a tertiary image (I_3) at the eye point, just above the EL of the ocular. This tertiary image can be caught on a screen held at this plane. This is also called Ramsden disc (Figure 2.15).

The ocular lens systems are of two types, namely positive oculars and negative oculars. The lens of our eyes receives this tertiary image (Ramsden disc) and forms the fourth image (I_4) on the retina.

By moving the body tube up or down, the microsection is made to be in between F and 2F of the objective lens systems. As a result, a magnified primary image (I_1) is obtained beyond the 2F of the objective lens on the other side.

The approximate magnification of a microscope can be given by the formula

$$\text{Magnification} = \text{ocular power} \times \text{objective power}$$

WORKING OF AN OPTICAL LIGHT MICROSCOPE

The following is a description of how a microscope works:

The first lens of a microscope is the one closest to the object being examined and, for this reason, is called the **objective**.

Light from either an external or internal (within the microscope body) source is first passed through the **substage condenser**, which forms a well-defined light cone that is concentrated on to the object (**specimen**).

Light passes through the specimen and into the objective which then projects a real, inverted, and magnified image (I_1) of the specimen to a fixed plane within the microscope that is termed the **intermediate** image plane (Figure 2.16).

The objective should have the following attributes:

⊙ The objective must gather the light coming from each of the various parts or points of the specimen.

⊙ The objective must have the capacity to reconstitute the light coming from the various points of the specimen into the various corresponding points in the image (sometimes called anti-points).

⊙ The objective must be constructed so that it will be focused close enough to the specimen so that it will project a magnified, real image up into the body tube.

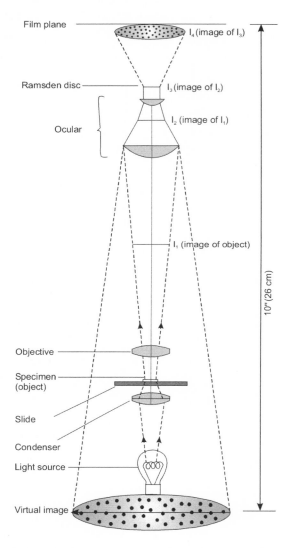

Figure 2.16 Schematic representation of the working of a light compound microscope

The intermediate image plane is usually located about 10 millimeters below the top of the **microscope body tube** at a specific location within the fixed internal diaphragm of the **eyepiece**. The distance between the back focal plane of the objective and the intermediate image is termed the **optical tube length**. Note that this value is different from the **mechanical tube length** of a microscope, which is the distance between the nosepiece (where the objective is mounted) to the top edge of the observation tubes where the eyepieces (oculars) are inserted.

The eyepiece or ocular, which fits into the body tube at the upper end, is the farthest optical component from the specimen. In modern microscopes, the eyepiece is held into place by a shoulder on the top of the microscope observation tube, which keeps it from falling into the tube. The placement of the eyepiece is such that its eye (upper) lens further magnifies the real image projected by the objective. The eye of the observer sees this secondarily magnified image (I_2) as if it were at a distance of 10 inches (25 centimetres) from the eye; hence this virtual image appears as if it were near the base of the microscope.

The distance from the top of the microscope observation tube to the shoulder of the objective (where it fits into the nosepiece) is usually 160 mm in a finite tube length system. This is known as the mechanical tube length.

The eyepiece has several major functions:

⊙ The eyepiece serves to further magnify the real image projected by the objective.

⊙ In visual observation, the eyepiece produces a secondarily enlarged virtual image (I_2).

⊙ In photomicrography, it produces a secondarily enlarged real image projected by the objective. This augmented real image can be projected on the photographic film in a camera or upon a screen held above the eyepiece.

⊙ The eyepiece can be fitted with scales, markers or crosshairs (often referred to as **graticules, reticules** or **reticles**) in such a way that the image of these inserts can be superimposed on the image of the specimen.

The factor that determines the amount of image magnification is the objective **magnifying power**, which is predetermined during construction of the objective optical elements. Objectives typically have magnifying powers that range from 1:1 ($1\times$) to 100:1 ($100\times$), with the most common powers being $4\times$ (or $5\times$), $10\times$, $20\times$, $40\times$ (or $50\times$), and $100\times$.

An important feature of microscope objectives is their very short focal lengths that allow increased magnification at a given distance when compared to an ordinary hand lens. **The primary reason that microscopes** are so efficient at magnification is the two-stage enlargement that is achieved over such a short optical path, due to the short focal lengths of the optical components.

Eyepieces, like objectives, are classified in terms of their ability to magnify the intermediate image. Their magnification factors vary between $5\times$ and $30\times$ with the most commonly used eyepieces having a value of $10\times$–$15\times$.

Total **visual magnification** of the microscope is derived by multiplying the magnification values of the objective and the eyepiece. For instance, using a $5\times$ objective with a $10\times$ eyepiece yields a total visual magnification of $50\times$ and likewise, at the top end of the scale, using a $100\times$ objective with a $30\times$ eyepiece gives a visual magnification of $3000\times$.

Total magnification is also dependent upon the tube length of the microscope. Most standard fixed tube length microscopes have a tube length of 160, 170, 200, or 210 millimeters with 160 millimeters being the most common for transmitted light biomedical microscopes.

Infinity-corrected microscopes also have eyepieces and objectives that are optically-tuned to the design of the microscope, and these should not be interchanged between microscopes with different infinity tube lengths.

Modern research microscopes are very complex and often have both episcopic and diascopic illuminators built into the microscope housing. This leads to design constraints in these microscopes and the standard tube length of 160 mm or so cannot be maintained in these microscopes. The body tube exceeds the standard tube length. Addition of a set of parallelizing lenses shortens the apparent mechanical tube length of such microscopes. These additional lenses will sometimes introduce an additional magnification factor (usually around 1.25–$1.5\times$) that must be taken into account when calculating both the visual and photomicrographic magnification. This additional magnification factor is referred to as a **tube factor** in the user manuals provided by most microscope manufacturers. Thus, if a $5\times$ objective is being used with a $15\times$ set of eyepieces, then the total visual magnification becomes $93.75\times$ (using a $1.25\times$ tube factor) or $112.5\times$ (using a $1.5\times$ tube factor).

Choice of Suitable Eyepiece/Objective Combination

Care should be taken in choosing eyepiece/objective combinations to ensure the optimal magnification of specimen detail without adding unnecessary artefacts. For instance, the microscopist could choose a $10\times$ eyepiece coupled to a $10\times$ objective to obtain a magnification of $100\times$. An alternative choice for the same magnification would be a $20\times$ eyepiece with a 5× objective. Because the 10× objective has a higher numerical aperture (approximately 0.25) than does the 5× objective (approximately 0.10), and considering that **numerical aperture** values define an objective's resolution, it is clear that the former choice would be the best. If photomicrographs of the same viewfield were made with each objective/eyepiece combination described above, it would be obvious that the 10× eyepiece/10× objective duo would produce photomicrographs that excelled in specimen detail and clarity when compared to the alternative combination.

These are the basic principles underlying the operation and construction of the compound microscope which, unlike a magnifying glass or simple microscope, employs a group of lenses aligned in series. The elaboration of these principles has led to the development, over the past several hundred years, of today's sophisticated instruments. Modern microscopes are often modular with interchangeable parts for different purposes; such microscopes are capable of producing images from low to high magnification with remarkable clarity and contrast.

In addition to the parallelizing lenses used in some microscopes, manufacturers may also provide additional lenses (sometimes called **magnification changers**) that can be rotated into the optical pathway to increase the magnification factor. This is often done to provide ease in specimen framing for photomicrography. These lenses usually have very small magnification factors ranging from 1.25× up to 2.5×, but use of these lenses may lead to **empty magnification,** a situation where the image is enlarged, but no additional detail is resolved.

BRIGHT-FIELD MICROSCOPY

Bright-field microscopy is the simplest of all the light microscopy techniques. The object is illuminated via white light, i.e., illuminated from below and observed from above.

Limitations

⊙ Very low contrast of most biological samples.

⊙ Low apparent resolution due the blur of the out-of-focus material.

Advantages

⊙ Simplicity of set-up with only basic equipment required.

⊙ No sample preparation required, allowing viewing of live cells.

The image may be improved by the following simple enhancements to this technique:

⊙ Reducing the size of the light source via the condenser aperture, although this reduces resolution.

⊙ Use of coloured or polarizing filters on the light source to highlight features not visible under white light. This is especially useful with mineral samples.

⊙ By use of oblique illumination, the image begets a 3-D appearance. More importantly this highlights the otherwise invisible features of the object.

The design of the microscope assumes that when the specimen is placed in focus, it is a few microns further away than the front focal plane of the objective. The distance from the plane of attachment of the objective to the collar of the nosepiece and the upper end of the draw tube is referred to as the mechanical tube length of the microscope. Objectives designed to be used with a microscope having a tube length of 160 millimetres are inscribed with this value on the barrel (Figure 2.17).

Typical NA Values

4× 0.1
10× 0.25
40× 0.65
100× 1.25

Figure 2.17   Typical NA values for objectives of various powers

Finite tube lengths were standardized at 160 millimetres during the nineteenth century by the Royal Microscopical Society (RMS) and enjoyed widespread acceptance for over 100 years.

BASIC CONCEPTS AND FORMULAE IN MICROSCOPY

In order to understand the full potential of the optical microscope, one must have a firm grasp of the following fundamental physical principles associated with its operation. The following terms are recalled with their definitions to link the present topic to the relevant units in the previous chapter:

Conjugate planes In a properly focused and aligned optical microscope, there are two sets of principal conjugate planes that occur along the optical pathway through the microscope.

One set consists of four **field planes** and is referred to as the **field or image forming conjugate set.**

The second set consists of four **aperture planes** and is referred to as the **illumination conjugate set.**

Each plane within a set is said to be conjugate with the others in that set because they are simultaneously in focus and can be viewed superimposed upon on one another when observing specimens through the microscope.

Depth of field The depth of field is the thickness of the specimen that is acceptably sharp at a given focus level.

Depth of focus Depth of focus refers to the range over which the image plane can be moved while an acceptable amount of sharpness is maintained.

Note The two concepts—depth of field and depth of focus—are often incorrectly used interchangeably while referring to the depth of field of a microscope.

Field of view In optical microscopy field of view is the diameter of the field of vision in millimetres measured in the intermediate image plane in an optical microscope. It is expressed by the field of view number or simply field number.

In most cases, the eye field diaphragm opening diameter determines the viewfield size.

Working distance Working distance of a microscope objective is the distance from the front lens element of the objective to the closest surface of the coverslip when the specimen is in sharp focus.

Objective lens systems are generally designed with a short free working distance.

Parfocal length Parfocal length represents the distance between the specimen plane and the shoulder of the flange by which the objective is supported on the revolving nosepiece.

Refraction index (index of refraction) Refraction index is a value calculated from the ratio of the speed of light in vacuum to that in a second medium of greater density. The refraction index variable is most commonly symbolized by the letter n or n' in descriptive text and mathematical equations respectively.

Numerical aperture   The numerical aperture of an objective lens system of a microscope is a measure of its ability to gather light and resolve fine specimen detail at a fixed object distance. All modern microscope objectives have the NA value inscribed on the lens barrel. This allows determination of the smallest specimen detail resolvable by the objective and an approximate indication of the depth of field.

Resolution   The resolving power of the microscope is the most important feature of the optical system and influences the ability to distinguish between fine details of a particular specimen.

Resolution is dependent on the following factors:

⊙   NA of the objective lens system (primary factor)

⊙   Type of specimen

⊙   Coherence of illumination

⊙   Degree of aberration correction

⊙   Contrast-enhancing methodology either in the optical system of the microscope (dark-field illumination, using phase contrast principle, etc.,) or in the specimen itself (staining)

Useful magnification range   The range of useful magnification for an objective/eyepiece combination is defined by the NA of the system. There is a minimum magnification necessary for the detail present in an image to be resolved. This value is rather arbitrarily set to a value between 500 and 1000 times the NA (500 or 1000 × NA) of the objective.

Image brightness   Image brightness is governed by the light-gathering power of the objective, which is a function of its NA. The image brightness is proportional to the square of the objective NA. This is regardless of the imaging mode utilized in optical microscopy.

Coverslip correction   Non-immersion microscope objectives (high-dry objectives) having a numerical aperture exceeding 0.75 are prone to introduction of aberration when imaging through coverslips that deviate from the standard thickness and refraction index.

To prevent artefacts, many objectives are equipped with correction collars that compensate for coverslip thickness variations.

Linear measurements (micrometry)   Performing measurements at high magnifications in compound optical microscopy is generally conducted by the application of eyepiece reticles in combination with stage micrometers.

A majority of measurements made with compound microscopes fall into the size range of 0.2 μm to 20 mm (the average field diameter of wide-field eyepieces). Horizontal distances below 0.2 μm are beneath the resolving power of the microscopes, and lengths larger than the field of view of a wide-field eyepiece are usually and far more conveniently measured with a stereomicroscope.

PHASE CONTRAST MICROSCOPY

Normal visible natural light is used in microscopes to form the image of the object. If there is no obstruction in the path of light, the light rays travel as undeviated rays. Thus, when no object is placed in a microscope, the light rays travel as undeviated rays forming a full bright field.

On the other hand, if an object is placed in the path of light in the light microscope, the light rays falling on the object (microsection) are deviated. The objective of the microscope condenses these deviated rays on the other side to form a primary image. We use the ocular to capture this image in our eyes (*see* Figure 1.2 in chapter 1).

Thus, the deviated rays create the image in the field of vision. Depending on the nature of the object (its transparent or opaque nature), the image is either bright or darker.

The undeviated rays travelling around the object form the bright background of the image.

If the image of the object differs from the background both in brightness as well as in colour, it is seen clearly. That is, the deviated rays should differ from the undeviated rays either in amplitude or in wavelength or in both.

In case of coloured objects, the deviated rays will differ from the undeviated rays in amplitude as well as in wavelength, rendering the object more visible against the bright white background.

On the other hand, if the object to be examined has no colour of its own, it can be coloured artificially by using stains, to make it suitable for microscopic observation.

Phase Shift

Light is regarded as a series of small particles, moving at the rate of 1,86,000 miles per second. A beam of light consists of millions of these particles, which are so close to each other, that it is simplest to draw them as continuous waves shown as sine curves. Therefore, when drawn as though it were flat, it has two dimensions. They are **amplitude** (depth of the curve) and **wavelength** (distance between crests).

Amplitude is felt as brightness and wavelength as colour by our eyes. Monochromatic rays of longer wavelengths are felt as red light, while those of shorter wavelengths are felt as blue lights. Natural daylight, which is nothing but the sun's rays reflected by the clouds in the sky, is in fact a mixture of light rays of different wavelengths. This is felt as white light.

The daylight that we see is nothing but the resultant light, which in fact is a mixture of deviated rays and undeviated rays (Figure 2.18a).

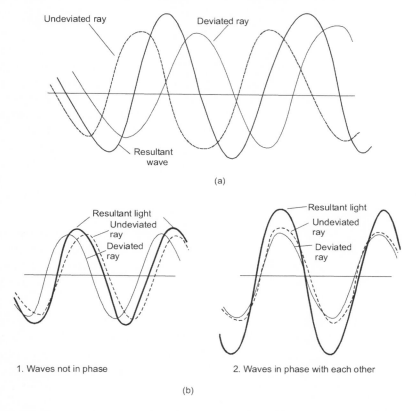

(a)

1. Waves not in phase   2. Waves in phase with each other

(b)

Figure 2.18   (a) Deviated and undeviated rays forming the resultant light
(b) Phase shift

If the deviated and undeviated rays travel in such a way, that their crests and troughs are not related to each other, then they are called "light waves not in phase with each other". The resultant light of such light rays "not in phase" will have amplitude slightly higher than that of the individual waves (Figure 2.18b(1)).

On the other hand, if the deviated rays and undeviated rays travel at the same speed, their crests and troughs will be "in phase with each other".

The resultant light of such rays "in phase with each other" will have amplitude, which is twice that of the individual waves (Figure 2.18b(2)).

Reducing the speed of the undeviated rays until they travel in phase with the deviated rays can double the positive and negative amplitudes. This increase in the amplitude is called phase shift (Figure 2.18b). If this phenomenon is used in microscopy, the image can be seen very clearly against the background.

Principle

Many biological structures such as cell walls and cell nuclei are transparent. They transmit as much light as the mounting medium that surrounds them. In other words, their light deflecting property is almost equal to that of the surrounding medium. There is no colour or transmission contrast in such objects, and therefore conventional microscopes are not useful to study such structures. However, the refraction index of the structure varies slightly from that of the surrounding medium. Thus, the light passing through such an object provides not only a change in the optical path across the object, but also a shift in the phase of the light that has passed through the structure relative to the light passing around.

This phase shift information can be used to form a visible image, if it is converted into intensity variations that are detectable by the observer. Frederick Zernike, a Dutch physicist developed a method in 1934 to achieve this and he was awarded the Nobel Prize in 1953 for his achievement.

In phase contrast microscope, the phase difference between the light that is diffracted by a specimen and the light that is direct and undeflected is one quarter of a wavelength or less. Zernike increased this phase difference by another quarter wavelength by placing a suitable mask in the back focal plane of the objective. Waves that differ in phase by half a wavelength cancel each other. Areas of the object that cause such an effect appear dark. Thus, phase differences caused by variations in the specimen appear as intensity variations in the image.

The following are the approaches to achieving phase image of good quality by this method.

- ⊙ Use of an annular light source imaged on to an annular mask in the back focal plane causing phase shift (most commonly used method)
- ⊙ Use of edges

⊙ Use of small dots

⊙ Use of other combinations of source shape and mask shape

Phase contrast microscopes use phase shift effect to create very accurate images of microsections.

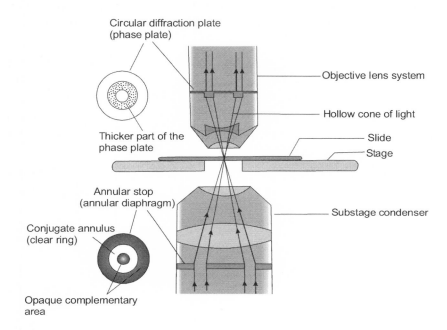

Figure 2.19   Phase contrast microscope

In phase contrast microscopes, an annular stop replaces the iris diaphragm of the substage condenser (Figure 2.19). This is a circular disc called annular diaphragm. It is opaque, except for a clear ring. The opaque area is called complementary area and the clear ring is called conjugate annulus. This clear ring permits a hollow cylinder of light, which becomes a hollow cone as it passes through the lens system of the condenser.

A cross section of this cone at the back aperture of the objective is a conjugate annulus. Both inside and outside of the conjugate annulus are comparatively darker areas called complementary areas. Rays deflected (deviated) by the microsection will be in the complementary area.

The objective lens system contains a circular diffraction plate (also called phase plate) at the focal point on the upper side. This is a transparent circular plate of differential thickness. The ringlike part corresponding to the conjugate annulus of the ring diaphragm is thick, while the other parts corresponding to the complementary area are thin. The thinner ringlike part of the phase plate is made of a substance that shifts the phase of the light passing through it by a quarter of its wavelength, creating an artificial phase shift.

The deviated and undeviated rays strike different parts of the plate. The plate can alter their phase relation. The relative amplitude (brightness) can also be altered.

By using transparent films of suitable thickness placed on the conjugate annulus, a bright or negative contrast is obtained. Thicker or more refractive parts of the section appear lighter than the background.

Alternately, the film can be placed on the complementary area, to get dark or positive contrast. Thicker or more refractive portions appear darker than the background.

In either case, an additional, partially absorbing film to reduce the intensity of the undeviated rays to additional contrast may cover the annulus.

Applications

- Ideal for examination of live cells and tissues.
- The nucleus in a cell for example shows up darkly against the surrounding cytoplasm. Contrast is excellent.
- Suitable to examine the cells grown in artificial media by tissue culture technique.
- The changes caused by chemical and physical factors on live cells can be studied by using phase contrast microscopes.
- The changes that occur during cell division can be studied.
- The nature and development of membranes and ultra-outgrowths can be studied.
- The empty spaces that arise in the cells and their nature can be studied.

FLUORESCENCE MICROSCOPY

Fluorescence is an optical phenomenon in which light absorbed by a substance is almost instantly emitted as a light of longer wavelength. George G. Stokes was the first to describe this phenomenon. He observed that the mineral Fluorspar emitted red light when illuminated with UV light. Such a substance is known as fluorophore and the change/shift in wavelength is known as Stokes shift.

As a result of absorption of light, the fluorophore molecules become excited, i.e., as they absorb the energy of light, their electronic state is changed to an excited state in which the energy of each molecule is higher than it is in its ground state. The excess energy may be dissipated as heat or emitted as fluorescence or may be used in photochemical reaction.

If a fluorophore is irradiated with light of constant intensity (in quanta/second) and varying wavelength, a proportion of the incident light will be absorbed in accordance with the absorption spectrum of the fluorophore. Only a part of the light absorbed is emitted as fluorescence. Each fluorophore has a characteristic excitation maximum and emission property.

Fluorophore	Excitation maxima	Emission maxima	Fluorescence colour
FITC	495 nm	525 nm	Green
RITC	550 nm	580 nm	Red to pink

Therefore, the intensity of fluorescence will vary with fluorophore.

Types of Fluorescence

Two different types of fluorescence are noticed in biological materials. They are 1. primary fluorescence and 2. induced fluorescence.

Primary fluorescence (autofluorescence)   Certain substances show some fluorescence by themselves, e.g. most tissue components. Proteins can be expected to fluoresce, if excited by UV light (250–280 nm) due to the presence of tryptophan, tyrosine and phenylalanine. Chlorophylls give a red fluorescence due to the presence of porphyrenes. Presence of lipid droplets in lipid storage tissues can be demonstrated by fluorescence microscopy. In this case, the fluorescence is due to the pigments dissolved in the lipids, rather than due to the lipids themselves.

Induced fluorescence   Some non-fluorescent substances can be converted into fluorescent compounds by simple chemical treatments. Fluorescence of this type is called induced fluorescence. Formaldehyde, glyoxylic acid, acetic acid, acetaldehyde and fluoresamine are some of the reagents, which can induce fluorescence in some substances.

Fluorescence microscopy also involves the use of fluorescent stains or dyes, which are known as fluorochromes, e.g. Congo red, eosin, basic fuchsin, thioflavin-T and BAO. While some of these stains are coloured in visible lights, others are colourless, but emit fluorescence. Fluorochromes are used in very low concentrations (1:10,000 or less).

Fluorescence microscopy involves illumination of the object with light of shorter wavelengths such as UV light, while fluorescence is seen at longer wavelengths. It uses the phenomena of fluorescence and phosphorescence instead of, or in addition to, reflection and absorption (the phenomena used in normal light microscopy).

Kohler (1904) was the first to report fluorescence of tissues when examined under UV irradiation, in a microscope.

Coons *et al.* (1942) introduced fluorescence antibody technique. This led to the development of fluorescence microscopy, which is extensively used in immunological studies. With the availability of more refined instruments, more general uses of fluorescence microscopy have developed, which help in studying the properties of organic or inorganic substances.

Photoluminescence, Fluorescence and Phosphorescence

Generation of luminescence through excitation of a molecule by ultraviolet or visible light photons is a phenomenon called **photoluminescence**. Absorption of visible or UV radiation raises the molecule to an **excited state**. Electron absorbs quantum of energy and jumps to a higher energy orbital. When electron drops back to the **ground state**, excitation energy can be liberated by either of the following two processes:

1. **Quenching or radiationless** transfer which is most common.

2. **Re-emission of radiation** which is less common gives rise to photoluminescence. Based on the electronic configuration of the excited state and the emission pathway, two different types of photoluminescence namely fluorescence and phosphorescence occur.

Fluorescence is the property of some atoms and molecules to absorb light at a particular wavelength and to subsequently emit light of longer wavelength after a brief interval of time called **fluorescence lifetime** which is normally within nanoseconds (10^{-9} seconds) of the excitation.

Phosphorescence on the other hand occurs in a similar manner but with a much longer excited state lifetime and hence a much slower process. Phosphorescence is caused by an electron becoming transferred into a triplet state. Triplet states have long lifetime, so phosphoresence persists. After the source of excitation radiation is switched off, phosphorescence emission continues for periods that vary from milliseconds to weeks.

Fluorescence Light Microscope

Fluorescence microscope has the same basic construction of light compound microscopes with the following additional parts.

Lamp house unit   Fluorescence microscope uses a xenon or mercury vapour arc lamp as a light source. The lamp house unit includes a condenser lens that controls the path of light.

The lamps produce short wavelength light of very high intensity. There is provision to vary the intensity from low to very high levels.

The working of the fluorescence microscope requires selection of specific wavelengths. Therefore, illumination of very high intensity is desired.

The lamps are provided with protective arrangement to minimize the heat generated when they are on.

Complementary filters   Fluorescence microscopes differ from the conventional microscopes in having a pair of complementary filters called excitation filter and emission filter.

Excitation filter   One filter is inserted in the pathway of illumination to give a monochromatic light (of shorter wavelengths), for the excitation of fluorescence. This is called excitation filter.

Emission filter (barrier filter)   The second filter is used in the body tube of the microscope to prevent the excitation light (wavelengths below 400 nm), from reaching the observer's eyes, while permitting the longer wavelengths emitted by the fluorescent object, so that the fluorescence will be seen against a dark background. This filter is called emission filter or barrier filter.

Dichroic mirror (dichromatic beam splitter)   A dichroic mirror is provided only in epi-illumination fluorescence microscope. This is nothing but a dichromatic beam splitter. It is placed in the body tube, between the objective below and the emission filter above in the path of light. It is oriented at 45° so that it can deflect the excitation light down through the objective on to the specimen and at the same time, allow the emission light from the specimen to reach the ocular through the emission filter.

Digital camera system   Expensive models are provided with digital camera systems to document the images obtained as digital data.

A schematic representation of the light path and the components in fluorescence microscopy is shown in Figure 2.20.

There are two types of fluorescence microscopes based on the positioning of the lamp house unit. They are 1. trans-illumination fluorescence microscope and 2. epi-illumination fluorescence microscope.

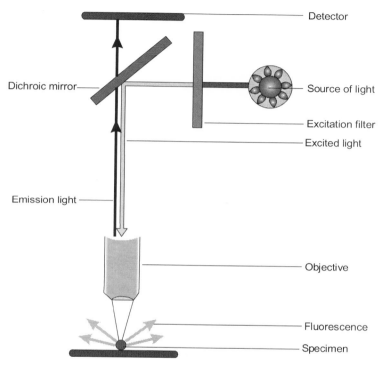

Figure 2.20 Schematic representation of the light path and the components in fluorescence microscopy

Trans-illumination Fluorescence Microscope

In this type, the lamp house unit is provided as a substage arrangement. The excited light is transmitted through the specimen. So this type is called trans-illumination fluorescence microscope.

The fluorochromes present in the specimen emit fluorescence. Therefore, in trans-illumination fluorescence microscope, both the excitation light and emission light travel through the objective and reach the emission filter.

The emission filter allows only the fluorescence to pass through and prevents the excitation light from reaching the ocular (Figure 2.21a).

The choice of a condenser is very important in trans-illumination fluorescence microscope. When a bright-field condenser is used, both the excitation light and emission light enter the objective. In such an event, separation of fluorescence from the excitation light becomes difficult. Therefore, a dark-field condenser is preferred.

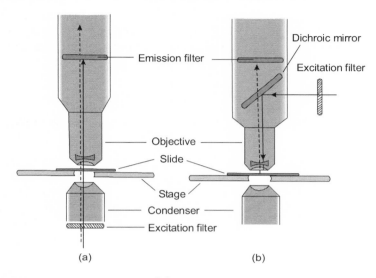

Figure 2.21   Optical principle of fluorescence microscope (a) Trans-illumination fluorescence microscope (b) Epi-illumination fluorescence microscope

Dark-field condenser emits a hollow cone of light. The specimen is illuminated by oblique rays only, most of which travel outside the objective lens. Only the emission light (fluorescence) travels directly through the objective. The very little amount of excitation that might travel alongside are easily separated and prevented.

Epi-illumination Fluorescence Microscope

This is an improved version of fluorescence microscope. In this type, the lamp house unit is located above the stage. It uses a mercury vapour lamp as light source.

The excitation filter attached with the light source lets out the excited light to fall on the dichroic mirror placed at a 45° angle in the body tube. The mirror deflects the excitation light downwards through the objective lens system.

The excitation light strikes the specimen which emits fluorescence. This emission light travels upwards through the objective. The dichroic mirror allows the emission to traverse it and reach the emission (barrier) filter (Figure 2.21b).

Thus, in epi-illumination fluorescence microscope, the separation of excitation light from the emission light is fully achieved.

Epi-illumination fluorescence microscopes are most widely used and have become an important tool in the field of biological science, opening the doors for the more advanced types of microscopes such as, confocal laser scanning microscope and total internal reflection fluorescence (TIRF) microscopes.

Applications

⊙ Fluorescence microscopy is useful in studying the location of molecules in the cell and their movements.

Since fluorescence emission differs in wavelength (colour) from the excitation light, a fluorescent image ideally only shows the structure of interest that was labelled with the fluorescent dye. This high specificity led to the widespread use of fluorescence light microscopy in biomedical research. Different fluorescent dyes can be used to stain different biological structures, which can then be detected simultaneously, while still being specific due to the individual colour of the dye.

⊙ This is an ideal approach to study the autofluorescent cell components.

⊙ Fluorophores are used as markers to locate and study the cell components that lack autofluorescence.

⊙ In recent years, antibodies labelled with fluorescent markers are used to locate specific proteins in the cells. Thus, fluorescence microscopy has lead to the development of a new technique called immunofluorescence. This is nothing but a technique of tagging fluorescent marker molecules with non-fluorescent antibodies so that the target protein can be located with the help of induced fluorescence.

This method is of critical importance in the modern life sciences, as it can be extremely sensitive, allowing the detection of single molecules. Many different fluorescent dyes can be used to stain different structures or chemical compounds. One particularly powerful method is the combination of antibodies coupled to a fluorochrome as in immunostaining. Examples of commonly used fluorochromes are fluorescin or rhodamine. The antibodies can be made tailored specifically for a chemical compound. For example, one strategy often in use is the artificial production of proteins, based on the genetic code (DNA). These proteins can then be used to immunize rabbits, which then form antibodies which bind to the protein. The antibodies are then coupled chemically to a fluorochrome and then used to trace the proteins in the cells under study.

⊙ Applications of fluoro-micro-chromy include quantification of DNA, chromosome banding, staining of amyloids, vital staining, etc.

In recent work, highly efficient fluorescent proteins such as the Green Fluorescent Protein (GFP) have been specifically fused on a DNA level to the protein of interest. This combined fluorescent protein is not toxic and hardly ever impedes the original task of the protein under study. Genetically modified cells or organisms directly express the fluorescently tagged proteins, which enables the study of the function of the original protein *in vivo*.

DARK-FIELD MICROSCOPY

Light optical microscopy works on the principle of light absorption and reflection. The non-deviated rays received at the other end of the objective lens system form a bright circular field of vision (field) while the deviated rays emanating from the specimen form the image.

The clarity of the image depends on the contrast between the image and field of vision. The contrast can be enhanced by any or a combination of the following ways.

1. Staining the specimen if it does not have colour of its own
2. Controlling the intensity of illumination

Use of conventional illumination produces a solid pencil cone of bright light to fall on the specimen. In this case both axial rays and inclined rays illuminate the object causing a very bright field of vision. Hence it is also called bright-field microscopy.

The disadvantage of bright-field microscopy is that colourless regions and those parts which do not have affinity to stains are not imaged properly owing to poor contrast. There are many alternatives to bright-field microscopy that increase the contrast between the background and the specimen without staining. This allows viewing live specimens with clarity. One of these alternatives is by rendering the field of vision dark so that contrast is enhanced. This is called dark-field microscopy.

Dark-field microscopy is an optical microscopy illumination technique used to enhance the contrast in unstained samples. In this, the specimen is illuminated by inclined rays and the field of vision is rendered dark by preventing the axial rays with the use of a circular stopper in the light path. The result is a bright image of the object against a dark background.

Dark-field microscopy uses a carefully aligned light source to minimize the quantity of directly transmitted light (i.e., unscattered light) entering the image, and only collected light scattered by the sample. This is done by confining the illumination to a ring of light.

This approach is akin to the visibility of dust particles laden in the air in a beam of light projected in a dark room. The same is invisible in a brightly illuminated room. In the dark-field microscopy also, the object under observation is brightly illuminated against a dark background. The object appears as a luminary body against a dark background. This is in contrast to the bright-field microscopy where, the object appears dark against a bright background (field of vision).

Improvising the Ordinary Light Optical Microscope for Dark-Field Microscopy

There is no special microscope model as a dark-field microscope. It is very simple to improvise an ordinary light optical microscope for dark-field microscopy work. The light passing through the central part of the condenser lens system is to be screened off allowing only the light in the periphery of the lens to pass. This ensures illumination of the object by inclined rays only.

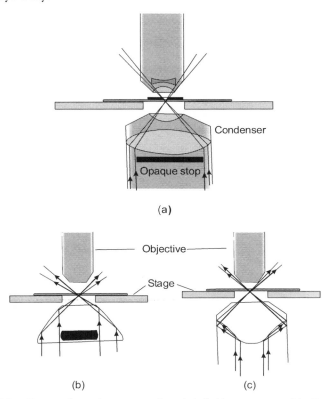

Figure 2.22 Types of condensers used in dark-field microscopy (a) Condenser with opaque stop (b) Paraboloid condenser (c) Cardioid condenser

This can be achieved by placing a circular disc called patch stop in between the iris diaphragm and the lens in the condenser. Special condensers (Figure 2.22) with such opaque patch stop (Figure 2.22a) are available. However, the same can be achieved by sticking a circular sticker in the centre of the condenser lens. This along with low-power objectives will suffice for ordinary dark-field observations. However, for higher power observations, special dark-field condensers with paraboloid and cardioid lenses are employed (Figure 2.22b and c).

Rheinberg illumination is a special variant of dark-field illumination and is named after its inventor, Julius Rheinberg. In this variant, transparent coloured filters are inserted just before the condenser so that light rays at high aperture are differently coloured than those at low aperture, e.g. the background to the specimen may be blue whilst the object appears self-luminous yellow. Other colour combinations are possible but their effectiveness is quite variable.

Principle

1. Light reaches the object mounted on the stage through the condenser.
2. The condenser lens focuses the light towards the sample.
3. The patch stop provided in the condenser lens blocks light around the central region allowing light to pass only along the periphery of the lens.
4. Of the light that enters the specimen, most is directly transmitted, while some is scattered from the sample.
5. The scattered light alone enters the objective lens and produces the image.
6. The directly transmitted light is not collected and is omitted.
7. Thus the field of vision is rendered dark and the image created is by the scattered light and therefore, cell components that reflect light are clear in the image.

Advantages

1. Dark-field microscopy produces a clear image in a dark background.
2. It is a very simple but effective technique for observing live and unstained biological samples such as smears from cultures and flagellates.
3. The sample/specimen has to be adequately illuminated. Sometimes strong illumination may become necessary and care must be exercised, so that the specimen is not damaged by strong illumination.

4. It clearly shows even transparent objects.

5. It is very simple to set up dark-field microscope with only basic equipment.

6. No sample preparation is required. Hence this allows viewing of live cells.

7. Images obtained in dark-field microscopy are almost free of artefacts. However, interpretation of the image requires caution as the dark features/components of the images of the same object obtained in the bright-field microscopy may be invisible and vice versa. Therefore, it is advisable to use both dark-field microscopy and bright-field microscopy as complementary to each other.

Limitations

⊙ Low light intensity in final image of many biological samples.

⊙ Low apparent resolution due to the blur of out-of-focus objects.

Applications

⊙ Ideal for the study of flagellated organisms.

⊙ Ideal for the study of cell suspensions from culture samples.

POLARIZED LIGHT MICROSCOPY

Principle

The light rays of ordinary visible white light travel in straight axes. If there is any obstruction in the path of light, the light rays are deviated.

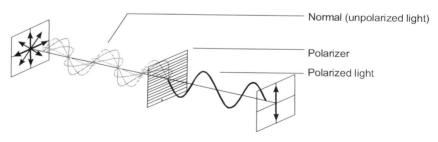

Figure 2.23 A wire grid polarizer converting normal light (unpolarized beam) into one with a single linear polarization

The light rays travelling in straight axes, exhibit movement in all directions when they hit or pass through any object on their way. There are some substances/materials that can re-orient the light waves passing through them in one plane. Such a substance is called a **polarizer**. All the rays of light that come out of a polarizer show movement in one plane only. Such a light is called polarized light (Figure 2.23). Therefore, the normal light is unpolarized.

A polarized light falling on or passing through a substance gets deviated or deflected either to the right or to the left depending on the structural chemistry of the substance. This ability of turning polarized light to the left or right is called the **optical property** of the substance. Based on the optical property, substances are of two types:

Optically isotropic substances   These deflect polarized light falling on them equally on all sides. The light waves that come out of the substance are of same wavelength and hence same refraction index in all directions. These substances exhibit a very limited degree of phase effect (phase change).

Optically anisotropic substances   These deflect polarized light falling on them to different extent on different sides. The light waves that come out of the substance on the other side are of two different wavelengths at mutually perpendicular planes. This phenomenon is called birefringence and these substances are called birefringent materials. The difference in the wavelengths at the two different planes is one-fourth of a lambda (λ).

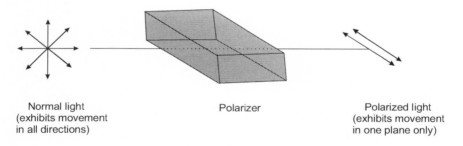

| Normal light (exhibits movement in all directions) | Polarizer | Polarized light (exhibits movement in one plane only) |

Figure 2.24   Polarization of light

Use of polarized light in microscopy has opened a new arena in biological research. Polarized light microscopy involves the use of polarized light (Figure 2.24) instead of the normal light.

Most biological compounds are stereo-isomers having asymmetric carbon atoms. These asymmetric carbon atoms render the molecules the property of turning the plane of polarized light impinging on them. Such compounds are said to be optically active. Every optically active compound has a corresponding isomer that rotates the plane of polarized light in exactly the opposite direction, e.g. dextro-sugars and laevo-sugars.

Polarimetry and Polarimeter

Polarimetry is the measurement of the polarization of light. It is an approach of measuring such deflections of polarized light by the chemical compounds. The scientific instrument used to make these measurements is called polarimeter (Figure 2.25).

Polarimetry is used to measure various optical properties of a material including linear birefringence, circular birefringence (also known as circular rotation or optical rotary dispersion), linear dichroism, circular dichroism and scattering.

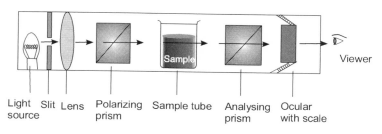

Light   Slit Lens Polarizing   Sample tube   Analysing   Ocular
source   prism   prism   with scale

Figure 2.25   Components of a polarimeter

A simple polarimeter consists of a long tube with flat glass ends, into which the sample is placed. Sodium lamp emitting light at 589 nm is used as a light source at one end. The light passing through a slit reaches a lens that focuses the light on to a Nicol prism or other polarizer. The prism works as a polarizer and therefore, the light coming out of the prism is polarized light. The sample contained in a 1 dm long tube, is introduced in the path of the polarized light. Another Nicol prism on the other side of the specimen tube functions as an analyser. The analyser is attached to an eyepiece which has a scale to measure the degree of rotation. The analyser–eyepiece unit can be rotated through 360°.

In the absence of an optically active substance (sample in the tube), the lens on the analyser side can be adjusted so that the intensity of light seen on the viewer side is maximum. When an optically active compound (specimen tube) is placed in the path of the polarized light, the plane of light is rotated. The viewing lens has to be rotated again until all light is shut off. The angle of rotation is read from reading on the scale. The specific rotation of the compound may then be calculated. If the analysing lens is rotated clockwise, the substance is said to be dextro-rotatory (+) and if it is rotated counter clockwise, the substance is said to be laevo-rotatory (−).

Thus polarimetry can be used for identifying unknown compounds and also for knowing the concentration of the known compounds.

The optical rotatory dispersion measurements can provide information about the atomic organization of a molecule.

The same working principle of a polarimeter is employed in polarized light microscopy so that the chemical nature of biological objects under microscopic observation can be understood by illuminating the object with polarized light, as every substance has a certain optical property, namely, dextro-rotatory or laevo-rotatory property, which is determined by its structural chemistry.

The polarized light microscope is basically a light compound microscope with the following additional components.

Polarizer and Analyser   Polarized light microscope contains a **polarizer** and an **analyser** in addition to the usual parts of the light microscope. Both the polarizer and analyser are made of **polaroid film** or **Nicol prism of calcite**.

Polarizer is fixed in the substage condenser. Therefore, only polarized light comes out of the condenser and falls on the object.

Analyser is present in the body tube on the other side of the objective. It is arranged in such a way that it can rotate in the horizontal plane.

When the polarizer and analyser are set at right angles to each other, light is screened or blocked for most part resulting in a dark field of vision.

When polarizer and analyser are set coinciding with each other, more of light passes through the object and the field of vision is bright (Figure 2.26).

Accessory slots   It is a semicircular plate provided above the objective lens system. It serves to eliminate the few rays that are vibrating in various other directions so that the image obtained will have a better contrast.

Circular Rotary Stage   The stage of the polarized light microscope is circular and can be rotated in the horizontal plane through 360°. This enables rotating/turning the object to either +45° or −45° of the median line.

Birefringence effect is obtained by setting the object mounted on the stage at either +45° or −45°, in between the polarizer and the analyser. Because of the birefringence, the image obtained is very clear. Birefringence or double refraction is the splitting of a light ray, generally by materials such as calcite crystal, into two components that travel at different velocities and are polarized at right angles to each other. This effect can occur only if the structure of the material is anisotropic. If the material is uniaxial (has a single axis of anisotropy), birefringence can be formalized by assigning two different refraction indices to the material for different polarizations.

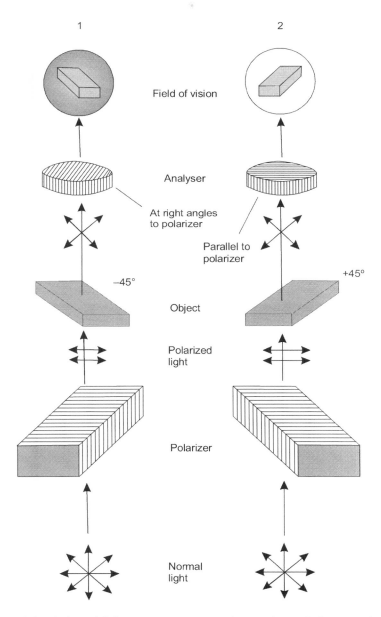

Figure 2.26   Polarized light microscopy—optical principle 1. Polarizer and analyser are set at right angles; object is turned to −45°. 2. Polariser and analyser are set parallel to each other; object is turned to +45°

Applications

1. The arrangement of the constituent molecules of the object under observation can be understood by using a polarized light microscope.
2. The spindle fibres of mitotic apparatus can be seen.
3. Parts of nerve cells can be seen clearly.
4. Grana and lamellae of chloroplasts can be seen clearly.

UV MICROSCOPY

The best resolving power that can be attained in a light microscope is approximately $0.2\ \mu$ as visible light has a wavelength of about $0.5\ \mu$ and the numerical aperture of the best lens is about 1.4.

The numerical aperture cannot be increased beyond this level and even by using the shortest possible wavelengths of visible light, namely about $0.4\ \mu$, the resolving power is not significantly improved.

Therefore, the only way to improve the resolving power is to use still shorter wavelengths to illuminate the object. Ultraviolet light, with a wavelength of about $0.3\ \mu$, offers the possibility of an approximately twofold improvement in resolving power.

However, the following hurdles are to be overcome in using UV light in microscopy.

⊙ UV light is not transmitted by glass. Therefore, the lenses as well as the slides and cover glasses made of quartz or fluorite are to be used. These are very expensive and are difficult to work with.

⊙ A special lamp is to be used as a source of UV light.

⊙ Our eyes cannot detect UV rays. Nor can the UV rays be allowed to fall on the eyes as they can damage the eyes.

Therefore, the image cast by the UV rays has to be captured on a screen for indirect viewing or be documented photographically.

Under optimal conditions, the UV microscope has a resolving power of $0.1\ \mu$. Until the advent of electron microscope, this was the upper limit of resolution available.

Certain cell components such as nucleic acids selectively absorb UV light of characteristic wavelengths. Therefore, such components can be identified and located in the cell using UV microscopy. The localization of various chemicals in cells is called cytochemistry.

With the advent of electron microscope, the use of UV microscopy has been limited to cytochemistry.

INTERFERENCE MICROSCOPY

The images obtained in conventional light microscopy have their own inherent limitations of resolution and contrast. The images do not present a relief and therefore lack three-dimensional effect.

Phase contrast microscopy was a step towards providing a better contrast to the image obtained using the normal visible light. The principle of obtaining increased or decreased amplitude by interference between out-of-phase waves and in-phase waves is used to produce contrast in the image. In phase contrast microscopy, light rays passing through the specimen alone are used to create the image.

Interference microscopy involves the principle of interferometry. In this approach light rays passing through the object and light rays passing through a reference slide minus specimen are made to interfere/coincide exactly to produce an interference pattern that helps to gain information about the optical density of the sample and to see otherwise invisible features.

Principle

Conventional interference microscope (Figure 2.27) uses two reflectors (M_1 and M_2) placed along the path of the light. A condenser lens (L_1) focuses the light on to M_2 placed at 45° in the path of light. The light is condensed on to the microslide containing the object (O). Light passing through the object is received by the objective lens L_2 and is diverted by 45° by a partial reflector S_2 placed in its path. The light diverted by 45° by this partial reflector is received by the ocular/eyepiece (E).

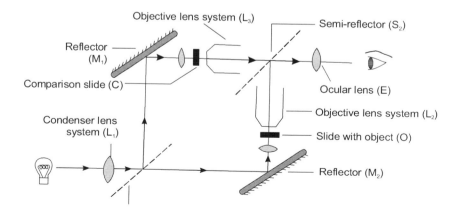

Figure 2.27 Interference light microscopy

An additional reflector system consisting of a partial- or semi-reflector (S_1) and a reflector (M_1) is provided to create interference effect. The partial reflector S_1 placed in the path of the light to M_2 reflects a part of the light on to the reflector M_1. The light reflected by M_1 is focused on to a reference slide (C) which does not contain object. The objective lens L_3 receives this light and focuses it on the partial reflector S_2.

The partial reflector S_2 is placed in such a way that the light wave passing through the object slide (O) and those passing through the reference or comparison slide (C) are made to coincide precisely and made to reach the observer's eye through the ocular.

DIFFERENTIAL INTERFERENCE MICROSCOPY

A more advanced approach used in interference microscopy is the use of polarized light and Nomarski prism to enhance contrast in unstained samples. This approach is also known as differential interference contrast (DIC) microscopy or Nomarski differential interference contrast (NDIC) microscopy or simply Nomarski microscopy.

It is a relatively complex lighting scheme that produces a black to white image on a grey background without the bright diffraction halo that is characteristic of the phase contrast image. Differences in optical density show up as differences in relief. For example, a nucleus in the cell appears as a globule.

Principle

The DIC microscope works by separating a beam of polarized light into two beams namely ordinary and extraordinary beams. These two beams travel at a minimal space from each other (say, less than the maximum resolution of the objective). After passing through the specimen, the two beams are re-united by a similar prism in the objective.

In a homogeneous specimen, there is no difference between the two beams, and no contrast is generated. However, near a refractive boundary (for example, a nucleus with the cytoplasm), the difference between the ordinary and extraordinary beams generates a relief in the image.

As polarized light is used, the DIC microscope is provided with a polarizer below the condenser and an analyser above the objective. In this respect the DIC microscope resembles the polarized light microscope.

A Wollaston prism or a Nomarski-modified Wollaston prism is used to split the polarized light into two beams.

Types of prisms

Wollaston prism Wollaston prism (Figure 2.28) is a birefringent polarizer. It consists of two triangular calcite prisms with orthogonal crystal axes that are cemented together. The normal light (unpolarized light) entering the Wollaston prism splits at the internal interface. The resulting linearly polarized rays leave the prism at a divergence angle of 15° to 45°.

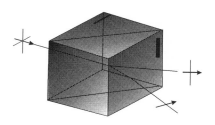

Figure 2.28   A Wollaston prism

Nomarski prism The Nomarski prism is a variant of Wollaston prism. This is used widely in DIC microscopes. The Nomarski modification causes the two rays to come to a focal point outside the body of the prism. This allows a greater flexibility when setting the microscope. The prism can be actively focused.

Components of Differential Interference Contrast (DIC) Microscope

The basic construction of the DIC microscope is the same as that of normal light microscope with the following additional components (Figure 2.29).

Polarizer A polarizer is provided next to the field diaphragm. This polarizes the unpolarized light received through the field diaphragm from the source.

Nomarski prism Two Nomarski-modified Wollaston prisms are used in the DIC microscope.

Main or first Nomarski (modified Wollaston) prism The first Nomarski prism is provided in between the analyser and condenser lens. This splits the polarized light entering into it into ordinary and extraordinary rays which are polarized at 90° to each other.

Auxiliary or second Nomarski (modified Wollaston) prism The second Nomarski prism is provided just above the objective lens system. It re-combines the two different beams into one polarized at 135°.

Analyser   An analyser is provided in the body tube below the ocular lens system. It can be rotated either to the right or to the left of the median line.

Working/Functioning of the DIC Microscope

The light source generates normal light (unpolarized light).

The field diaphragm in the condenser regulates the light path.

The unpolarized light is polarized at 45° by the polarizer. The polarized light reaches the main (first) Nomarski-modified wollaston prism (Figure 2.29). The prism splits the polarized light into two rays namely ordinary and the extraordinary rays, polarized at 90° to each other.

The condenser lens focuses these two rays onto the specimen. The two rays pass through the specimen at a very minimal distance from each other, around 0.2 μm apart.

Thus the sample is illuminated by two coherent light sources, one with 0° polarization and the other with 90° polarization. These two illuminations are not quite aligned. One is slightly offset with respect to the other.

The two rays traverse different, though adjacent, areas of the specimen. The difference in optical density of the two areas causes a change in phase of one ray relative to the other. Thus the two rays experience different optical path lengths.

The image of the specimen will now be carried by both the 0° and 90° polarized light. Individually, these two would be bright-field images of the sample, though slightly offset from each other.

The two rays do not interfere at this stage because of different polarizations.

These rays which also differ in phase relative to each other, are focused on to the second Nomarski-modified Wollaston prism.

The second prism recombines the two rays into one, polarized at 135°. This recombination of the rays leads to interference resulting in brightening or darkening the image at that point according to the optical path difference.

The two bright-field images are overlaid and their polarizations aligned by the prism, so that they can interfere.

The images do not line up or superimpose because of the offset in illumination, i.e., the ray that passed through a particular point in the specimen interferes with a ray that passed through a different point and has a slightly different phase.

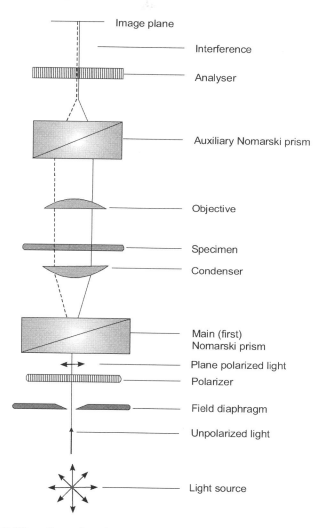

Figure 2.29 Optical path and working of the NDIC microscope

As the difference in phase is caused by the difference in optical path length, the recombination of the rays causes "optical differentiation" of the optical path length giving a three-dimensional quality to the image obtained.

The interference of the rays may be either constructive or destructive giving rise to the characteristic appearance of three dimensions.

Generally, the phase difference giving rise to the interference is very small, very rarely being larger than 90° which is one-fourth of the wavelength. This is because the refraction indices of the specimen and the medium it is in (the mounting medium) are almost similar. For example, a cell mounted in water has a refraction index difference of only around 0.05. This kind of small phase difference leads to proper functioning of the DIC.

If the difference between refraction indices of the two points/medium and specimen is too large, the phase difference between the two rays would reach 180° (half of a wavelength). This is a complete destructive interference resulting in a dark region.

Any further increase in the difference in the refraction indices would cause further increase in phase difference moving toward 360° (a full wavelength). This is a complete constructive interference resulting in an anomalous bright region.

Advantages

- Most suitable for observing live and unstained biological samples.
- Smear samples from tissue culture or aquatic unicellular organisms which cannot be viewed satisfactorily in conventional light microscopes can be viewed very clearly in DIC.
- The image obtained in DIC has very good contrast.
- In DIC, the condenser aperture can be used fully open which reduces the depth of the field and maximizes resolution.
- When used in optimal conditions, the image is entirely free of artefacts and is of outstanding quality.

Limitations

- DIC requires transparent/thin samples with a refraction index very similar to that of the surrounding medium.
- It must be kept in mind that the three-dimensional effect of the image obtained is an optical effect and that the relief does not necessarily resemble the true shape.
- The interpretation of the image obtained in DIC should take into account the orientation of the Nomarski prisms and the apparent lighting direction, as features parallel to this will not be visible. This is, however, easily overcome by simply rotating the sample and observing the changes in the image.

CONFOCAL MICROSCOPY

In a conventional wide-field microscopy, the entire specimen is bathed in light from the light source and can be viewed directly by eye. The image thus created may be projected on an image-capture device and viewed or may be photographed.

The method of image formation in a confocal microscope is different. The specimen is illuminated by one or more focused point beams of light, usually from a laser source. The point of illumination is brought to focus in the specimen by the objective lens and laterally scanned using some form of scanning device under computer control. The sequences of points of light from the specimen are detected by a photomultiplier tube (PMT) through a pinhole or a slit. The output from the PMT is built into an image and displayed by the computer.

Although unstained specimens can be viewed using light reflected back from the specimen, they are usually labelled with one or more fluorescent probes (dyes).

Confocal microscopy (CFM) provided a leap over the conventional light microscopy. The greatest advantage in this approach is that the out-of-focus details are automatically eliminated from the image formed, thus rendering it blur-free.

Though the principle for this special kind of microscopy was developed by Marvin Minsky in 1953, it was not until the end of the 1980s that confocal microscopy could become a standard imaging technique.

The key feature of CFM is its ability to produce blur-free images of thick specimens at various depths. A laser beam is used for scanning the object at different planes. It combines fluorescence microscopy with electronic image analysis to obtain three-dimensional images of the specimen. Images are taken point by point and reconstructed with a computer, rather than being projected through an eyepiece.

In CFM, all out-of-focus structures are suppressed at image formation. This is made possible by an arrangement of diaphragms situated at optically conjugated points of the path of rays. Of these diaphragms, one acts as a point light source and the other as a point detector respectively. The latter (detection pinhole) suppresses the rays emanating from the planes out of focus (Figure 2.30).

The depth of the focal plane is determined by three parameters namely, wavelength of light, numerical aperture (NA) and diameter of the diaphragm (diameter of the light path). Of these, the diameter of the light path is the most important. In CFM, the confocal effect and diameter of detection pinhole are inversely related. At a wider detection pinhole, the confocal effect is reduced.

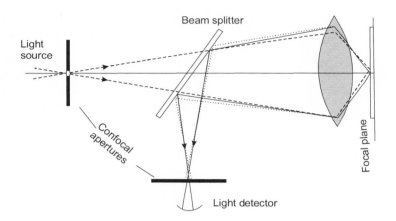

Figure 2.30   Principle of confocality

Since laser beam is used, confocal microscopy is also called laser confocal microscopy (LCFM).

Mirror scanners are provided to obtain full image. These scanners help in moving the image point across the specimen so that a full image is obtained and hence the microscopy is also called laser scanning confocal microscopy (LSCFM).

A photomultiplier transforms the reflected/emitted light passing through the detector pinhole into electrical signals.

A computer converts the signals, and the image thus constructed is displayed on a monitor screen.

Working Principle of CFM

The optical path and working principle of CFM (Figure 2.31) is as follows:

A very small/narrow beam of light is supplied by a laser. The lasers used in CFM are high intensity, monochromatic light sources.

The laser beam of light is passed through an excitation filter (fixed or programmable) and a lens and made to fall on a diaphragm, whose pinhole serves as a point light source.

A beam splitter, fixed or programmable (F/P) placed on the light path deflects the beam down on to the fluorescent specimen.

The light emanating/reflected from the focal plane is a mixture of fluorescence emission from the specimen and the reflected laser from the illuminated spot in the specimen. The objective lens picks this mixture and passes the same through the beam splitter.

The beam splitter separates the light mixture. It allows the laser light to pass through and reflects the fluorescence to fall on the second diaphragm, whose pinhole serves as detector pinhole.

The detector aperture obstructs the light that is not coming from the focal point, as shown by the dotted grey line in the image resulting in sharper images, compared to those obtained in conventional fluorescence microscopy. It also makes imaging of various z-axis planes of the sample possible.

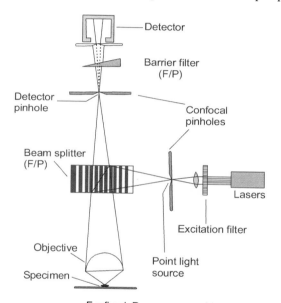

F = fixed; P = programmable

Figure 2.31   Optical path and working principle of confocal microscope

The two diaphragms are confocal and the pinholes function confocally.

The term confocal arises from the presence of the diaphragm in the conjugated focal plane (confocal plane).

The reflected light converged by the detector pinhole passes through a barrier filter (fixed/programmable).

A photodetection device consisting of either a photomultiplier tube (PMT) or Avalanche photodiode serves as a detector. It captures the spectral composition of the reflected light and transforms it into electrical signals.

The detected light originating from the illuminated point (volume) in the specimen represents one pixel in the resulting image.

As the laser scans over the plane of focus (plane of interest), a whole image is obtained pixel by pixel and line by line. The brightness of the resulting image-pixel corresponds to the relative intensity of detected fluorescent light.

The beam is scanned across the sample in the horizontal plane using one or more oscillating mirrors. This scanning method is rather slow and the scan speed can be varied.

Slower scans provide a better *signal-to-noise ratio* resulting in better contrast and higher resolution.

Different focal planes of the specimen can be scanned by raising or lowering the stage of the microscope.

The computer analyses these signals and produces an image that is displayed on the monitor screen. The computer can also generate a three-dimensional image of the specimen by assembling a stack of these two-dimensional images from successive focal planes.

Construction of a Confocal Microscope

The confocal microscope, complete with the work station, is an elaborate set-up which includes the following components (Figure 2.32):

Microscope   The microscope has all the components of a conventional microscope built to a very high precision. The objectives are precision-built to work precisely at wide wavelengths and very low levels of light.

The body of the microscope is fixed while the stage is vertically movable. Therefore, the stage is called focusing stage. The stage is an intricate high-precision mechanism providing movement of the specimen in the x, y and z axes. The x, y stage is electronically driven. This is inclusive of z stage which is galvanometrically driven.

A confocal scan head is provided on top of the body of the microscope.

The microscope unit is placed on an antivibration table which is separated from the large, shielded rack, which houses the lasers and electronics of the CFM.

Shielded rack cum computer table   A large shielded rack houses the laser and electronic components of the CFM.

The laser/electronics control panel and programmable manual control panel are positioned on the rack.

The laser is housed in a shielded box on the side of the rack.

The PC workstation is provided on the side next to the laser box.

Monitor(s) is/are placed on top of the table surface.

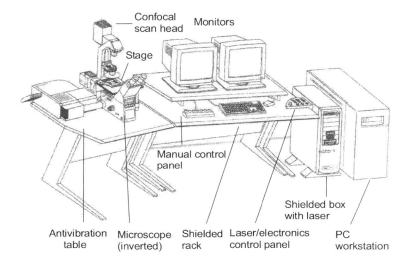

Figure 2.32   Confocal microscope (complete with workstation)

Improvements over Conventional Light Microscopy and Fluorescence Microscopy

1. Light rays from focal plane alone are recorded. The light rays from outside the focal plane are eliminated by de-focusing. The parts outside the focal plane are gradually cut off and they become darker and eventually disappear. This feature is called optical scanning.

2. The object can be scanned in x/y direction as well as in z direction. This allows viewing the object on all sides.

3. The small dimension of the illuminating light spot in the focal plane minimizes stray light.

4. Image processing is possible, i.e., many sectional views/images can be superimposed giving an extended focus image. Since it is done without reducing the aperture, resolution is not sacrificed. (In conventional light microscopy, it can be achieved only by reduction of aperture, thus sacrificing resolution.)

5. Optical scanning/section and image processing help in recording three-dimensional data of the object.

6. With CFM, extremely high-quality images can be obtained from specimens prepared for conventional optical microscopy.

7. CFM is most suitable for the ever-increasing number of applications in cell biology that rely on imaging both fixed and living cells and tissues.

8. The capability of collecting serial optical sections from thick specimens has rendered confocal technology to be one of the most important advances ever achieved in optical microscopy.

9. Poor contrast is inherent with imaging thick specimens in a conventional microscope. The thickness of the specimen under observation is a very important criterion deciding the quality of the image in conventional light microscopy, where best results are obtained in thickness below 10 to 15 μ. This is because thick specimens suffer from a tremendous amount of extraneous light in out-of-focus regions. Confocal technique is the best suited for thick specimens, as this eliminates the light emanating from the out-of-focus regions in the specimen.

Advantages

In CFM, multiple images are collected simultaneously in digital form into a computer. This affords a high degree of flexibility in image display and analysis. This is the greatest advantage in confocal microscopy.

Important Aspects of Confocal Microscopy

Confocal principle and resolution   Enhancement of resolution by the confocal principle is best understood by comparing it with yet another scanning technique namely, scanning electron microscopy (SEM).

In LSCFM, a fluorescent specimen is illuminated point by point by a laser source. Each volume element is associated with discrete fluorescence intensity.

The size of scanning volume is determined by the diffraction limit of the optical system. This is due to the fact that the image of the scanning laser is not an infinitely small point, but a three-dimensional diffraction pattern.

The size of this diffraction pattern and the focal volume it defines are controlled by the numerical aperture of the system's objective lens and the wavelength of the laser used. This is the classical resolution limit of conventional optical microscopes using wide-field illumination.

However, LSCFM overcomes this resolution limit of wide-field illuminating techniques as only light generated in a small volume element is detected at a time. It is to be noted that the effective volume of light generation is usually smaller than the volume of illumination, i.e., the diffraction pattern of detectable light creation is sharper and smaller than the diffraction pattern of illumination.

In other words, the resolution limit in CFM depends not only on the probability of illumination, but also on the probability of creating enough detectable photons, so that the actual addressable volume being associated with a generated light intensity is smaller than the illuminated volume.

The fluorescent dyes used in CFM contribute to improvement in lateral resolution, depending on their fluorescence properties.

The use of light creation processes with much lower probabilities of second harmonic generation (SHG) reduces the volume of addressing to a small region of highest laser illumination intensity.

The probability of decrease in creation of detectable photons has a bad effect on the signal-to-noise ratio. This is compensated by using more sensitive photodetectors. Increasing the intensity of the illuminating laser point source also helps, but this approach is to be avoided as it may result in bleaching of the fluorescence or may damage the specimen.

Resolution and contrast In a perfect optical system, resolution is limited by numerical aperture (NA) of the optical components and the wavelength of the light, both incident and detected. The concept of resolution is inseparable from contrast. Resolution is defined as, "the minimum separation between two points that results in a certain contrast between them." However, in a CFM, contrast is determined by the following factors: 1. number of photons collected from the specimen, 2. the dynamic range of the signal, 3. optical aberrations of the imaging system and 4. the number of picture elements (pixels) per unit area.

Imaging modes Many different imaging modes are used in CFM to suit a vast variety of specimens.

- ⊙ High-resolution images called optical sections are produced in sequence through relatively thick sections of more than 20 μ thickness or whole mounts of specimens.

- ⊙ The optical sections are the basic image units from which data are collected from the specimens in single-, double-, triple- or multiple-wavelength illumination modes.

- ⊙ Images collected with the various illumination and labelling strategies are stored.

- ⊙ Live cell imaging and time-lapse sequences are possible.

⊙ The digital image processing allows z series and 3-D representation of specimens. Time-lapse sequencing of images enables presentation of 3-D data as 4-D imaging.

⊙ The early versions of confocal microscopes reflected light as imaging mode. Later versions incorporated the use of laser scanning as the imaging mode. Any of the transmitted light imaging modes commonly employed in microscopy can also be used in the laser scanning confocal microscopes.

⊙ The LSCFM is routinely used to produce digital images of single-, double- and triple-labelled fluorescent samples. The use of red, green and blue colour is called RGB staining.

Factors affecting the images   Quantitative 3-D imaging is complicated by the following factors.

1. Artefacts due to specimen preparation
2. Controllable and uncontrollable experimental variables
3. Configuration problems with the microscope
4. Objective magnification
5. Coverslip thickness
6. Specimen embedding medium

Objectives of a CFM

In any optical microscope configuration, the objective is the most critical component determining the information content of the image.

The design of the objective and its performance under the specific conditions employed for the observation has a bearing on the following:

1. The contrast and resolution of fine specimen detail
2. The depth within the specimen from which information can be obtained and
3. Lateral extent of the image field

In CFM, the objective also serves as the illumination condenser and is required to perform with high precision, at a wide range of wavelengths and at very low light levels, without introducing unacceptable **image-degrading noise**.

Scanning Systems

The following sequential events are involved in confocal imaging.

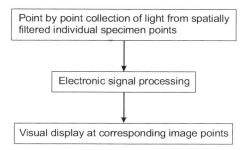

In order to achieve confocal operation, any one or a combination of the following scanning approaches, each of which is meant for a specific application, are to be incorporated.

- ⊙ Laterally translating specimen stage coupled to a stationary illuminating light beam (stage scanning)
- ⊙ A scanned beam with a stationary stage (beam scanning)
- ⊙ By maintaining both the stage and the light source stationary while scanning the specimen, with an array of light points transmitted through apertures in a spinning Nipkow disc

Signal-to-Noise Considerations

In case of imaging techniques including confocal imaging that employ digital imaging technique, the effect of signal sampling on contrast and resolution must be considered.

The measured signal-level values do not directly represent the number of photons emitted or scattered by the specimen, but are proportional to that number.

Each individual sample of signal intensity is only an approximation of the number of collected photons. It will vary with repeated measurement. The variation, referred to as noise, imparts an uncertainty in the quantification of intensity, and therefore in the contrast and resolution of the image data.

Electronic Light Detectors

In modern wide-field fluorescence and LSCFM, the collection and measurement of secondary emission gathered by the objective can be accomplished by many classes of photosensitive detectors, including photodiodes, and solid state charge-coupled devices (CCDs).

In CFM, fluorescence emission is directed through a pinhole aperture positioned near the image plane, to exclude light from fluorescent structures located away from the objective focal plane, thus reducing the amount of light available for image formation.

The low light levels thus encountered in CFM necessitate the use of highly sensitive photon detectors that do not require spatial discrimination, but instead respond very quickly with a high level of sensitivity to a continuous flux of varying light intensity.

Specimen Preparation for CFM

CFM is suitable for observing specimens either alive or fixed. Staining of the specimen is not a must, but if stained, gives better images.

The procedures that have been developed over many years for preparing (fixing, staining, sectioning, etc.) specimens for imaging with conventional wide-field microscope, form the basis of specimen preparation for CFM.

Fluorescent dyes that stain specific cellular organelles and structures are used as probes. Fluorescently labelled phalloidins that target polymerized actins in the cells are also used.

Use of fluorescence as an imaging mode in LSCFM has the following advantages: 1. High degree of sensitivity, 2. Structural components of cells can be targeted and 3. Even dynamic processes in the cells can be targeted. Because of these advantages, biological LSCFM relies heavily on fluorescence as imaging mode.

It is now possible to construct synthetic aromatic organic compounds for specific purposes in molecular biology. Many fluorescent probes are designed using such synthetic compounds, for the following purposes.

1. to bind with a biological macromolecule such as a protein or nucleic acid, and

2. to localize within a specific structural region in the cell such as cytoskeleton, mitochondria, Golgi apparatus, ER and nucleus.

Probes are employed to monitor cellular dynamic processes and also the localized cellular environmental variables such as concentrations of inorganic metallic ions, pH, reactive oxygen species and membrane potential.

Fluorescent dyes are also useful in monitoring cellular integrity (live versus dead and apoptosis), endocytosis, exocytosis, membrane fluidity, protein trafficking, signal transduction and enzyme activity.

Fluorescent probes are widely applied to genetic mapping and chromosome analysis in the field of molecular genetics.

A number of relatively simple protocols have been developed for the large number of fluorescent probes that are available.

Spectral Bleed-through Artefacts in CFM

Sometimes, a photomultiplier channel or the filter combination reserved for a fluorophore detects the emission of a second fluorophore. This is called spectral bleed-through of fluorescence often termed crossover or crosstalk. This complicates the interpretation of experimental results.

Therefore, while planning multiple-label fluorescence staining protocols, fluorophores (probes) should be chosen in such a way that bleed-through artefacts are very minimal.

Laser Safety

The following are some of the major safety concerns in CFM.

1. Exposure to the laser beam.
2. Electrical hazards associated with high voltages within the laser and its power supply.
3. Damage to eyes that can be caused by laser beam.
4. Beams of high power can burn the skin and can burn or damage other materials.

There have been instances of deaths attributable to contact with high-voltage laser-related components.

USEFUL TIPS ON HOW TO USE AND MAINTAIN MICROSCOPES

Microscope is the most extensively used tool in biology. As with any other scientific equipment or tool, microscopes also need to be cared and maintained properly, so that they will serve the user for several decades.

A book on microscopy will be incomplete without a unit on important tips (do's and don'ts) on how to use and maintain microscopes.

The purpose of this unit is therefore, to draw the attention of the teachers and the taught of biology, towards the importance of maintaining microscopes clean and in ready-to-use state.

General Guidelines

1. Always keep the microscope covered with a polythene cover inside the wooden cabinet meant for it.

2.   It is advisable to inscribe the stock serial number on the body of the microscope. It is imperative to inscribe the number on all detachable accessory parts especially oculars and objective lens systems.

3.   Avoid using the oculars and objectives of different microscopes interchangeably.

4.   There is always a tendency to separate the additional oculars in all kinds of microscopes and hand-rests and contrast plates of dissection microscope for safe-keeping! This is a wrong practice. Students should be trained to be the microscopes with all the accessories.

5.   During transportation, always keep the microscope in the wooden cabinet covered with a polythene bag/pouch.

6.   When the microscope is to be carried, always carry it with both the hands. Grasp the arm firmly with one hand and support the base with the other arm.

7.   The body tube along with the stage and illuminating system can be inclined to convenient angle in students' compound microscopes. Repeated inclination loosens the hinge joint. Moreover, it is a common practice for students to tilt the body with the microslide mounted loosely, resulting in breakage of the slide. As far as possible, practice to use the microscope keeping the body of the microscope vertically.

Guide to a Beginner

The stepwise instruction on using a microscope for routine observation are given below.

1.   Keep the compound microscope on a firm clean surface/table top near a light source, be it natural daylight or artificial electric lamp.

2.   Clean the body with the help of a clean soft white cloth. Keep a piece of soft white cloth always handy for this. **Dust is the first enemy in microscopy.**

3.   Turn the revolving nosepiece so that the lowest power objective lens system is clicked into position. The lowest power objective is the shortest.

Focusing the light into the optical path

1.   Focusing the light into the optical path of the microscope is the most important next step.

2.   If the microscope is provided with a condenser, open the iris diaphragm fully.

3. If there is no condenser and only a disc diaphragm is provided, turn the disc so that the largest aperture (circular window) is brought in line with the optical path.

4. Look through the ocular lens system and turn the reflector towards the light source, until the field of vision becomes fully bright.

5. Remember that the plane side of the reflector is to be used if a condenser is present. If otherwise, only the concave side is to be used.

Mounting the slide

1. Always use clean microslides. Keep a separate piece of soft, white cloth for cleaning the microslides.

2. Place the microslide on the stage. Looking from sides, move the slide in such a way that the object is brought to the path of light. Now secure it with the stage clips.

Focusing

⊙ The proper way to focus a microscope is to start with the lowest power objective lens system first.

⊙ Looking from the side, bring down the objective lens as close to the specimen as possible without touching it.

⊙ Now, look through the ocular and *focus upward only* until the image is sharp.

⊙ If unable to get the object in focus, the process is to be repeated again.

⊙ Once the image is sharp with the low-power lens, turn over to the objective of the next higher power and fine-focus it.

Under low power

1. Looking at the objective lens system and the stage from the side, turn the coarse focus knob so that the objective moves down.

2. Move the objective as far as it will go, without touching the slide.

3. In case of models with fixed body and vertically movable stage, move the stage upwards as far as it will go.

4. Now looking through the ocular, turn the coarse focus knob and move the objective lens system upwards until the object on the slide is brought to clear focus. In case of movable stage, move the stage down away from the objective lens until the object comes to clear focus.

5. Unfasten the slide, and move the slide while continuing to look through the microscope to bring the desired area for observation. Once it is achieved, fasten the slide again.

6. Now turn the fine focus knob to get a clearer image.

Under high power

1. Once the object is brought to clear focus under low power, focusing with further higher power objectives will be easier with the minimal use of focusing adjustment.

2. Looking from the side, rotate the nosepiece so that the next higher power objective is brought in the optical path.

3. If the microscope is built parfocally, the object will be in perfect focus once the high-power objective is clicked to the optical path. Further focusing will not be necessary. Unfortunately, most makes lack parfocality, necessitating further focusing on switch over with objectives.

4. Always use fine focus knobs to focus while working under high-power objectives.

5. Working distance decreases with objectives of higher powers. Objectives of most students' compound microscopes have NA of 0.85. The thickness of the slide and coverslip are to be discounted in this. This is the reason why objectives of most students' microscopes are not able to work beyond a distance of 0.6 mm. This has to be remembered while using high-power objectives.

6. Do not allow the lens of the objective to touch the slide.

Keeping the microscope back after use

1. When finished with the microscopy work under high-power objective, always raise the body tube a little, by turning the coarse-focus knob and then click the low-power objective back to position.

2. Clean the microscope and put back the dust cover on it.

3. Keep the microscope in its wooden cabinet and lock it.

General Tips on Usage of Microscope

1. Most of us tend to close the other eye while viewing through the ocular, in a monocular microscope with one eye. This leads to eye strain, hindering prolonged observation. Keeping the other eye open is the proper way to use a monocular microscope. It may be difficult in the beginning but one gets used to, with practice.

2. Remember that the image obtained is inverted. When the slide is moved to the right, the image goes to the left.

3. Do not ever touch the optics of the oculars and objectives with fingers. Always use "lens-cleaning papers" to clean them.

4. Many have a tendency to blow through the mouth over the optics. This is to be avoided as the moisture-laden air from the mouth, leads to fungal growth on the optics.

Microscopes are expensive instruments. Most makes are built sturdily for a long life. Handled and maintained properly, they will last for many years.

Attributes/Parts that are to be Checked while Purchasing a Microscope

Size   Generally students' compound microscopes are available in two sizes, namely junior model and senior model.

Junior model, also known as introductory or elementary model, is ¾ size or smaller, measuring 11 to 12 inches in height. These are suitable for students, younger than 13 years.

Senior models, also known as full size, are generally 14 inches in height.

Mobility   Two types of focusing arrangements are available in microscopes.

Fixed stage and movable body tube   In this type, the body tube moves vertically up and down while focusing. The stage remains fixed. Most students' microscopes meant for routine class work and demonstration purpose are of this type.

Movable stage and fixed body tube   In this type, the stage moves up and down vertically while focusing. The body tube remains fixed. This is preferred in case of research microscopes, as the fixed body can support the weight of photomicrographic attachment. However, this type, in junior models, is reported to give problems.

Material and finish   Basic frame and most components should be made of metal. Look for the general finish and weight of the microscope. Sturdier, the better is the microscope. Evaluate the general appearance of all metal and optical surfaces.

Rack-and-pinion   Rack-and-pinion mechanism is the most important for focusing. Rack is visible and pinion is invisible (refer Figure 2.10). Ensure that the rack-and-pinion is made of copper/brass. The teeth of the cog-wheel (pinion) should neatly engage the teeth in the rack. Then only, the movable part (stage/body tube) will move smoothly when the focusing knob is turned. There should be no rough spots.

⊙   Models with two separate focusing knobs (coarse and fine) are preferred for use, by beginners (students).

- ⊙ Single "intermediate" focusing knob is suitable only in expensive models meant for finer handling.

- ⊙ Check if the "dovetail" (Figure 2.13) is machined properly and fits accurately. Improper cut may lead to problems later.

- ⊙ Excess of grease on moving parts may be an attempt to cover deficiencies in any of these aspects.

- ⊙ Backlash in operation of rack-and-pinion shows that the gear wheel and rack are not engaged properly. Move the body tube/stage all the way up and down and try to turn the knob a little further. Any slight movement on the part of the body tube/stage indicates that the gear wheel and rack are not engaged fully.

- ⊙ Also check the strength of the slip clutch (check nut) by continuing to turn the knob after reaching some resistance.

Drift   The movable part should not drift down on its own.

- ⊙ In models with movable stage, gently press down the stage with a finger. The stage should not drift down.

- ⊙ Similarly, in models with movable body tube, gently press down the ocular with a finger without touching the lens. The body tube should not move.

- ⊙ If drift is felt, ask the service engineer to set it right. Drifting stage and body tube will frustrate the user.

Alignment of nosepiece and stage   The nosepiece and the optical path (circular window) of the stage should be perfectly aligned. After fine-focusing of the mounted slide, tilt the stage slightly. The specimen should continue to be in focus, in the whole field of vision. If the stage is not aligned properly with the nosepiece, the specimen will be out-of-focus, on one side or the other.

Parfocality

- ⊙ With a slide mounted on the stage, the image should remain close to focus when changing objectives. Only a slight adjustment of fine focus should be required to sharpen the image as objectives are changed.

- ⊙ Parfocality is a very important requisite in a compound microscope.

Parcentricity

- ⊙ While at the lowest power objective, move and position the specimen to the centre of the field of vision. The area of observation should remain relatively centred with every move up, to successive objectives.

- ⊙ Parcentricity is a very important attribute of the nosepiece design. If the objectives are not parcentric, then the observer will have to search for the area of interest every time, he shifts to the next higher power objective. This is a manufacturing defect which cannot be corrected.

Cleaning the lenses (optics) Optics are the most important components of the microscope. They are to be kept clean to obtain the best images in the microscope. The best way to avoid having to clean the lenses of the microscope is to use the microscope carefully and keep it covered when not in use. Following are the useful tips to be followed meticulously to clean lenses which are dirty or gummed up with mounting media or stain:

- ⊙ Clean the microscope lenses (optics) only when they are dirty.
- ⊙ Use only proper materials for cleaning.
- ⊙ If the field of vision appears dirty probably the dirt is on the lenses. Try to find whether it is on the ocular lens system or objective lens system.
- ⊙ If the dirty spot turns when the eyepiece (ocular) is turned, probably it is on the eyepiece lens.
- ⊙ If the dirty spot does not move when the eyepiece is turned but seen at all powers of objective, it is internal. It warrants cleaning by a professional.
- ⊙ If the dirt is seen at one power, it is most likely on that particular objective lens.
- ⊙ Use a squeeze bulb or a camera lens cleaner bulb with the camel hair brush on the end to blow off the dirt. If more air pressure is needed, compressed air cans can be used. **But never use sprays with cleaners.** Once blown clean, wipe the lens with lens-cleaning paper (Kodak Lens Tissue).
- ⊙ Swipe the lens with the tissue paper in one direction rather than rubbing in a circular motion. **Do not clean lenses with ordinary cloth, paper towels or fingers.**
- ⊙ A regular lens brush can hold grit and cause scratching. Therefore the tissue can be rolled into a tube and one end of the tube can be torn to form a feathery brush like end. It can be used as a one-time brush. Use several for very dirty lenses.
- ⊙ If the dirt is present even after blowing and swiping operations, one may need to use a solvent.
- ⊙ When using solvents, put a drop or two on the lens cleaning tissue paper and hold it against the lens for a few seconds to dissolve the dirt (cud or grime). Then wipe it free.

- Distilled water is the first solvent to try. If it does not work, alcohol can be tried.

- Isopropyl alcohol is one of the best solvents recommended for cleaning lenses. It must be at least 90% pure.

- If balsam is stuck to the lens, a stronger solvent such as acetone or xylene is to be tried. It has to be borne in mind that acetone and xylene dissolve plastic and paints.

- When using organic solvents, put only a small amount on the tissue paper. Always apply it from underside going upwards to the lens. This will keep the liquid from running down into the lens. Do not remove the lens from the assembly unless absolutely necessary. Never soak even the tip of an objective lens in a container of solvent. It could dissolve the cement used to hold the glass lenses in place.

- If the objective lens gets smeared with glycerine, blood or other albuminous material, swipe it with lens paper dipped in a weak ammonia solution (one dropper full of household ammonia in ½ cup water).

- While using 100× objective with immersion oil, always swipe the excess oil off the lens with tissue paper after every use. Dust may build up on the lightly oiled surface of the lens. To remove the oil completely, use a solvent that can dissolve the immersion oil used. Consult the MSDS info that is supplied with the immersion oil to see what solvents are recommended. Always remember to clean the immersion objective lens, top lens of the condenser and the two surfaces of the slide every time after use.

- Professional cleaning and adjusting should be performed whenever necessary.

- Do not attempt to clean or adjust the inner optics of your microscope.

- The microscope should be kept in a low-vibration smoke-free room that is as clean as possible and has minimum disturbance of the circulated air.

- When not in use, keep the microscope covered in its cabinet.

- If a heavy-duty vinyl dust cover is available use it to cover the microscope. Dust may accumulate on the dust cover. Therefore, double-cover it with a plastic shopping bag. When dust builds up on the shopping bag, replace it.

- Keep all the accessories in air-tight containers.

- Avoid using corrosive solvents to clean any part of the microscope. Use only diluted soapy water to clean non-optical surfaces.

TECHNICAL TIPS FOR OIL-IMMERSION MICROSCOPY

While using 100× oil-immersion objectives, keep the following techniques and precautions in mind:

- ⊙ Locate the sample with a low-power objective and position the slide so that the area of interest in the specimen is exactly in the centre of the field of vision.

- ⊙ It is always desirable to swing the immersion objective into place to ensure the correct location of the specimen before applying oil to the front lens of the objective.

- ⊙ Now swing the immersion objective away from the optical path and raise the body tube using coarse-focusing knob.

- ⊙ To achieve optimum results while using immersion objectives, it is important to apply oil also to the underside of the slide and to the top lens of the condenser to exclude air from underneath the slide. In most microscopes, the central window in the stage is designed in such a way that the top lens of the substage condenser can reach and touch the underside of the slide.

Application of oil to the front lens of the substage condenser

- ⊙ Raise the condenser so that its top lens comes into contact with the underside of the slide. Make a mental note of the area of contact in the slide.

- ⊙ Remove the slide and using a piece of tissue paper or an eye-dropper, place a small oil drop on the underside of the slide exactly in the place of contact with the condenser lens.

- ⊙ Place a drop of oil on the top lens of the condenser in the same manner.

- ⊙ Now mount the slide carefully on the stage in such a way that the oil drop on the underside of the slide merges with the oil drop on the condenser lens.

Application of oil to the front lens of the immersion objective

- ⊙ Place a small drop of oil directly on the front lens of the immersion objective using a piece of tissue paper or an eye-dropper. Next place a drop of oil on the coverslip in the area to be viewed. This prevents entrapment of tiny air bubbles in the concave cavity at the tip of the immersion objective. Such an air bubble will cause image degradation.

- ⊙ Now swing the immersion objective back to position and carefully lower it so that the oil-covered front lens of the objective touches the oil droplet on the cover glass. A small flash of light emitted at the oil junction indicates that the two oil drops have merged. One has to be very careful in this step. Racking the objective too close to the coverslip may damage the slide.

⊙ Viewing through the ocular, bring down the immersion objective slowly into focus with the coarse-focusing knob. Switch to fine-focusing knob once the details just begin to become visible.

⊙ Even though front lens assembly in immersion objectives are spring-loaded it is very important that the approach of the objective is to be carefully monitored.

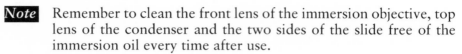 Remember to clean the front lens of the immersion objective, top lens of the condenser and the two sides of the slide free of the immersion oil every time after use.

Some Useful Tips for Comfortable Microscopy

Biologists may have to spend as much time each day working with a microscope as others spend working with their computers. Here are some useful tips on optimization of working conditions and practices to reduce the fatigue and increase the enjoyments offered by the occupation at hand:

⊙ The bilateral symmetry of both the instrument and its user determines many of the common-sense requirements for an optimized working space (which are largely personal and ergonomic in nature).

⊙ The physical arrangements of the working space include stable worktable to seat the microscope and a seating arrangement offering convenient posture of looking into the microscope rather comfort.

⊙ Unwanted reflections of the surrounding light sources in many optical surfaces of the microscope, especially those of eyepieces, are the main detractor from image quality and a major cause of eye fatigue in routine microscopy.

⊙ If there is a window in the room, it is best to set up the microscope facing the opposite wall, so that the eyepieces of the instrument are in the shadow of the observer's body.

⊙ The microscope should be seated on a preferably dark surface to minimize reflections and glare.

⊙ A well-balanced angle poise lamp with an easily accessible dimmer control is ideal.

⊙ Eye cups with extended side-pieces (like the ones bird watchers have on their binoculars) fitted to the eye piece(s) of the microscope are very effective in enabling a reflection-free image.

⊙ A binocular viewing system (binocular head) is itself an aid to comfort as both eyes share their intensive task with much less strain than is often the case with a monocular microscope.

⊙ Users of monocular microscopes should cultivate the habit of using each eye in turn, and of keeping both eyes open at all times. This is difficult at first, but the brain soon learns to ignore the image from the unoccupied eye, and the task is made much easier if the ambient lighting level is lower than the microscope illumination.

Very worst situation   A monocular microscope set up on a shiny white bench in a brightly lit lab with no lighting controls, and an observer who keeps one eye closed whilst the other does all the work.

The best situation   The best situations begin with the ownership of your on microscope. Apart from anything else, one's home is usually warmer and more comfortable than most laboratories, and the grease-lubricated adjustments of a microscope run more smoothly in a warm setting.

A comfortable working temperature also reduces the inconvenience of eyepiece misting and breath condensation on colder parts of the microscope.

In conclusion, it can be said that the possession of a good quality, well equipped light microscope, set up in a situation optimized for personal convenience so that any specimen (that one comes across) which suggests itself may be examined quickly and easily, is one of the most rewarding luxuries (experiences a biologist with inquisitions can hope to enjoy) a technological world can offer the intelligently curious person.

Basic Requirements for Successful Microscopy

1. Be patient.
2. Know the basic principles of microscopy especially the relationship between magnification, resolution and contrast.
3. Take care of the microscope.
4. Understand the nature of the specimen observed.

ELECTRON MICROSCOPY

An object becomes visible in a microscope as a result of its interaction with the light waves used to illuminate it. This interaction which causes a disturbance or deviation of the waves as they pass through the object is called diffraction.

The most important point about light microscopy is that the light waves will be disturbed only by an object which is sufficiently large in relation to the wavelength. Very small objects will not bring about any detectable deviation in the waves, and therefore will remain invisible (unresolved). The resolving power of a microscope is directly related to the wavelength of light used to illuminate the object.

Resolution depends mainly on

1. numerical aperture (NA) of the lens used and
2. wavelength of the light used to illuminate the object.

The nature of light itself sets a limit to the amount of detail that can be resolved in a microscope. With the visible light having a wavelength of $0.5\ \mu$ and the NA of the best lens being 1.4, the best resolving power that can be obtained in light microscopes using lenses made of glass is approximately $0.2\ \mu$. The NA cannot be increased any further. Using visible light of the shortest possible wavelength (about $0.45\ \mu$) also does not improve resolution appreciably.

Ultraviolet light, with a wavelength of about $0.3\ \mu$ offers the possibility of an approximately twofold increase in the resolving power. Unfortunately, the following practical difficulties are to be overcome in UV microscopy.

 ⊙ Glass is impermeable to UV radiation. Therefore, the lenses, slides and cover glasses used in UV microscopy are to be made of quartz or fluorite. These are very expensive and difficult to work with.
 ⊙ Our eyes cannot detect UV rays, nor can they be exposed to UV rays. Therefore, the image is to be captured on a screen and viewed or photographed.
 ⊙ Special precautions are to be exercised in using UV radiation.

Under the best conditions, the UV microscope has a resolving power of about $0.1\ \mu$. Until the advent of electron microscopy this represented the upper limit of resolution.

For a really significant improvement in resolution, it is necessary to turn from visible light and UV light to some other form of radiation. It is here that the development of electron microscope began.

PARTICULATE AND WAVE PROPERTIES OF ELECTRONS

After the discovery of electrons by Thompson in the year 1897, knowledge about the use of electrons grew multifold.

The wave properties of electrons were predicted on theoretical grounds by the French physicist Louis-Victor de Broglie in the year 1924, and confirmed experimentally a few years later.

It was learnt and shown that like all matter, electrons have particulate character and that under appropriate conditions exhibit wave properties. They have some of the characteristics of visible light, UV light and X-rays and can be treated theoretically much in the same way. In particular, electrons just like visible light have a wavelength associated with them. A beam of electrons can in some circumstances be made to behave like a beam of radiation. The wavelength is dependent on their energy, and so can be tuned by adjustment of accelerating fields. Though their wavelength can be much smaller than that of light, they can interact with the sample due to their electrical charge.

The wavelength of electrons is 0.5 Å. A very high voltage of electricity (50,000 volts) is used to generate electrons. When electrons are used in microscopy, a resolution equal to their wavelengths can be obtained. But, there are practical difficulties in employing electrons of such low wavelengths. That is the reason why the maximum resolution possible in the present-day electron microscope is from 2.5 Å to 3 Å.

The first electron microscope was designed by the German scientists M. Knoll and E. Ruska in the year 1932. Later, Prebus and Miller of Belgium, made some improvements in the electron microscope.

In the year 1939, the German company, Siemens, manufactured electron microscopes for marketing. In the year 1941, the American Company, RCA, started manufacturing electron microscopes on large scale.

COMPONENTS OF ELECTRON MICROSCOPE (EM)

In its general layout, EM is very similar to a light microscope, except that it is inverted.

The electron microscope has parts that are similar in name and function to their counterparts in the light microscope.

The electron microscopes have a mechanism to generate electrons, a mechanism to generate vacuum, electromagnetic lenses to condense the electron beams on the object and electromagnetic lenses to create magnified image of the object. These mechanisms are common to all the types of electron microscopes.

The following is an account of the various components special to electron microscopy.

Source of Electrons (Electron Gun)

All electron microscopes have an electron gun (Figure 2.33) which serves as a source of electrons. It consists of an anode and a cathode.

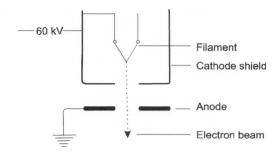

Figure 2.33 Diagram of electron gun

A 'V' shaped tungsten filament serves as the cathode. When electricity of very high voltage is passed through this filament it emits electrons. This property of emitting electrons when heated is common to all metals and is called **thermionic emission.** This property is used in cathode ray tubes, valves and in various other electronic devices.

The higher the temperature, the more are the electrons emitted. In practice, tungsten filaments that can withstand temperatures of over 3,000°C without melting are used. Usually electricity of 40,000 to 100,000 volts (40 to 100 kV) is used in electron microscopes to generate electrons.

As very high voltage of electricity is used, the electron gun is covered with a metallic cap called **Wehnalt cylinder (Wehnalt cap).** This cap also prevents dissipation of electrons. The wehnalt cap has a circular opening at its lower end. The tip of the cathode is near this circular opening. A negative voltage on this Wehnalt cap helps control emission of electrons and the shape of the electron beam.

A little away from the wehnalt cap is the anode. The anode has a circular opening which is in the same axis as of the opening in the Wehnalt cap.

The anode is kept at zero volt current while the cathode is kept at high voltage (50–100 kV). This difference in voltage causes the electrons to accelerate as they pass through the cylinder and so is called **accelerating voltage.**

The accelerating voltage also determines the wavelength of the electrons generated which can be obtained by the following formula

$$\lambda = \frac{150}{\sqrt{V}}$$

where,

λ = wavelength of electrons in Angstrom unit and

V = volts.

Thus, for example, when an accelerating voltage of 60 kV is used, the wavelength of electrons generated would be $\sqrt{150/60,000}$, which is 0.05 Å. Comparing this with the wavelength of the shortest visible light which is 0.5 μ or 5000 Å, we can understand that the effective wavelength of an electron beam is about 10,000 times less than that of light waves. This helps greatly in increasing the resolving power.

Electromagnetic Lenses

In the beginning of the 20th century, it was discovered that an electron beam is deflected by a magnetic field. This was made use of in cathode-ray tube. In the 1920s it was demonstrated that a "radially symmetrical" magnetic field acts as a lens. These important discoveries led to the development of electromagnetic lenses that are used in electron microscopes.

The **electron lens** (Figure 2.34) used in electron microscopes consists of a coil, consisting of a few thousand turns of wire (**lens coil**), with a current of about 1 amp or less passing through it. Since the path of electrons is helical, the same principle applied in designing the coils in electric motors is used in designing electron lenses.

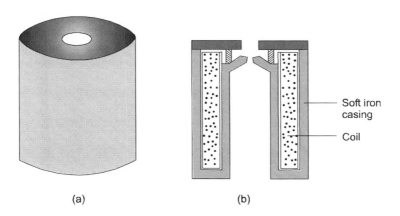

Soft iron casing

Coil

(a) (b)

Figure 2.34   Electron lens (a) Entire (b) Sectional view

The lens coil is encased in a soft iron casing. The casing helps in concentrating the magnetic field produced. In some cases, the concentration is enhanced by specially shaped pieces of soft iron called **pole pieces** in the centre of the coil.

The strength of the electric current passing through the electron lens can be varied and the focal length of the lens depends on this. In actual practice, at maximum excitation of the coil, a focal length of a few millimetres is achieved in most electron microscopes.

The focal length of the electron lens is variable and depends on the following other factors:

1. The design of the electron lens—this is constant.
2. Wavelength of the electron beam used—this is a variable. It depends on the value of the current passing through the electron lens.
3. Voltage of the electric current passing through the lens coil—can be varied as desired.
4. Accelerating voltage—can be varied.

Aberrations of Electron Lenses

Electron lenses also suffer from aberrations as do the glass lenses of light microscopes. Both chromatic aberration and spherical aberration do occur in electron lenses. The correction of these aberrations in electron lenses is a little different from the methods adopted in glass lenses of light microscopes.

For example, unlike the polychromatic light (natural white light/daylight) employed to illuminate the object in light microscope, the light source used to illuminate the object in electron microscopes is an electron beam which can be maintained "monochromatic". The wavelength of the electron beam used in EM depends on the voltage used in electron lens to accelerate the electrons. If this voltage is not kept constant, the wavelength will vary. Therefore, the high-voltage current supply has to be stabilized very accurately to the order of 1 in 100,000 to provide a sufficiently "monochromatic" beam.

As the focal length of the electron lens depends on the value of the current passing through the lens coil, this also has to be precisely stabilized to the tune of 1 in 100,000.

As for spherical aberration, the method of combining lenses which correct each other's faults in case of glass lenses is not practicable in electron lenses. Restricting the path of light which is effective in glass lenses is the only solution available to correct the spherical aberration in electron lenses. This is achieved by building an aperture of smaller diameter into the lenses. This restriction of the aperture of the lens beyond a certain limit will affect the quality of the image obtained. Spherical aberration is considered as one of the main obstacles to achieving the theoretical limit of the resolving power.

Resolving Power of Electron Microscope

Wavelength of electrons is only a fraction of an Angstrom unit (Å). But the resolving power which it should theoretically make possible has not been achieved in practice. The following are the impediments in achieving this:

1. Electron lenses are highly imperfect compared with glass lenses used in the light microscope.
2. All electron lenses suffer from aberrations, both chromatic and spherical.

The best resolution ever obtained in electron microscopes is from studies on crystals where spacing of crystal lattices of around 2 Å units has been resolved. With biological materials, the best resolution that has been obtained is around 10 Å. This is about 200 times greater compared to the best resolution obtained in light microscopes (0.2 m or 2000 Å).

In practice, the resolving power of electron microscope depends on the following factors.

1. Design and construction of the microscope
2. Skill and experience of the operator
3. Nature of the specimen examined

Vacuum System

Electrons cannot travel far in air. Collision with the gas molecules will stop them. Therefore, the entire path of the electron beam in an electron microscope has to be evacuated for which about 10^{-4} mm Hg of vacuum is required and this is achieved with the help of vacuum pumps.

Vacuum is developed at two levels in electron microscopes. When the instrument is first started, an initial low vacuum is developed using a **standard rotary pump**. Later operations require high vacuum and this is achieved by an **oil diffusion pump**. The diffusion pump is an oil-filled reservoir. In this pump the oil is vaporized by heating. The rising oil vapour traps air molecules and is condensed by vanes. The condensate is cooled by cold water circulation system. The trapped air molecules from the condensate are removed by the rotary pump. Thus, the rotary pump and the oil diffusion pump work in unison.

High vacuum is obtained in some electron microscopes by a special device called **coldfinger**. This consists of a metal that is cooled by liquid nitrogen. The coldfinger installed in the microscope attracts gases and any other contaminating molecules. These solidify on the cold surface of the device. Coldfinger is incorporated in certain electron microscopes to obtain very high vacuum of 1×10^{-4} mm Hg or less.

IMAGE FORMATION IN ELECTRON MICROSCOPE

In electron microscopy, electrons are used to illuminate the object under observation.

Electrons are particulate in nature and display wave properties as does visible light. The high-voltage electricity of the electron gun generates a stream of such particles constituting the electron beam.

As mentioned earlier, the electrons are stopped or diverted by collision with atoms or molecules. This is the reason why we have to pass the electron beam through vacuum in the electron microscope. The specimen also has to be supported (mounted) on an extremely thin plastic film.

The specimen itself is made of atoms and will therefore act as an obstacle to the passage of electrons.

While passing through the specimen, some of the electrons in the beam will encounter atoms and as a result of collision, will be diverted or scattered. If the angle of divergence is quite large, they will be lost to the electron beam as all the lenses of electron microscope are fitted with very narrow apertures. In the other regions of the specimen where there are no obstacles (structural details), the electrons will pass straight through and will end up in the viewing screen or photographic plate (Figure 2.35).

The degree of diffraction of electrons by a particular area of the specimen depends on the following two factors.

1.   the number of atoms per unit volume of the specimen in that area

2.   the size of the atoms in question

The more atoms there are and the larger they are, greater are the chances that an electron passing through will collide with one of them. Therefore, areas of the specimen where electrons are scattered appear dark on the screen or on a positive image.

The darker regions in the image therefore, correspond to regions in the specimen which scatter larger number of electrons, thereby removing them from the beam, while the lighter areas correspond to less dense regions which allow electrons to pass through freely. The distribution of densities in the final image is closely related to the distribution of matter in the specimen. Elements with high atomic number diffract electrons to a greater degree than do elements with low atomic number.

Thus, the diffraction pattern obtained in the final image corresponds exactly to the nature of the various regions in the specimen. The darkest (electron-opaque) regions in the image indicate regions with more number of atoms per unit volume of the specimen. The brighter (electron-dense) regions in the image indicate regions in the specimen without any structure (obstacle).

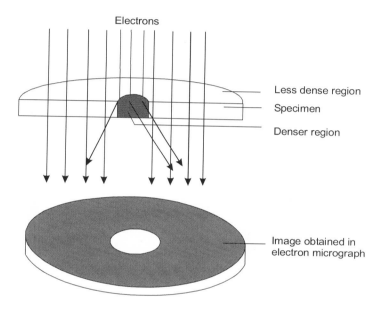

Figure 2.35 Diffraction/scattering of electrons by different areas of the specimen

ELECTRON MICROSCOPES

There are two types of electron microscopes—transmission electron microscope (TEM) and scanning electron microscope (SEM).

Both are similar in that each uses a beam of electrons to produce an image. However, the two use quite different mechanisms to form the final image.

Transmission electron microscopy (TEM) is an imaging technique whereby a beam of electrons is focused onto a specimen and the diffraction pattern caused by the different internal regions of specimen creates an enlarged image on a fluorescent screen or on a photographic film.

In SEM, the electron beam is directed to scan the surface features of the specimen so that the diffraction pattern caused by the surface features creates the image.

TRANSMISSION ELECTRON MICROSCOPE (TEM)

The first practical TEM was built by Albert Prebus and James Hillier at the University of Toronto in 1938 using concepts developed earlier by Max Knoll and Ernst Ruska. Though they contained all the essential features of the modern electron microscope, the early versions were primitive in design and difficult to operate.

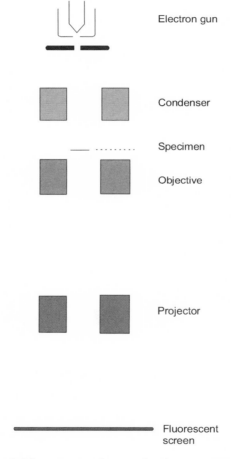

Figure 2.36   Layout of a simple electron microscope

The early simple electron microscope had an electron gun, a single condenser lens, an objective lens, a projector lens (equivalent to the ocular of light microscope) and a fluorescent screen (Figure 2.36).

Later a large number of technical refinements were incorporated leading to the development of modern electron microscopes capable of higher resolution. JEOL, Hitachi High-Technologies, FEI Co., Philips and Carl Zeiss are the major TEM manufacturers.

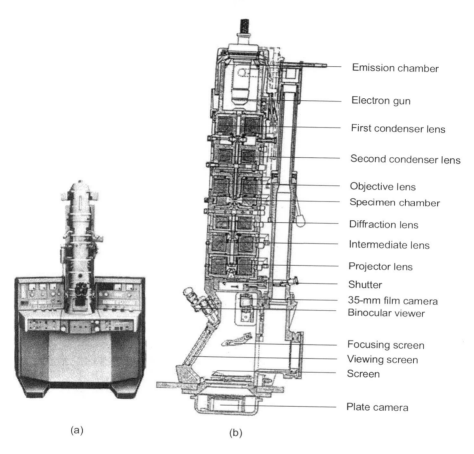

Emission chamber

Electron gun

First condenser lens

Second condenser lens

Objective lens
Specimen chamber

Diffraction lens

Intermediate lens

Projector lens

Shutter

35-mm film camera
Binocular viewer

Focusing screen
Viewing screen
Screen

Plate camera

(a)   (b)

Figure 2.37   (a) Siemens Elmiscop 102 TEM (b) A high-resolution transmission electron microscope (a vertical sectional view)

A high-resolution transmission electron microscope has the following components in a vertical column from top to bottom (Figure 2.37).

Electron-Generating Arrangement (Emission Chamber)

The arrangement used to generate an electron beam in TEM is called **electron gun**. It has a cathode and an anode.

A tungsten filament functions as cathode. It emits electrons from its surface when it gets heated by passage of high-voltage electricity (50–100 kV). The cathode is safely housed in a metallic housing called

Wehnalt cylinder (also called Wehnalt cap or cathode shield). The negative charge of this shield helps in concentrating the electrons generated by the cathode into a beam along the axis of the gun. The tip of the cathode terminates near the circular opening of the Wehnalt cap. The diameter of the electron beam is regulated by this opening.

The anode consists of a metal plate with a hole drilled in its centre. The circular hole of the anode is exactly in line with the circular hole of the cathode shield. Thus the path of the electron beam is defined.

The topmost part of the TEM is the sturdily built emission chamber. It houses the electron gun. The electron gun takes the place of the lamp and acts as the source of illumination. The circular opening of the cathode shield and that of the anode are perfectly aligned to permit the electron beam to travel down.

Electromagnetic Lenses

Conventional lenses made of glass or quartz such as those used in light microscopy are not used in electron microscopes. Instead, a radially symmetrical magnetic field such as that formed by a coil of wire with current passing through it is used as a lens. Such a kind of virtual lens is called electromagnetic lens.

An electromagnetic lens consists of a lens coil made up of a few thousands of turns of wire and a soft iron casing around it. Electric current of about 1 amp or less passing through the coil produces electromagnetic field. This magnetic field is concentrated by the outer casing.

The focal length of the electromagnetic lens depends upon the value of the current passing through it. This can be varied. At maximum excitation, the focal length of the lenses used in electron microscopes is usually a few millimetres.

Lens systems in EM   The modern electron microscope has four lens systems each serving a specific purpose.

Condenser lens system   This is located below the electron gun assembly. The purpose of this is to condense (focus) the electron beam precisely on the object. It is equivalent to the condenser of the light microscope in function. The early versions had a single condenser lens while the modern TEM is provided with two condenser lens systems—the first and the second.

The additional condenser lens helps to produce a narrower illuminating beam limiting the area of the specimen which is irradiated by electrons.

Thus, damage to the specimen by continued irradiation in a larger area is prevented.

Metallic magnetic deflectors are used to focus the travelling electrons precisely on the object.

Objective lens An electron lens located exactly in line with and below the specimen chamber acts as the objective lens.

The objective lens captures the electron beam emerging from the object.

Additional lenses Early version of TEM was provided with a projector lens below the specimen chamber. Modern versions incorporate two to four additional intermediary lenses in between the specimen chamber and the projector lens. The intermediate lenses allow the magnification to be changed over a wide range.

The magnified versions of the diffraction pattern of electrons caused by the structure of the specimen are made to fall on the projector lens below.

Projector lens The projector lens corresponds to the eyepiece (ocular) of a light microscope. It magnifies the image several times.

It collects the magnified image (diffraction pattern) from the objective and intermediary lenses, and projects the final image on a fluorescent screen. Hence it is called projector lens in electron microscope.

Specimen Chamber

The specimen to be observed is to be positioned exactly in the path of electron beam in between the condenser lens and objective lens. The space provided for this purpose is called specimen chamber.

In electron microscopy, all operations such as introduction and subsequent changing of the specimen are to be carried out without breaking the vacuum that has been built in the column of the microscope when the instrument is switched on.

The specimen chamber is provided with an air-lock system so that the specimen can be introduced into the column and subsequently changed without breaking the vacuum while working.

The microsections to be used in electron microscopy are to be ultra thin. They should be less than $1\ \mu$ thick. Such ultra-thin sections are mounted on a microgrid, which is placed on the specimen holder. The specimen holder is a metallic block, which is pushed into a slot so that the ultra-thin sections mounted are right in the path of the electrons.

Viewing Chamber

Our eyes are not sensitive to electrons. So the final image is projected on a screen coated with some material which fluoresces, when irradiated with electrons.

This screen (with its image) can be viewed through a binocular viewer provided at the base of the microscope column.

A low-power binocular microscope is also provided at the bottom, outside the column. The image on the screen can be examined through this microscope. This helps in critical focusing of the microscope.

The screen can be tilted to permit this kind of viewing.

Photographic Arrangement

A plate camera is situated at the lowest end of the column below the fluorescent screen. The screen can be raised out of the way to allow photographing the enlarged image with the help of this camera.

Additionally, there is also a 35-mm film camera or a digital camera fitted in the viewing chamber to capture the image projected on the screen.

Vacuum System

Vacuum is developed at two levels—first at low level and then at high level. When the instrument is first started, a standard **rotary pump** is used to develop initial low vacuum. The high vacuum required for the operation is developed by using the **oil diffusion pump**. The diffusion pump requires the back up of the rotary pump to expel the trapped air molecules from the system.

In some electron microscopes, a metal insert called **coldfinger** is incorporated in the vacuum system to help establish a high vacuum. This metal insert is cooled by liquid nitrogen. Gases and all other molecules present in the system are attracted by the cold metal surface.

The vacuum pumps are located in the desk on which the microscope column is mounted. The first step in the operation of electron microscope is to establish vacuum in the path of electrons. The vacuum should not be broken when the specimen is introduced in the path of electron and during subsequent changing of the specimens. This problem is solved by providing an air-lock in the column through which the specimen can be introduced into the microscope, with only a very small amount of air.

Electrically Operated Mechanical Controls

The various lenses and the gun, have to be accurately lined up on a common axis. There are electrically operated mechanical controls for moving them about.

The specimen itself is moved on a special stage equipped with delicate controls operated by fine micrometer screws. With the help of these screws, the specimen can be moved accurately over small distances and placed in any desired position.

The focal length of an electron lens varies with the wavelength of illumination and value of the current flowing through the coil. Therefore, the electricity used is to be highly stabilized to a permissible variation of about 1 in 100,000. Each lens is provided with a separate stabilizer. The precise value of each lens current can be controlled by means of resistances. The lenses can also be switched off completely if necessary.

The high-voltage supply of the gun and the filament-heater current can also be adjusted by electrical controls.

Thus, an electron microscope has an array of control panels of knobs and switches. These electrical controls aid in carrying out all the operations such as changing the objective or eyepiece to alter the magnification, or moving the specimen to bring it to sharp focus.

Modern research TEM's include aberration correctors, which reduce the amount of distortion in the image. They also incorporate monochromators to reduce the energy spread of the incident electron beam to less than 0.15 eV.

Dimension of the Microscope

The whole microscopic column, from the electron gun at the top to the plate camera at the bottom, is about six feet high. It is fairly and massively constructed to ensure mechanical stability against vibrations.

Other Versions of Transmission Electron Microscopes

Scanning transmission electron microscope (STEM) This is another type of TEM where the beam of electrons can be rastered across the sample to form the image.

Analytical TEM In this type, the elemental composition of the specimen can be determined by analysing its X-ray spectrum or the energy loss spectrum of the transmitted electrons.

Applications

⊙ The TEM is extensively used both in material science (metallurgy) and in biological sciences. In both cases, the specimens examined should be ultra-thin and be able to withstand the high vacuum present inside the instrument.

⊙ For biological materials, the maximum permissible specimen thickness is about 1 μ.

⊙ Biological specimens are held at liquid nitrogen temperatures after embedding in vitreous ice, or fixed by plastic embedding to withstand vacuum in the instrument.

Limitations

The following are the drawbacks of the TEM technique.

⊙ Many materials require extensive sample preparation to produce a sample thin enough to be electron-transparent. The techniques involved are time-consuming.

⊙ The sample preparation process may bring about structural changes in the sample.

⊙ As the field of view is very small, the area or region of the sample observed may not represent the whole.

⊙ Biological samples may be damaged by prolonged exposure to electron beam.

SCANNING ELECTRON MICROSCOPE (SEM)

C.W. Oatley designed scanning electron microscope in the year 1965 to study the surface characteristics of objects.

Scanning electron microscope is chiefly used for examining the surface of the solid specimens. In this instrument, a fine beam of electrons is made to scan the specimen, just as an electron beam scans in a television picture tube.

Depending on the chemical composition and topography of the surface of the specimen, electrons are reflected or absorbed to different extent in different regions.

The reflected electrons can be collected and can be made to form an image by some electronic device.

An image is built up sequentially. The image of the surface can be obtained directly. It can also be photographed directly.

The resolving power of such an instrument is limited by the size of the electron beam used to scan the specimen, and is rarely better than 100 Å.

SEM is extremely useful to study the surface features of the objects.

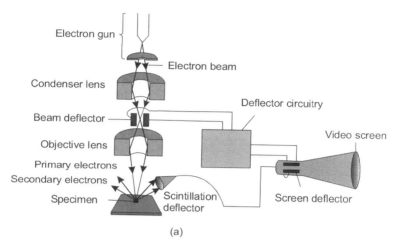

(a)

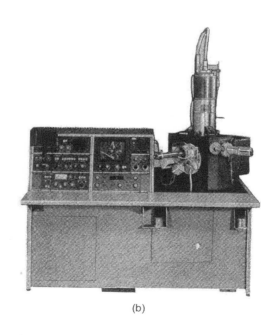

(b)

Figure 2.38 Scanning electron microscope (SEM) (a) Optical path (b) Philips PSEM 500

Optical System and Components of SEM

Scanning electron microscope works on the same principle as does the TEM. The difference is that, in SEM the final image is formed by an electronic device such as a picture tube (Figure 2.38a and b).

The electrons generated by the electron gun are condensed by the first condenser lens. A very narrow fixed aperture directs this condensed beam onto the second condenser lens.

An adjustable objective aperture directs the narrowed beam of about 20 nm thickness on to an objective lens through the scanning coil.

The scanning coil directs the beam on points along grids for specific microsecond period of time as determined by scan speed in the same manner as are signals scanned in a picture tube.

The objective lens focuses the scanning beam on the desired area of the specimen.

The electrons that are incident on the surface of the object are called primary electrons. Depending on the topography and chemical composition of the surface of the specimen, the electrons are either absorbed or deflected variously. The electrons that are deflected by the object are called secondary electrons. The secondary electrons are gathered together by a positively charged grid arrangement. Signals are sent from the grid to the television picture tube. The image is formed on the television screen.

The number of scanning lines in the picture tube of SEM is far more when compared to the picture tube of an ordinary television, making a very clear image. The resolution of SEM is a maximum of 100 Å.

Certain substances have the property of absorbing electrons. So to prevent such an incident, the objects scanned in SEM are coated with gold. This is done by metal vaporization method. Internal structure of the object cannot be seen in SEM. Only surface characteristics can be studied.

REVIEW QUESTIONS

Light Microscopy

1. Distinguish between magnifying power and field of view of a simple magnifier.
2. Distinguish between a simple dissection microscope and a stereo-binocular dissection microscope.

3. Describe the construction and optical principles involved in a compound light microscope.

4. Explain the working of an optical light microscope.

5. What is bright-field microscopy? Add a note on the advantages and limitations of bright-field microscopy.

6. Define phase shift. Add a note on its applications in microscopy.

7. Describe a phase contrast microscope and its functioning.

8. What is fluorescence? Describe the various types of fluorescence.

9. Describe trans-illumination fluorescence microscopy.

10. Describe epi-illumination fluorescence microscopy.

11. What is dark-field microscopy?

12. Describe the method of improvising the ordinary (bright-field) light optical microscope for dark-field microscopy.

13. Describe the principle and functioning of a polarized light microscope.

14. Give an account of UV microscopy.

15. Define interference microscopy and differential interference microscopy.

16. Describe the components of a differential interference contrast (DIC) microscope and its functioning.

17. Describe the working principle and construction of a confocal microscope.

18. List the advantages of confocal microscopy and its improvement over conventional light microscopy and fluorescence microscopy.

19. Write notes on:
    i. Objectives of a CFM
    ii. Scanning systems of CFM
    iii. Signal-to-noise considerations
    iv. Electronic light detectors of a CFM
    v. Specimen preparation for CFM
    vi. Spectral bleed-through artefacts in CFM
    vii. Laser safety in CFM

20. Write an account of the general guidelines on how to use and maintain microscopes.

21. Narrate the technical tips on oil-immersion microscopy.

Electron Microscopy

1. Explain the particulate and wave properties of electrons.
2. Describe the source of electrons (electron gun) in an electron microscope.
3. Describe electromagnetic lenses.
4. Write notes on:
    i. Specimen chamber
    ii. Viewing chamber
    iii. Vacuum system
    iv. Cold finger
5. Describe the components and functioning of a transmission electron microscope (TEM).
6. Describe the optical system and components and functioning of a scanning electron microscope (SEM).

3

DOCUMENTATION OF IMAGES OBTAINED IN MICROSCOPY

INTRODUCTION

Documentation is a very important aspect of science. It is the basic requirement for development of science. The scientific observations are to be carefully documented so that they form the foundation for future development of science.

Textual description, tabular representation of data, diagrammatic representation of the structure observed or phenomena hypothesized, true to life drawings and paintings and photographs are the various possible types of scientific documentation. In the field of biology, preserved specimens either in fluid such as museum specimens or in dry state such as herbarium are two more important types of documents. The permanent microslides themselves are a form of scientific document.

The images obtained in microscopic observation are to be given in the form of illustrations or photographs while describing the structure under observation. In the beginning, free-hand drawings were used for this purpose. Later in the beginning of the 19th century, camera lucida was used to draw very accurate cellular drawings to a specific scale and magnification. This was followed by the era of photomicrography with the invention of the camera. All these are the different methods of documenting the images obtained using microscope, as supportive evidence for the textual description and for posterity.

CAMERA LUCIDA

Camera lucida (Latin—light chamber) is an optical instrument invented in the year 1807 by William Hyde Wollaston to facilitate accurate sketching of objects. It consisted of a four-sided prism mounted on a small stand above a sheet of paper. By placing the eye close to the upper edge of the prism so that half of the pupil of the eye is over the prism, the observer is able to see a reflected image of an object situated in front of the prism apparently lying on the paper.

In its original form, the camera lucida was extremely difficult to focus properly, and a weak spectacle lens was added between the prism and the paper.

A latter form developed about the year 1880 for use with a microscope substituted two diagonal mirrors for the prism. One transparent mirror was positioned above the microscope's eyepiece and the second at a short distance above the paper. It is designed to aid in tracing images of the cells or organisms (mounted in microslides) caught on a white sheet of paper spread on the table, on the side of the microscope. Camera lucida drawings are exact representations of the objects examined under microscope, magnified to a definite scale.

Camera lucida drawings can bring out greater details observable under different foci, which is hardly possible in photomicrographs. For this reason, though cumbersome, they are preferred in biological researches that require documentation of microscopic details of the parts investigated.

Principle

The image of a drawing sheet and pencil tip placed at the table level on the right side of the microscope can be caught by a reflecting prism reflector set at an angle of 45° at the level of airy disc (Ramsden disc) just above the eye lens of the eyepiece. The prism whose surface is silvered except for the circular path of light (of the size of airy disc) placed over the eyepiece, superimposes the image of the object mounted in the slide and the image of pencil tip.

Looking through the camera lucida, one can carefully see the image on the paper and can trace the outline of the cellular details accurately.

The two kinds of camera lucida available are: 1. mirror type and 2. prism type.

Camera Lucida—Mirror Type

In this type of camera lucida, there is a mirror (Figure 3.1) attached to the prism. The adjustable mirror can be inclined so that it will be at 45° both to the desk and to the prism. The resultant light rays (the image of the object mounted, in the background of the field of vision) coming out of the object mounted on the slide is deflected by 90° by the prism and reaches the mirror. The mirror further deflects the light by 90° so that the virtual image falls on the paper which is on the table.

Similarly, the light rays deflected by the paper and the pencil are reflected by the mirror towards the prism. The prism superimposes the two images at the level of Ramsden disc and these are caught by the observer's eye.

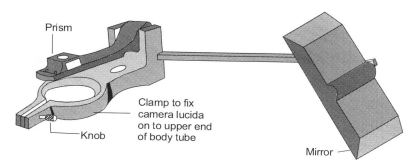

Figure 3.1   Camera lucida—mirror type

Camera Lucida—Prism Type

In prism type camera lucida, the reflecting mirror is avoided. An ingeniously shaped glass prism (Figure 3.2) whose surface is silvered, combines the functions of reflecting prism and the reflecting mirror. The prism is positioned in such a way that only one-half covers the pupil of the eye of the viewer.

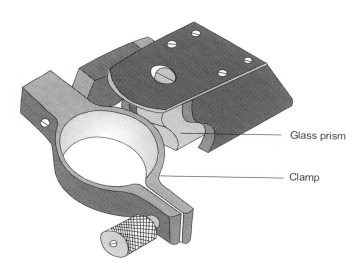

Figure 3.2   Camera lucida—prism type

Useful Tips on Using Camera Lucida

1. Proper illumination of the object mounted on the slide, and that of the paper and pencil placed on the table is essential for making camera lucida drawings.

2. The user will have to get his eyes trained to see the two images superimposed.

3. It takes a few days/weeks of training and patience to master the art of making drawings using a camera lucida.

4. Proper understanding of the principles of microscopy and working of the camera lucida are a prerequisite for making clever use of this simple instrument. It calls for patience and perseverance to master this art. The students will understand that it is worth all the trouble, once they have mastered the art of using a camera lucida.

PHOTOMICROGRAPHY

The ocular (eyepiece) that is provided with microscopes is intended to relay an image obtained through it for direct viewing by an observer. The image thus obtained can very well be documented by photographic recording or by making pencil drawings to exact magnification using camera lucida.

The photographic recording method requires a real image be provided to a film holder or a camera without lens.

One approach is to remove the eyepiece (ocular) and place the film holder directly in the focal plane of the eyepiece and thus intercept the image from the objective directly.

A better approach is to use a specially designed projection eyepiece, which can be adjusted to provide the appropriate magnification coupling the image to the film. Such an eyepiece can incorporate a change in the chromatic aberration correction to accommodate the requirements of the photographic system.

With the advent of electronics and computing technology, electronic detector is employed to capture the magnified image as a video signal. The video signal can be observed directly on a monitor or sent to a computer via a frame "grabber" that can capture a single frame or perhaps several averaged frames of video data. A computer is then used to provide some image processing.

Photomicrography is nothing but the use of photography to capture the images obtained in microscopes. It is the art and science of taking photographs using a microscope to visualize an unseen world. Photomicrography is also known as photomicroscopy.

Photomicrography as a method of documentation, dates back to the invention of the photographic process.

The early photomicrographs were remarkable in their quality, but the techniques involved were laborious, involving very long exposures and very difficult process of developing emulsion plates. This was followed by the period of 2B cut films and later by 120 film rolls and 35-mm film rolls.

Until recently the medium of photomicrography was 2B cut films, 120 film rolls and 35-mm film rolls. With the advent of electronic camera and computer technology, digital imaging has become very inexpensive and user-friendly than the conventional photography using film rolls.

Students of biology indulging in microscope work will at some point, have the need to document (record) the images obtained through the microscope. Photomicrography using either film roles or digital technology is the most ideal technique for this purpose. Therefore, it is desirable that students of biology working with microscope, get themselves acquainted with photomicrograph techniques.

PRINCIPLE

The magnified image obtained in the microscope is to be captured in a photographic film.

One can try to capture the final image obtained at the level of Ramsden disc on the viewfinder of an SLR camera by holding the field lens of the camera exactly at the Ramsden disc. However, this is a difficult exercise as the field lens of the camera is much wider in diameter, and it is also difficult to hold the camera in position at the level of Ramsden disc (eye point) without damaging the lens of the camera.

An adapter is required to fix the body of the camera to the body tube of the microscope. The optics of the microscope is used to image the mounted object to a magnified scale. The lens of the camera with its diaphragm and aperture control lever is removed and not used in photomicrography. Only the body of the camera with its shutter speed-control wheel and the shutter-release cord are used. The intensity of illumination and the diameter of the optical path are controlled through the substage condenser of the microscope.

The quality of photomicrographs is dependent mainly on the quality of the microscopy. In fact, the photographic film is the best judge to endorse how good the microscopy was prior to capturing the image.

Therefore, it is imperative that the student learns the basic principles of microscopy before attempting photomicrographs. The following are the most important precautions.

- ⊙ The microscope should be properly configured using Kohler illumination.
- ⊙ The field and condenser diaphragms are to be adjusted correctly.
- ⊙ The condenser's height is to be optimized.

A properly adjusted microscope will yield images that have uniform illumination over the entire field of view and display the best compromise of contrast and resolution. (Contrast and resolution are inversely related.)

The following are the three important goals a photomicrographer should aim at

- ⊙ Accuracy of image reproduction
- ⊙ True to life representation of colour when colour film is used
- ⊙ Getting excellent pictures

IMAGE OBTAINED IN MICROSCOPE

The final image obtained in the ocular of a microscope is a virtual image formed at infinity. It cannot be captured on a screen, CCD, or film emulsion surface.

Parallel light rays emerging from the ocular are focused by the lens of the observer's eye on to the retina. The details are transmitted to the brain and interpreted.

To form a real image that can be projected on to a film plane, the distance between the object and objective lens system is often changed by turning the focusing knobs.

Sometimes, the position of the eyepiece should be changed to place the image formed by the objective beyond the focal point of the eyepiece. This helps to avoid spherical and field curvature aberrations caused by changing the objective focus position, after the microscope has been visually focused.

Photoeyepiece (Projection Lens)

Normal eyepieces have an infinite projection distance. Therefore, the final image formed by a normal eyepiece is a virtual image that cannot be captured on a screen.

This infinite projection distance is truncated in a photoeyepiece, which is also called projection lens.

This is a specially designed eyepiece for projecting images at short distances of around 125 mm, between the ocular exit pupil and the camera film plane.

Projection lenses used in photomicrography have magnification factors of 2.5× to 3.3× and higher magnifications of up to 7×.

PHOTOGRAPHIC FILMS

Photographic films are coated with a number of very thin light-sensitive emulsion layers (gelatin anti-halation layer, anti-curl backing, adhesion promotion layer, film base emulsion layer and gelatin-protective layer) consisting of silver salts and/or dyes.

When exposed, the regions exposed to light (active centres) combine to form a latent image.

The latent image formed in the exposed film must be developed through the use of photographic chemicals. This is achieved by appropriately subjecting the film to a series of solutions in a darkened container. Development of the film is done in a controlled manner with respect to temperature, developing time and proper mixing of the solutions.

The developing process must then be halted by means of a stop solution.

This is followed by fixing the film. During this process, the unexposed emulsion material which consists of non-reacted silver salts and dyes is cleared. The fixed film is washed and dried for use.

The development, stoppage, fixing, and clearing must be done under dark room conditions or in lightproof developing tanks. The film must be handled in complete darkness.

The rigours of temperature, duration and agitation depend on the film being used.

Film Speed

Film speed is nothing but the emulsion speed. It determines as to how much light must be used to expose the film in a given time period. Film speed is indicated according to ISO number. There are two standard methods of designating film speed namely, ASA designation and the logarithmic DIN speed ratings.

The ASA (American Standards Association) number is directly proportional to the film speed.

The DIN (Deutsches Industrie Norm) system uses a logarithmic scale in which an increase of three DIN degrees represents an increase in film sensitivity by a factor of two.

For example, the ISO designation for Fujichrome Velvia 100 transparency film is 100/21° which refers to an ASA of 100 and a DIN of 21°. Where the ISO number is abbreviated as a single number (100 for example), only the ASA rating is provided.

Larger ISO numbers indicate faster films. Thus an ISO of 25 is one of the slowest films available and ISO 1600 is one of the fastest. A film with ISO rating of 200 is twice as fast as a film with an ISO rating of 100.

Because the microscope and the object observed under microscope are relatively stable with good illumination properties, films of 50–200 ISO range are commonly used for photomicrography.

The exposure meters of the camera are calibrated according to ISO numbers. Those of American cameras are calibrated according to ASA numbers while those of European cameras are calibrated according to DIN number.

The higher the speed of the film, the coarser the grain and the less fine the resolution. For best resolution and smallest grain size, films of ISO 100 or lower are recommended. Sometimes, as in fluorescence photomicrography, the light intensity is so weak that one has to sacrifice some resolution and grain fineness and choose films of ISO from 200 to 400 or even higher.

Slow films Films with ISO between 25 and 100 are classed as slow films because they are less sensitive to light and produce more contrast than do the faster films. A slow film reveals the maximum image detail, but takes maximum amount of illumination and requires much longer exposure times. This renders photomicrography with slow films prone to artefacts such as inherent vibrations in the laboratory and furniture or wind currents from air circulators.

Medium-speed films Films with ISO rating between 125 and 400 are classed as medium-speed films. They represent a compromise between long exposures with fine grain of slow films and very short exposures with much larger grain size of fast films.

Bright-field microscopy requires fairly short exposure times. On the other hand, contrast-enhancing optical microscopy techniques such as polarized light microscopy, phase contrast microscopy, fluorescence microscopy and differential interference contrast microscopy require longer exposure times. Photomicrography with medium-speed films will yield better images when using these specialized techniques.

Fast films Films with an ISO rating between 400 and 3200 are classed as fast films. They respond very well to low light levels with short exposure times. However, they suffer from enlarged grain size which affects the quality of the final image.

Many photomicrographers resort to fast films while photographing images under fluorescence microscopy. When changing to fast films, it is advisable to experiment to determine the lowest ISO number film (longest exposure times) that will produce satisfactory images.

Film Types

Black/white films Black/white films are those that record the details of the object in various shades ranging from black to white. All the different colours of the object are compromised in varying grey tones between black and white.

Colour films Colour films on the other hand record the various details of the object in colour tones. Colour transparencies record the colour details true to the source. On the other hand, colour negative films record the colour details in complementary tones such as green for magenta and blue for yellow. When printed on special photographic papers, the final image will present the true colours.

Positive films Positive image is a true representation of the object where the black area is represented as black area and white as white.

A film which records positive image is called a positive film. It can be used as a transparency for projection on a screen through a film projector. Transparencies cannot be used to make prints on conventional photographic papers. However, through special techniques, colour transparencies are used to make colour illustrations in offset printing industry.

Positive films are available in both black/white film category and colour film category, e.g. film rolls used for cinematography. Colour positive films have the suffix "chrome", e.g. Kodachrome, Fujichrome, etc.

Negative films Negative image is one in which the details of the object are represented by complementary tones, such as the black area being represented as white area and white as black. Printed on photographic paper, a final image true to the object is obtained.

A film which records negative image is called a negative film from which any number of positive prints can be made on photographic papers. Photographic film roles normally used for photo-documenting objects, persons and events belong to this category.

Negative films are also available in both black/white category and colour film category. Colour negative films have a suffix "color", e.g. Kodacolor, Fujicolor, etc.

While using the negative films, it is in the intermediate step, from negative to print, that the photomicrographer loses control over the reproduction of the image. The "non-thinking machines" with automatic colour filters may sometimes result in disappointing rendition of colour.

Balancing of Film for Illumination

When the film is exposed to light of any source, daylight or artificial light emanating from tungsten–halogen lamp, etc., the temperature of the illumination is an important function in the reactions of the emulsion. Therefore, the manufacture of the film also involves a balancing for the temperature of exposure.

The colour temperature of tungsten–halogen lamps used in modern microscopes varies between 2900 K and 3200 K, depending upon the voltage applied to the lamp filament. Films balanced for 3200 K are in fact available in almost all makes. Film manufacturers indicate the suitability such as indoor or scientific use, on the cassette.

Daylight-balanced films are the most commonly available films and these are available in a wide variety of ISOs. These can be used for photomicrography with an appropriate filter in the light path of the microscope. Most manufacturers supply daylight colour temperature conversion filter with their microscopes. When any colour print or transparency film designed for 5500 K colour temperature is used for photomicrography, the daylight-balanced filter is to be used and for film balanced for tungsten illumination (3200 K), the filter is to be removed.

Film packages show the ISO of the film and whether the film emulsion has been balanced for daylight or indoor/tungsten illumination. Modern 35-mm film cassettes have a code, termed the DX number that allows specially designed camera-backs to automatically recognize the film speed and number of exposures.

Film Size Formats

Black/white as well as colour films are available in a number of size formats for use in a variety of types of camera. The following are the formats that are useful in photomicrography.

35-mm film   The most commonly used format is a 35-mm film which is available in individual cassettes (Figure 3.3). These cassettes are of uniform size and accommodate film lengths capable of producing 12 to 36 full-frame exposures of the size 24 × 36 mm. The film is wound on a single spool that is encased in a lightproof metal or plastic sleeve with end caps. The film exits the sleeve through a black-velvet-lined, lightproof slot. When the cassette is loaded into the camera, the film is drawn through the camera with a set of driver sprockets that match a pre-cut pair of sprocket holes on each edge of the film. After exposure in the camera, the 35-mm film is rewound into the cassette before being removed from the camera black box.

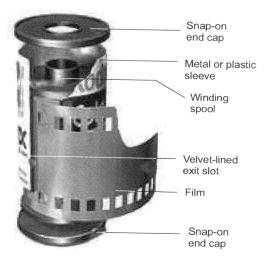

Figure 3.3 35-mm film cassette

Most SLR cameras are designed to accommodate 35-mm film cassettes and are provided with quick loading devices that do not require any dark room conditions for loading the film into the camera.

120-format film This is widely used by professional photographers. The film is available as a roll of 12 frames of size 6 × 6 or 6 × 7 cm. The 120-format film is wound on a spool with only a paper sheet protection on the back. Therefore, loading of the 120-format film into a camera requires dark room condition. Though it is seldom used in photomicrography, many manufacturers have produced cameras that accommodate this film.

4" × 5"-sheet film This is the most widely used film format. The film sheet is to be loaded in the specially designed 4 × 5-inch film holder (Figure 3.4). The loading requires dark room conditions. The 4 × 5-inch sheet film is the most widely used format, for which a number of popular microscopes have been adapted. Larger format films are more difficult to use, but their larger size produces photographs of higher quality that can be enlarged to a greater degree. When great enlargements are required, larger format films are preferable to reduced grain size in the final enlargements.

Figure 3.4   Film holders for photomicrography

Useful Tips on Selection and Use of Films for Photomicrography

⊙ Avoid colour negative films because, you lose control of the step between negative and print.

⊙ Use colour negative films if you have a custom printer.

⊙ The filters of automatic film processors are geared to reproduce skin tones accurately and, as a result, may be very inaccurate in reproducing colours of photomicrographic subjects. Therefore, if your local processor is willing to hand-manipulate the built-in filters of the machine, the results will be good.

⊙ Positive transparency films are very sensitive to underexposure or overexposure. On the other hand, negative films do not exaggerate underexposure or overexposure.

⊙ Always check the film box to make sure that the film is not an expired one.

⊙ For more critical work, it is better to buy films in large batches with a consistent lot number, manufactured at approximately the same time.

⊙ Once exposed, the film should be processed promptly.

The following films are recommended.

Colour negative films Daylight-balanced Kodak Porta, Fujicolor Superia and Agfa Futura give fine results.

Colour positive (transparency) films Kodachrome daylight ISOs 25, 64, 200 are recommended for colour photomicrography.

Kodachrome Elite daylight ISOs 100, 200 and 400 are better suited for fluorescence micrography.

Ektachrome daylight ISO 100 is a good general purpose transparency film.

Fuji Velvia (ISO 50), Fuji Astia (ISO 100) and Fuji Provia (ISOs 100, 400 and 1600) are good daylight-balanced transparencies.

Ektachrome 64 T and Ektachrome 160 T are balanced for colour temperature of 3200 K and yield high resolution and colour rendition.

Fujichrome 64 T is a tungsten-balanced colour transparency, specifically designed for push processing with a minimum grain size.

Black/white negative films Ilford XP2 (ISO 400), Kodak T-max 100 (best all-purpose film), Kodak T-max 400 CN can be used where light is scant; Kodak technical plan ISO 25 to 200 is the highest resolution b/w film.

Critical Information to be Sought about the Film

The following is a list of critical information to be noted on film packages.

1. Film speed, e.g. ISO 100/20°
2. Catalogue number, e.g. CAT 111 3612
3. Number of exposures, e.g. 24 □
4. Processing suggestions
5. Lot number, e.g. 2991
6. Expiration date

Before opening and loading into the camera, it is better to examine each film package to make sure that it fulfills the requirements for photomicrography.

Use of Polaroid Films

Polaroid films come in handy when the photomicrograph is to be secured almost immediately. These films are available in the following size formats.

1. 35-mm polachrome (colour transparency)

2. Polapan (black/white) $3\frac{1}{4}$" $\times$ $4\frac{1}{4}$"-film packs and 4"× 5" individual film packets

3. Larger formats in colour (ID numbers 668/669 or 58/59) or in black/white (ID numbers 667, 52, 665,55, etc.)

Polaroid films are produced by Kodak, Fuji, Konica and Agfa. These are more expensive compared to their corresponding normal films of the same brand. This has to be borne in mind when large number of photomicrographs are to be made.

Preservation of Old Transparencies and Negatives for Posterity

Prized old transparencies and negatives collected over several years of work can be scanned and written on a Kodak photo CD which can hold up to 100 images stored at several levels of resolution. The digital images burnt on to the photo CD can be displayed on a good monitor by means of a photo CD player. These images can be opened on a computer screen through programmes such as Adobe Photoshop, Corel Photo-Paint or Picture Publisher and a CD drive. With the help of a computer, these images can be manipulated and/or enhanced and printed using a digital printer. Dye sublimation printers are marketed by Kodak, Fuji, Olympus, Tektronix and Sony. These printers produce prints of same quality as those printed with usual colour enlarger in a dark room.

35-mm negative and positive transparency scanners and flat-bed scanners can directly scan transparencies or negatives or prints into a computer for storage and/or manipulation. The images can be stored on the hard drive of the computer or stored on floppy discs in JPEG or TIFF files. Floppy discs have limited storage capacity (1.44 MB) and therefore sip discs or magneto-optical drive discs are preferred, as they have storage capacity of 10 MB or more. Recordable CD-ROM is another popular storage medium. Commercial printers can print images with stunning colour fidelity and resolution from magneto-optical discs or CD-ROMs.

ART OF PHOTOGRAPHY IN PHOTOMICROGRAPHY

A photomicrography is not merely a scientific document. It is a "photograph" as well. Photomicrography should also include the aesthetic values of photography. The following are some tips to achieve this goal.

⊙ Compose photomicrographs with a sense of balance of colour elements across the image frame.

- ⊙ Use diagonals for greater visual impact.
- ⊙ Exclude unwanted debris or other artefacts from the image frame.
- ⊙ Select a suitable magnification that will readily reveal the detail sought.
- ⊙ Keep detailed records/notes to avoid repeating mistakes. These notes will also help in reviewing the images that are very old.
- ⊙ All microscopists can make excellent photomicrographs. Pay attention to the details. The overall image will assemble itself.

CAMERAS AVAILABLE FOR PHOTOMICROGRAPHY

Photomicrography involves capturing images obtained in the microscope, on the emulsion of a photographic film or into the pixel array of a charge-coupled device (CCD). This allows the biologist to produce a hard copy for documentation.

In photomicrography, the optical path of the microscope itself constitutes the image-forming lens assembly and illumination system. Therefore, the regular camera lens is not used.

The camera body alone is used in photomicrography. It discharges the following functions.

- ⊙ Protects the film in a lightproof compartment.
- ⊙ Positions the film within the focal plane for exposure.
- ⊙ Advances the film roll one frame at a time, after each new photomicrograph is recorded.

Photomicrographic equipment ranges from makeshift arrangements with simple point-and-shoot cameras to highly sophisticated automatic, integral photomicrographic systems with light metering systems, exposure meters and computer system compatibility.

The following is a brief account of the various types of photomicrographic systems available which will prove useful for students of different levels.

ADAPTING ANY AVAILABLE CAMERA TO THE MICROSCOPE

Makeshift Arrangements

Not all laboratories can afford automatic photomicrography system. Many a fund-starved laboratories have good microscopes not equipped with photomicrography system. By makeshift arrangements, any available camera can be adapted to the microscope available in the laboratory.

The simplest configuration is a compact view camera having an integral lens system (Figure 3.5). Any see-and-shoot camera or even a lens in a box can be coupled to the eyepiece of the microscope for photomicrography.

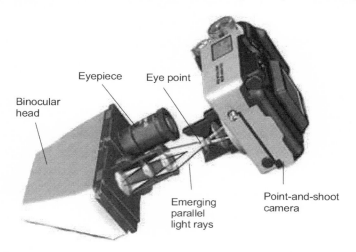

Figure 3.5   Photomicrography using an integral lens camera

The camera should be so positioned that the front surface of the lens (integral/detachable) is exactly at the eye point of the eyepiece and concentric with the optical axis of the microscope. This allows the image to be focused on the film plane.

Adapting the camera to the eyepiece of the microscope is the most difficult part of this configuration. Any support in the form of a ringstand available in the laboratory, camera tripod, copystand or any other support bracket can be used to secure the camera in position.

One problem with this improvisation is that stray light enters into the junction of the microscope and camera. This can be minimized by using some rubber coupling that is lighttight or at least as lightproof as possible.

Irrespective of the type and make, any camera that is available may be employed for this configuration. At the lowest end, inexpensive cameras contain fixed-focus integral lens having a single shutter speed and fixed aperture. At the higher end, modern cameras have detachable field lens attachments, built-in exposure meters, several shutter speeds and two or more aperture settings, and so on.

Whatever be the camera that is used in this manner, it is to be set at infinity focus. Cameras with integral lens are set for infinity focus as a default. When using more sophisticated types, care is to be taken to set it at infinity focus.

The following are the steps in locating the eye point.

- ⊙ Looking through the eyepiece, focus the light through the optical path of the microscope and open the diaphragm fully.
- ⊙ If the condenser is movable, raise it.
- ⊙ With the microscope thus turned on and fully focused, hold a white cardboard or frosted paper just above the eye lens of the ocular.
- ⊙ A bright circle of light can be seen projected by the ocular on to the paper under surface.
- ⊙ The circle of light becomes larger or smaller with the movement of the paper upward or downward.
- ⊙ The position where the circle of light is the smallest, is the eye point. This is where the front lens surface of the camera should reside.

Use of Specially Designed Camera Adapters

Specially designed adapters that aid in adapting the available camera to the microscope are available in the market.

Adapters for integral lens camera   In the recent years, adapters designed to attach integral lens digital cameras have been introduced in the market for adapting the simple integral lens digital cameras to microscopes. It is possible to use one of these adapters with some slight improvisation or modification to adapt integral lens 35-mm film cameras to the microscope (e.g. adapters of Nikon Cool PIX or Olympus C2020/C3030).

The adapter is fitted into the camera tube of the trinocular head with an ocular inserted into it. A small thumbscrew secures the camera lens inside the bracket, with the front lens resting at the eye point of the ocular.

If adjustable aperture settings are available in the camera, set the aperture to the largest value available. This will minimize the vignetting of the image.

The camera aperture setting does not control image intensity or exposure timing. It only serves to reduce the illumination at the edge of the viewfield.

At the lowest aperture setting, the diaphragm severely restricts the image field size so that only a small circular image is recorded in the centre of the film. Even at the largest aperture setting, vignetting is unavoidable and will occur to some degree.

The greatest disadvantage with adapting point-and-shoot cameras to a microscope is the very fast shutter speeds such as 1/25 to 1/50 of a second used by these models. Unless the amount of light focused into the ocular is great enough, images will be dark. Therefore, always set the microscope's illumination intensity to the highest available position when using cameras of this type.

Another disadvantage with integral lens (point-and-shoot/see-and-shoot) cameras is that the field size recorded on the film emulsion is only about half of the available area in the frame. Often the peripheral area of the photomicrograph is out-of-focus due to lens aberrations both in the microscope and camera. Use of the widest camera lens such as 80-mm lens instead of 28-, 35- or 50-mm lenses and oculars of higher magnifications will reduce/minimize this effect.

Reflections from multiple lens elements present in the camera produce bright spots in the photomicrographs taken with these cameras. Therefore, the simpler the camera lens system, the better the quality of photomicrographs.

Adapting single lens reflex (SLR) cameras   It is easier and straightforward to adapt a 35-mm single lens reflex (SLR) camera to the microscope. Since the 35-mm film format is the most popular and widely used, a wide range of accessories (Figure 3.6) and aftermarket products exist for these camera systems.

Figure 3.6   SLR camera mounting accessories

A hollow cylindrical extension or phototube called tube adapter is fastened to the straight tube of the trinocular head or straight to the monocular tube of the microscope.

A "T-mount adapter" is used to secure the body of the SLR camera to the tube adapter. The T-mount adapter has a bayonet mount on the upper side that receives the body of the camera whose field lens has been removed. The lower side of the T-mount adapter has internal screw threads with which it can be threaded to the upper end of the tube adapter.

The entire assembly is called an L-adapter and is marketed by many camera distributors. T-mount adapters to fit most popular camera bodies are available in the market.

To set up the SLR camera on a microscope,

- a photoeyepiece is inserted in the straight tube of the trinocular head,
- the L-adapter is tightened in place, and
- the camera body loaded with film is attached to the upper end of the L-adapter.

The image of the object mounted and focused in the microscope is visible on the camera viewing screen.

The shutter-release button can be pressed preferably with the help of a shutter-release cable, to capture the image as a photomicrograph.

Attributes of SLR camera   Knowledge of the various attributes of SLR camera such as functioning of the exposure meter, working of the shutter release mechanism, etc., will be useful for any student of biology desirous of developing photomicrography skills.

- Many SLR cameras have a built-in exposure meter that can automatically measure light and control shutter speed, i.e., opening and closure of the built-in camera shutter.
- These devices work well in shutter speeds between 1/3 of a second to a few seconds.
- In SLR cameras, a mirror behind the lens reflects an image on a ground glass screen that is positioned at the same distance from the lens as the film plane. A penta-prism inverts this image to yield an erect and laterally corrected image for viewing on the viewfinder.
- When the camera shutter release is activated, the mirror swings out of the light path and the shutter opens to allow light to expose the film emulsion.

⊙ After the specified exposure time, the shutter closes and the mirror swings back into position allowing the photographer to compose the next frame.

There are two types of measuring the light by exposure meters.

⊙ The built-in integral metering system measures the light " through-the-lens" (TTL) falling directly on the ground glass screen.

⊙ An alternate method is to measure the amount of light reflected from the film surface during exposure and it is called "off-the-film" (OTF) method.

⊙ Therefore, when adapting a modern autofocus SLR camera to a microscope using a T-mount adapter, be sure of the type of light metering in the camera. Some cameras require an autofocus lens to be in place before the metering and exposure systems will activate. These cameras consider a microscope adapter to be a manual focus lens and behave accordingly.

⊙ Focusing through the viewing screen of SLR cameras is always a little tricky and focusing images obtained through a microscope is really difficult. Especially at magnifications higher than 100×, critical fine focusing of details becomes almost impossible. This is because the surface of the viewing screen is too rough. The best solution is to replace the viewing screen of SLR camera, with a ground glass or equivalent plastic screen having cross hairs and a clear, central and circular area. This is available from camera manufacturers and aftermarket product distributors.

⊙ There are two types of shutters namely, focal-plane shutter and leaf shutter. While both are reliable, the leaf shutter has lightweight moving parts and produces less vibration during shutter activation. This type of shutter is to be preferred while purchasing a 35-mm SLR camera for photomicrography.

⊙ Another moving part of the camera that causes vibration which is undesirable in photomicrography is the internal mirror. It is a source of significant vibration when it swings out of the way during the exposure sequence. Some of the more advanced models of SLR camera have a mirror pre-release system that swings the mirror up, before the shutter mechanism is activated. This reduces or even eliminates vibration errors in the photomicrograph.

Adapting a manual photomicrographic camera   Manual photomicrographic camera also known as eyepiece camera or attachment camera is shown in Figure 3.7.

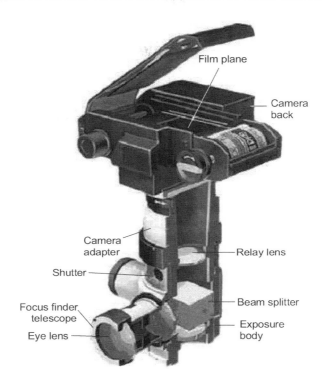

Figure 3.7   Manual photomicrographic camera (eyepiece camera)

This camera system consists of a vertical camera adapter, to the top of which a camera body can be attached. It can accept a manual 35-mm film back or an adapter for standard medium-format polaroid film (3¼" × 4¼") or a large-format (up to 4"× 5") polaroid or sheet film.

The greatest advantage of this camera system is the presence of a leaf-type shutter mounted in a vibration-free rubber mounting and set by hand.

Another advantage is the provision of an attachable focusing telescope, mounted at right angles to the adapter and parallel to the table top, which renders focusing of the image more convenient. The telescope has built-in reticles that contain rectangular grid and cross hairs for adjusting parfocality between the telescope and camera film plane. The portion of the image to be photographed can be brought within the confines of the grid. This will prove to be very useful in composing the photomicrograph.

The disadvantage is that, it is not provided with exposure meter. Therefore, the exposure time for each frame is to be determined by experience or by running trial-and-error tests. However, there is provision for attachable exposure meter which is optional.

In this type of "eyepiece camera system", the distance between the eye point and the film plane ranges between 100 and 150 mm. This is significantly less than the normal close focus distance of human eye which is 250 mm. This necessitates the use of a correcting lens to compensate for the microscope tube length and to allow parfocalization between the viewing telescope and the film plane. So, a photoeyepiece is to be positioned in the microscope body tube head, just above the intermediate tube if present, and beneath the exposure body of the camera tube.

DIGITAL IMAGING—NEW OPPORTUNITIES FOR PHOTOMICROGRAPHY

- When compared to the traditional mechanism of image capture namely photomicrography on film, digital imaging and post-acquisition processing enables a reversible, essentially noise-free modification of the image as an ordered matrix of integers rather than a series of analog variations in colour and intensity.

- Image capture for microscopy is an area that demands high resolution, colour fidelity and careful management of limited light conditions. Digital imaging offers new opportunities for photomicrography.

- The latest digital cameras combined with powerful computer software offer image quality that is comparable with silver halide film photography.

- Digital cameras are easy-to-use and offer greater flexibility for image manipulation and storage.

- The electronic devices accurately record image data by sequencing electrical fluctuations which vary continuously over all dimensions of the image.

- These image data are to be first converted into a computer-readable form or **digital format** in order to be processed and displayed by a computer.

- This applies to all images regardless of origin and complexity and whether they exist as black-and-white images (greyscale) or full colour images.

- A digital image is composed of a rectangular or square pixel array representing a series of intensity values and ordered through an organized x, y coordinate system.

- When first acquired by a charge-coupled device (CCD) or complementary oxide semiconductor image sensor (CMOS), digital images from the microscope suffer from the following setbacks that degrade overall image quality.

1. Poor signal-to-noise characteristics
2. Uneven illumination
3. Focused or unfocused dirt and debris that may be present in the specimen
4. Glare
5. Colour shifts

⊙ Thus digital images captured in the optical microscope may require a considerable amount of rehabilitation to achieve a balance between scientific accuracy, cosmetic equilibrium and aesthetic composition.

⊙ Deconvolution is a computationally intensive image-processing technique that is being increasingly utilized for improving the contrast and resolution of digital images captured in the microscope. Any image acquired on a digital fluorescence microscope can be deconvoluted.

⊙ When a dynamic event such as process of cell division must be recorded in real time, a video camera is often the most suitable resource for the task.

WHY DIGITAL IMAGING?

The most important point to be borne in mind is that the quality of the final image, whether it is digital or film, depends solely on the quality of the original microscope image.

Both film and digital imaging systems can reveal imperfections that are not immediately visible when looking through the microscope eyepiece.

Information storage, archiving, retrieval and transmittance have become very easy, fast and cheaper with the advent of electronic medium of communication and internet. Growth and development of electronic medium/mode of documentation has led to the digital technology.

With the advent and growing popularity of electronic communications, there is an ever-increasing demand/requirement/necessity for images in digital format which can be transmitted to a wide number of users through internet which has become an indispensable "information highway".

The following are the advantages of digitizing the images:

⊙ It is easier to e-mail digital images than sending hard copies of images such as photographs through conventional mail.

⊙ Transmitting images for consultation and discussion in digital format through e-mail is quicker and time-saving when compared to transmission of photoprints through post.

⊙ Digital images can be incorporated into other digital documents.

⊙ They can be easily transmitted to image analysis systems.

⊙ Digital images are easy to copy, store and archive.

⊙ Photographic images can also be scanned into a computer to produce digital images for copying, storing and archiving.

⊙ Capturing the image in digital format from the start saves time and effort.

Digital imaging offers a world of opportunity for the microscopist. It provides an easy-to-use image acquisition system that enables easy image storage, manipulation and management.

ADVANTAGES AND ATTRIBUTES OF DIGITAL CAMERAS

Digital cameras have the following advantages over the traditional film cameras:

⊙ Most digital cameras are of the "point-and-click"/"see-and-shoot" types requiring little or no photographic skill.

⊙ On the contrary, traditional film cameras require some basic knowledge of photographic techniques. The user needs to understand the advantages and disadvantages of the different kinds of films used, the need for using filters, the relationship between lens apertures, shutter speeds, depth of field, and for colour photography, the colour temperature.

⊙ Results in traditional film camera can vary. Hence it is advised to follow the practice of "bracketing exposure" for critical images. (This is done taking at least three separate pictures to ensure that at least one of the pictures is successful. But this escalates cost.)

⊙ Digital photography, on the other hand, does not incur ongoing costs. There is no film-processing fee.

⊙ Digital imaging is almost instantaneous. The LCD (liquid crystal display) screen enables viewing the image before taking pictures, and once recorded, the image can be quickly transferred to a PC. It can be immediately evaluated for its usefulness and accuracy. If the exposure is not satisfactory, one can try some more exposures until the required results are obtained.

⊙ Photographic film on the other hand needs developing and processing before it can be seen. By the time the film is developed and prints are made, the object may not exist any more! Therefore it may not be possible to shoot it again in order to obtain a better image.

When selecting a digital camera, resolution, image transfer speed and colour fidelity are good starting points. Software and ease of operation are also important considerations. Thanks to the simplicity of digital imaging, high-quality images are now within everyone's reach.

⊙ The latest generation of digital cameras designed for wide-ranging applications in optical microscopy combine excellent resolution, high sensitivity and rapid data transfer to a host computer.

⊙ Most models and makes available incorporate the latest innovations in imaging technology enabling the user to capture the superb images in the most demanding microscopy applications of the present day.

⊙ Some stand-alone models offering the advantage of independent operation including image storage to a compact flash card housed in the control/monitor unit have the versatility of full network capabilities if desired. Connection is possible to PCs through a USB interface and to local area networks (LANs) or the internet via ethernet port.

⊙ The camera control units of many models support Hyper text Transfer Protocol (HTTP), Telnet, File Transfer Protocol (FTP) server/client, and are Dynamic Host Configuration Protocol (DHCP) compatible.

⊙ Digital network camera which is a platform-independent, internet-capable digital camera system that can be used to deliver live or captured images to a local computer in the laboratory or to a remote computer anywhere in the world is also available.

SOFTWARE FOR DIGITAL IMAGING

⊙ Some manufacturers offer application software programme termed as "automatic camera tamer software" (ACT) designed to allow operation of the digital camera control unit from a networked high-performance PC (Figure 3.8). Such a programme allows basic digital imaging operations such as image capture, saving, printing and deletion, and also provide access to more advanced image processing, display manipulation and image analysis functions, e.g. digital sight ACT-1 for L-1 software.

⊙ Some manufacturers have developed screensavers for computers utilizing Windows 95, 98, NT and 2000 operating system. This screensaver is available as a free download from certain websites.

⊙ Software is an important feature of a digital camera. More powerful software undoubtedly confers greater flexibility to the user. However, one should keep the laboratory's needs in mind while deciding on a purchase. ACT-1 image acquisition software supplied with DXM 1200 provides sophisticated functions with ease of use.

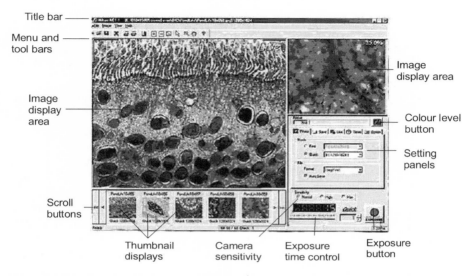

Title bar
Menu and tool bars
Image display area
Scroll buttons
Image display area
Colour level button
Setting panels
Thumbnail displays
Camera sensitivity
Exposure time control
Exposure button

Figure 3.8   DXM 1200 digital eclipse ACT-1 control software window elements

The proprietary direct PC connection technology without an interesting name (TWAIN) software loaded on a CD-ROM disc is supplied with certain digital cameras. This facilitates recording of the digital images directly on to the hard drive of a PC.

'TWAIN' is a widely known bacronym. Not an officially known acronym. TWAIN is a standard for acquiring images from image scanner— an image capture protocol for Microsoft Windows and Apple Macintosh operating systems.

TYPES OF DIGITAL CAMERAS AVAILABLE

⊙ Olympus DP-70 digital camera system is a 12.5-million-pixel cooled digital colour camera system.

⊙ Nikon's DS-5M-L1 digital sight camera system (5 megapixels).

⊙ Nikon digital eclipse DXM 1200—high resolution colour digital camera exclusive for photomicrography (resolution up to 12 million pixels) with superb colour rendition.

⊙ Nikon DN-100 digital network camera.

⊙ Olympus DP-10 digital camera designed specially for critical colour photomicrography.

PURCHASE OF DIGITAL CAMERA

At the time of purchasing a digital camera, the following are some of the attributes that one has to look for:

Nature of Output

⊙ One has to know whether the output is analog or digital as cameras available are either of these two types.

⊙ Analog signals must be transformed into digital signals using a frame grabber before they can be sent to a computer. In a digital camera, the signal to the computer is already in digital format and this reduces **noise** and omits the need for a frame grabber.

Transference of Digital Signals to a Computer

⊙ Digital signals can be transferred to the computer using a serial or parallel port (slow), Universal serial bus (USB) port (faster and available in all modern computers), fire wire (faster than USB but rare) or through boards for the PCI bus (fastest, widely available but requires board installation).

Speed of Transferring the Images to the Computer

⊙ Digital imaging systems vary in the speed at which images can be transferred to the computer.

⊙ The speed at which the images can be transferred to the computer is an important consideration for laboratories taking larger numbers of pictures. While a wait of a minute for downloading a picture to the PC may be acceptable for low-volume user, it can be severely rate-limiting for a busy lab.

⊙ Some digital cameras require a proprietary card to be inserted into the motherboard of the computer and the input/output is controlled through the accompanying automatic camera tamer (ACT) software.

⊙ Focusing and positioning of the image is an important attribute. A digital imaging system will have either an LCD monitor or will be PC-compatible so that the user will be able to view the image to be recorded on a PC screen. The LCD monitor if present should be large enough to get a clear image. Some imaging systems may have LCD screens that can be tilted towards the user for easy viewing. This facility may prove to be very useful to photomicrographers.

⊙ Digital camera models that can be easily attached and removed from the microscope will be an advantage to the microscopist.

Resolution

⊙ The most important attribute of a digital camera is resolution. The camera should be able to record the finer details that are revealed by the microscope. Digital images are made up of millions of tiny squares called picture elements or pixels. The higher the resolution of the image the greater will be the number of pixels in a given area. Beyond a certain point in enlargement of digital images, the individual picture elements become visible as separate dots. The more pixels an image contains, the more it can be enlarged before the separate pixels start to show.

⊙ The size of the image is described by its dimensions, e.g. 1500 × 1700 pixels or by the total number of pixels present, 2.55 million in this case.

⊙ Resolution is also indicated as the size of the charge-coupled device (CCD). A CCD is effectively the number of pixels on the chip. The size of each pixel varies among the different types of CCDs. For photomicrography, a pixel size (square) of 6.7 μ is said to be ideal.

⊙ A filter in the camera pixellates the light entering into the camera into red, green, and blue tone pixels, the colours used to create the overall colour image. The light rays are directed to the CCD which is a semiconductor that transforms the light rays into electrical charges. The intensity of the electrical charges is proportional to the intensity of the light coming from the specimen/subject. Values stored in the digital image specify the brightness and colour of each pixel.

Facilities to achieve high resolution   One of the following facilities is available in some digital cameras to achieve high resolution.

1. Some digital cameras are provided with an additional extrapolation step to achieve high resolution. These models use a software that guesses the values between two pixels. This value is used in the final "extrapolated" image.

2. Other cameras acquire three separate images, one each for red, green, and blue, which are then combined into a full-resolution (non-extrapolated) image. The disadvantage of this method is that exposure time is tripled.

3. Nikon has introduced a novel technology for its DXM 1200 digital camera to achieve high resolution (Figure 3.9). This technology is known as interpixel stepping (IPS) which uses a piezoelectric mechanism to increase the resolution of the chip by moving it back and forth, in a total of nine steps, by around 1/3 of a pixel. In this example, this increases both the resolution and the size of

the image by a factor of 9. Using this method several images are averaged out to produce a sharper image with less noise.

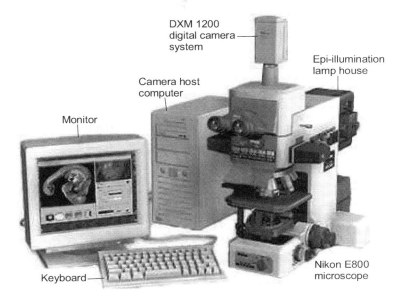

Figure 3.9   Nikon eclipse E800 microscope with DXM 1200 digital camera system

The DXM 1200 produces high-quality images with approximately 12-million output pixels. This is roughly equivalent to the number of silver halide grains in a conventional 35-mm film.

Its low-noise design makes it suitable for capturing low-light images as for example in fluorescence studies.

The long exposure time of up to 170 seconds ensures the capture of dim specimens.

USING AN ADVANCED DIGITAL PHOTOMICROGRAPHIC CONFIGURATION

Several models of different makes of digital photomicrographic systems are available in the market. Each manufacturer offers several models, each meant for a specific level of end use.

The following is a general account of digital photomicrographic configuration meant for high-end research needs (Figure 3.10). In equipment of this kind of configuration, the digital images can also be recorded directly on to the hard drive of a PC or a Macintosh computer connected to the DP-10 through an RS-232 serial port.

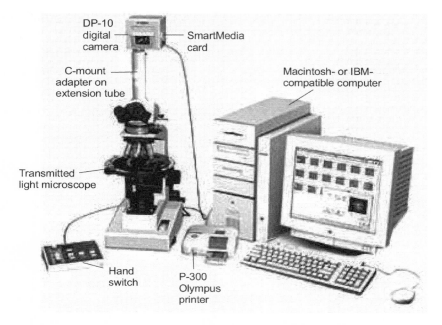

Figure 3.10   An advanced digital photomicrographic configuration

The following is the outline procedure of using a high-end digital photomicrographic configuration.

- ⊙ Carry out all the necessary optical adjustments on the microscope. Configure the illumination to Kohler and any special contrast-enhancing technique necessary.
- ⊙ Mount the specimen on the stage.
- ⊙ Choose any desired objective and adjust the focus in the field of vision.
- ⊙ Ensure that the digital camera LCD is parfocal with the microscope's eyepieces by adjusting the C-mount adapter on trinocular microscopes. In many cases, it may be difficult to focus the specimen using only the LCD monitor particularly at lower magnifications. In such cases, mount a focusing telescope on the LCD monitor and adjust the parfocality. This will allow using the eyepieces to focus the specimen prior to capturing the digital images (Figure 3.11).
- ⊙ If the camera is provided with a smart card, insert the same into the slot meant for it to make connection to a computer through the PC cable.

⊙ If the camera is supplied with "image capture software", load the same on to the computer prior to initiating photomicrography.

⊙ Activate the electronics of the camera by depressing the button/ switch. A green light inside the switch will glow, indicating that the camera is ready to record images.

⊙ With whatever electronic control hand switch (Figure 3.12) or panel the camera is supplied with, ensure that the camera is in record (REC) mode.

⊙ Also make sure that the light path of the microscope is set to send images to the digital camera CCD.

⊙ Set the voltage indicator of the microscope to the optimum range.

⊙ Place any necessary filters into the light path.

⊙ Also set polarizers (in case of polarizing microscope), colour temperature balance, colour compensation, etc.

⊙ Check brightness of the field of vision. If the field is too bright, reduce it preferably using neutral-density filters or by reducing the lamp voltage. If brightness is too low, increase the same by increasing the voltage. But always remember that the adjustment of brightness control may alter the colour temperature of the illumination light.

⊙ Using the menu button on the control panel fix the modes for the different aspects of the image to be recorded.

⊙ After all the adjustment of the modes are over, exit the menu to return to the microscope's field of vision which is projected on the LCD screen.

⊙ Fine-focus the image. If the microscope has been configured for parfocality between the eyepieces and the camera, use the eyepieces. If otherwise, adjust the focus through the LCD monitor using the telescope.

⊙ Choose whether to use the spot meter, the automatic exposure lock, or adjust the over/under exposure setting, etc., in the menu.

⊙ Appropriately select the image quality.

⊙ When everything is okay, record the image by pressing the expose button. Look out for any warning such as "over" or "under" displayed on the LCD monitor superimposed over the image. If there is any such warning, adjust the same through the menu controls.

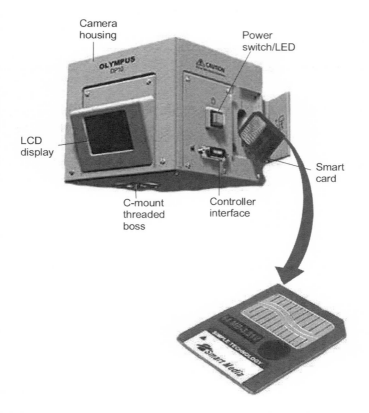

Figure 3.11   Olympus DP-10 digital camera with SmartMedia card

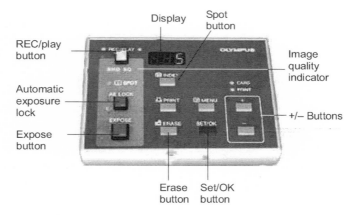

Figure 3.12   DP-10 digital camera hand switch

MICROMETRY

PRINCIPLE

Micrometry is the measurement of microscopic objects. The unit of measurement in micrometry is micron (μ), which is one-thousandth of a millimetre. Microscopic objects are seen with the help of microscopes. Therefore, the scale that is used for micrometry is to be somewhere in the microscope. For this purpose, a micrometric scale is lodged in the ocular lens system of the microscope. Hence, this scale is called ocular scale or ocular micrometer or reticles (pronounced as 'ret-eh-huls', with the accent on the "ret").

Though they are relatively simple to install, mounting the reticle is a somewhat critical operation. They sit right on the focal plane. Therefore any dust on the reticle will be quite apparent when looking into the microscope. Therefore, it is essential to wipe the reticle gently with a lens-cleaning tissue before mounting.

Eyepiece lens systems can be very different in different makes of microscopes. In some the reticle retainer ring is set at the outer edge. In others, it may be deep inside. The user may have to unscrew the lens housing to get to the ring. One has to be sure to remove the retainer ring and not a ring that secures the lens elements in place. Once the ring is removed, the reticle can be dropped and the retainer ring reinstalled. It is recommended that any dust remaining on the reticle may be blown out using compressed air.

Using an ocular micrometer, dimensions of the object under observation (cells, microbes, etc.) are measured only as number of ocular divisions covered along the length and breadth of the object. This is because the value of the divisions in the ocular scale is not known. Moreover, the object mounted on the stage for observation, is magnified variously under different ocular and objective power combinations. Therefore, the ocular scale is to be calibrated for each power combination, using a known scale. This is done with the help of stage micrometer which is mounted on the stage like the object.

The exact degree of magnification differs from microscope to microscope and therefore, each microscope is to be calibrated. This is called calibration of microscopes.

MICROMETERS

Ocular Micrometer (Eyepiece Reticle)

Eyepiece reticles are circular glass inserts with micrometer scales, circles or other shapes inscribed on them for effective use in counting, size comparison and measurement of specimens during microscope studies. Reticle patterns are opaque black on a clear ground positioned between laminated glass discs 16 mm in diameter.

Reticles of these varieties are available in different diameters. Choice of eyepiece micrometer (reticle) depends entirely on one's needs. The reticles of the following two standard sizes fit into eyepiece tubes of varying internal diameter.

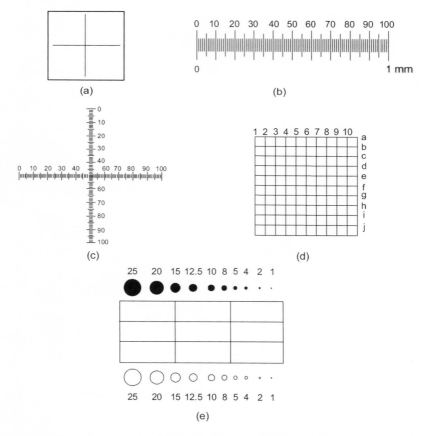

Figure 3.13 Various types of ocular scales (a) Crosslines (b) Horizontal micrometer (c) Crossed micrometer (d) Indexed squares (e) Patterson globe and circle

16-mm reticle   They are used to fit into eyepiece tubes of internal diameter 17 mm to 22 mm*.

21-mm reticle   They are used for eyepiece tubes of internal diameter 22 mm* to 28 mm.

(* Reticles of both the sizes fit the eyepiece tube of internal diameter 22 mm.)

The following reticle patterns (Figure 3.13) are available for the use of microscopist.

1.   Crosslines (Figure 3.13a) (line width 0.015–0.02 mm; line length 2.5 mm).
2.   Horizontal micrometer line (Figure 3.13b) (about 10 mm long divided into 100 equal parts).
3.   Crossed micrometer (Figure 3.13c) (each arm is about 10 mm long divided into 100 equal parts).
4.   Indexed squares (Figure 3.13d) (dimensions of each square are 0.5 mm).
5.   Patterson globe and circle (Figure 3.13e) (overall length of the grid is 4.5 mm).

An ocular micrometer serves as a scale or rule. It is a clear circular glass insert with a scale with 100 equally spaced divisions inscribed on it. It is a "scale of unknown value". The scale has 10 larger divisions marked from 0 to 10 by unitary steps or from 0 to 100 by steps of ten. Each larger division has 10 smaller divisions which are not numbered.

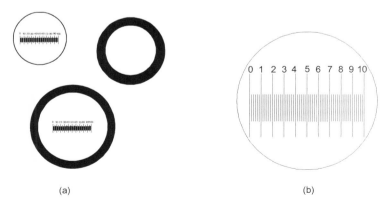

(a)   (b)

Figure 3.14   Ocular micrometer reticle (a) Ocular micrometer and rings (b) Ocular micrometer as viewed in the microscope

The reticle or ocular micrometer (Figure 3.14) sits right at the focal plane inside the eyepiece lens system. When placed in the ocular lens system (eyepiece), the ocular scale appears superimposed on the image of the object seen in the field of vision. The eyepiece that holds the reticle must have a reticle retainer (sleeve ledge) ring and the reticle must be of the proper diameter of the particular eyepiece lens.

The divisions in the ocular do not have a specific value. The actual distance between any two marks on the reticle are a function of the objective lenses only. The ocular scale is fixed, in the sense that neither the size of the markings nor the distance between the markings change with change of objective lens systems from low power to high. But the size of the image of the mounted object superimposed under these markings will get larger with higher magnification. Therefore, as one changes from low- to high-power objectives, the value between the markings of the ocular scale will change proportionately. For example, if each mark (division) represents 0.1 mm with a 1× objective lens, then with a 4× objective lens, each mark will roughly represent ¼ of 0.1 mm or 0.025 mm (which is equal to 25 μ, since there are 1000 microns in one millimetre).

Therefore it is important to find out the actual value of distance between the markings of the ocular scale as obtained with each change of objective power. It achieved by comparing markings (divisions) of the ocular scale with a known scale, namely, the stage micrometer.

Ocular scale is used to measure the cell dimensions. The number of ocular divisions, along the length and the breadth of the object (cell or organism) under the power combination in use (i.e., ocular and objective powers), is noted. If the microscope is calibrated already, this value can be converted into microns using the calibration chart.

Stage Micrometer

Stage micrometers are measuring standards that may be used with all microscopes. The stage micrometer is simply a glass microslide in which a micrometric scale is mounted, encircled and covered with a cover glass. The majority of microscopes are corrected to permit examination of specimens through a micro-cover glass by transmitted light and all stage micrometers are available in this form.

Stage micrometers (Figure 3.15a) with micro-cover glasses are suitable for use in transmitted light. The overall length of the micrometer scale may be 1 mm divided into 100 equal parts (Figure 3.15b) or 2 mm divided into 200 equal parts (Figure 3.15c). Those without micro-cover glass are also available for use in reflected light. These are for use in metallurgical microscopes. The scale length in this type is 1 mm divided into 50 equal parts (Figure 3.15d).

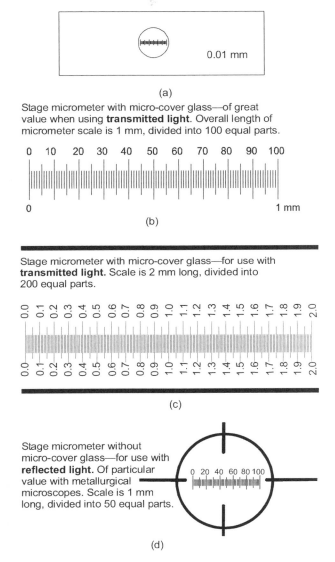

(a)

Stage micrometer with micro-cover glass—of great value when using **transmitted light**. Overall length of micrometer scale is 1 mm, divided into 100 equal parts.

(b)

Stage micrometer with micro-cover glass—for use with **transmitted light**. Scale is 2 mm long, divided into 200 equal parts.

(c)

Stage micrometer without micro-cover glass—for use with **reflected light**. Of particular value with metallurgical microscopes. Scale is 1 mm long, divided into 50 equal parts.

(d)

Figure 3.15 (a) Stage micrometer (b) Micrometer scale 1 mm long divided into 100 equal parts (c) Micrometer scale 2 mm long divided into 200 equal parts (d) Stage micrometer scale for metallurgical studies (1 mm divided into 50 equal parts).

The scale on stage micrometer is a "scale of known value". There are 10 large divisions each having 10 smaller divisions. Thus if

1000 microns (1 mm) are divided into 100 divisions, each small division in the stage micrometer equals 10 μm (=0.01 mm, which is marked at the right lower corner of the micrometer as an index of the scale). With changes in the objective lens systems from low to high power, the distance between the divisions in stage micrometer is enlarged correspondingly, the same way a mounted object does. Thus the divisions of the stage micrometer scale (Figure 3.16) represent a known value under whichever power combination they are viewed (10× eyepiece/10× objective; 10× eyepiece/45× objective; 10× eyepiece/100× oil-immersion objective; 15× eyepiece/10× objective; and so on).

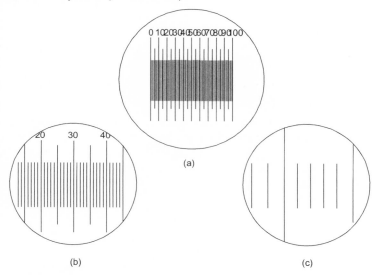

Figure 3.16   Stage micrometer scale as seen under different magnifications (a) Low power (b) High power (c) Oil-immersion

By determining how many ocular divisions exactly correspond to a known distance in the stage micrometer, the value of one ocular division under the power combination in use can be found out. This is called calibration.

Stage micrometers are expensive. More often, stage micrometers are broken by entry-level students. Therefore, a cruder but less expensive method to train entry-level students in calibration of ocular micrometer is to use a clear plastic metric ruler instead of stage micrometer until they get the dexterity to handle delicate instruments and glassware.

Calibrating the Ocular Scale and the Microscope

For accurate results, the reticle (ocular micrometer) is to be calibrated using a stage micrometer for each objective lens. Even objectives of same power from the same manufacturer may show variation by a few per cent.

Unscrew the eye lens of the ocular. Place the ocular micrometer disc on the retainer ring. Screw the eye lens back in position.

Replace the ocular lens system in the body tube of the microscope. Adjust the light source and view through the ocular system. The ocular scale is seen in the field of vision.

Mount the stage micrometer and bring its scale to the field of vision and focus it under 10× objective.

Bring the stage micrometer scale parallel to the ocular scale in such a way, that the lines of the latter superimpose the former (Figure 3.17).

Move the stage micrometer scale to line-up the left edges of each, i.e., a particular division exactly coincides with the zero of the ocular (zero coincidence). It can be seen that the two scales again coincide after a few divisions farther from zero coincidence.

Count the intervening divisions of ocular and stage scales between the zero coincidence and the next point of coincidence.

For example, let us say, 15th division of the ocular from the zero coincidence lines up with 3rd division on stage micrometer scale. That means 15 divisions of the ocular equal 30 μm. Therefore one division of the ocular under that power combination equals $30/15 = 2\ \mu$m. This is a simple ratio relationship.

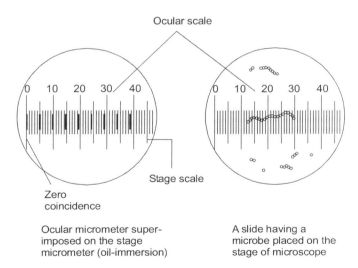

Figure 3.17   Ocular scale superimposed on stage micrometer scale

Thus we can find out how many divisions of ocular scale (unknown) equal how many divisions in the stage micrometer scale (known) for objectives of different powers including oil-immersion objective.

Now transfer the ocular micrometer scale to an ocular of another power (15× oculars and 4×/6× oculars if available), and repeat the exercise for all the power combinations.

Once the calibration of ocular scale in different power combinations is over (Table 3.1), record the values in a card and paste it in the wooden cabinet of the microscope for future reference with a copy for your file.

Table 3.1   Sample calibration value sheet

Microscope accession no:		Date of calibration:	
Make:			
Eyepiece	Objective	Ocular division	= μ
8×	10×	1 division	= 1.8 μ
	45×	1 division	= 0.4 μ
	60×	1 division	= 0.28 μ
	100× (oil)	1 division	= 0.19 μ
10×	10×	1 division	= 0.96 μ
	45×	1 division	= 0.24 μ
	60×	1 division	= 0.18 μ
	100× (oil)	1 division	= 0.12 μ
15×	10×	1 division	= 1 μ
	45×	1 division	= 0.23 μ
	60×	1 division	= 0.18 μ
	100× (oil)	1 division	= 0.11 μ
20×	10×	1 division	
	45×	1 division	
	60×	1 division	
	100× (oil)	1 division	

MICROMEASUREMENTS (MEASUREMENT OF CELL DIMENSIONS)

1. Micromeasurement is measuring the cell dimensions using a calibrated ocular micrometer scale mounted in an ocular lens system.
2. Dimensions of cells or organisms mounted on a microslide can be measured using a calibrated ocular scale.

3. The ocular scale mounted in the ocular can be rotated in its plane so that it can be conveniently oriented with reference to the length and breadth of the cells or the organisms mounted.

4. The length and/or breadth of the object are measured as the number of ocular divisions, which can be converted into μm from the calibration chart.

5. The calibration chart is permanent for a microscope, unless and until the eyepieces and oculars are changed.

Marking the Scale of Magnification on Camera Lucida Drawings and Photomicrographs

Camera lucida drawings and photomicrographs are exact representations of the images of the objects on a magnified scale. Such illustrations are complete only if the scale of magnification is indicated in them.

In the case of camera lucida drawings, the degree of magnification increases with each increase of ocular and/or objective power. In case of photomicrographs, the image recorded in the film or electronic chip is further magnified variously in the final print. Therefore it is always essential to mark the scale of magnification on such illustrations to indicate the size relationships (Figure 3.18).

Camera lucida drawings   Camera lucida drawing is an exact reproduction of the virtual image of the object obtained in the microscope.

The dimensions of the drawing (length and breadth) can be measured in centimetres. These measurements are multiples of the dimensions in microns of the object under observation.

The relationship of the dimensions of the object in microns and the dimensions of the drawings in centimetres represents the scale of magnification of the camera lucida drawing under that particular power combination (ocular and objective) in that microscope.

This relationship can be found out by making a camera lucida drawing of the stage micrometer scale under the same power combination. It is known that one small division in stage micrometer is equal to 10 μ (0.01 mm). Therefore, a camera lucida drawing of the stage micrometer scale of the following lengths represent the corresponding magnifications.

- ⊙ scale line of 1 division in the drawing $= 10 \mu$ (0.01 mm)
- ⊙ scale line of 10 divisions in the drawing $= 100 \mu$ (0.1 mm)
- ⊙ scale line of 100 divisions in the drawing $= 1000 \mu$ (1.0 mm)

Therefore, as soon as a camera lucida drawing is made, mount the stage micrometer in the same power combination (ocular and objective lenses) and draw a scale line of the micrometer scale on the same paper to a suitable length by the side of the drawing (1 division or 10 or 100 divisions) and write the distance it represents in the diagram, preferably in microns.

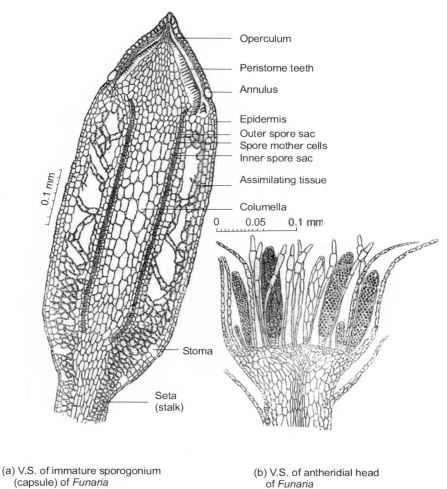

(a) V.S. of immature sporogonium
    (capsule) of *Funaria*

(b) V.S. of antheridial head
    of *Funaria*

Figure 3.18 Scale line showing magnification in a camera lucida drawing (*Continues*)

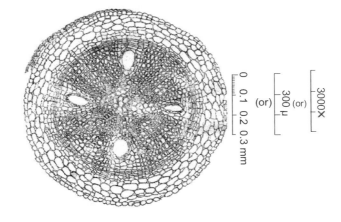

(c) T.S. of old root of *Pinus sylvestris*

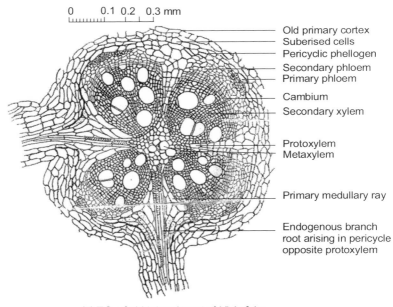

(d) T.S. of old tetrarch root of *Vicia faba*

Figure 3.18   Scale line showing magnification in a camera lucida drawing

Alternatively, just as done for calibration of the microscope, make a permanent set of scale line drawings each for the particular power combination and indicate the distance each represents in the drawing in microns. This comes in handy as a ready reckoner for future camera lucida drawing exercises.

The scale of magnification can be drawn by referring the permanent chart prepared earlier for the microscope. If such a chart is available it will be enough if the ocular/objective power combination is noted by the side of every drawing as soon as it is made (Table 3.2).

Table 3.2   Magnification sample chart

Microscope No:
Make:

Eyepiece	Objective		Magnified to
8×	10×	1 μ	0.13 cm
	45×	1 μ	0.58 cm
	60×	1 μ	0.76 cm
	100× (oil)	1 μ	1.22 cm
10×	10×	1 μ	0.17 cm
	45×	1 μ	0.82 cm
	60×	1 μ	1.1 cm
	100× (oil)	1 μ	1.84 cm
15×	10×	1 μ	0.25 cm
	45×	1 μ	0.58 cm
	60×	1 μ	0.71 cm
	100× (oil)	1 μ	2.24 cm
20×	10×	1 μ	0.31 cm
	45×	1 μ	1.56 cm
	60×	1 μ	1.35 cm
	100× (oil)	1 μ	3.4 cm

Photomicrographs   In photomicrographs, the magnified image recorded in the photographic film or in the electronic device is further magnified in the final print. The stage micrometer scale cannot be recorded direct on the photomicrograph either. Therefore, it is advisable to make photomicrographs of the stage micrometer scale under different objective powers (ocular and objective power combinations if ocular is also used in photomicrography) and make prints. The scale in the print represents the magnification (in mm) of the micrometer scale divisions (in microns) (Figure 3.19).

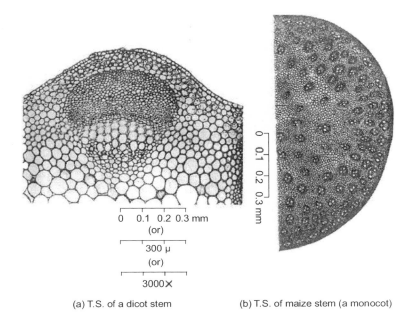

0   0.1 0.2 0.3 mm
(or)

300 μ
(or)

3000×

(a) T.S. of a dicot stem   (b) T.S. of maize stem (a monocot)

Figure 3.19 Scale line showing magnification in a photomicrograph

In the final presentation of the photomicrograph, the scale of magnification can be indicated by a scale line of suitable length with the magnification inscribed in mm.

Procedure

1. Place the stage micrometer on the microscope stage.
2. Focus on an area containing ruled parallel lines of known separation distance.
3. Capture the image on a photomicrograph with the camera.
4. Process the film, and make a print.
5. Measure the distance between two successive lines and compare this distance to the known distance of the micrometer scale.

For example,

Micrometer line spacing (actual) $= 10 \, \mu$ (0.01 mm)

Line spacing in the photomicrograph print $= 0.1$ mm

Therefore, magnification obtained
in the photoprint $= 0.1/0.01$

$= 100×$ (100 times).

REVIEW QUESTIONS

Camera Lucida

1. Describe the principle involved in the working of camera lucida.
2. Describe a mirror type camera lucida.
3. Describe a prism type camera lucida.

Photomicrography

1. Write notes on:
    i. Film speed
    ii. Film types
    iii. Balancing of film for illumination
    iv. Film size formats
    v. Tips on selection and use of films for photomicrography
    vi. Critical information to be sought about the film
    vii. Polaroid films
    viii. Preservation of old transparencies and negatives
    ix. Art of photography in photomicrography

Cameras available for photomicrography

1. Describe the various methods available for adapting any available camera to the microscope.
2. Write notes on:
    i. Camera adapters
    ii. Eyepiece camera/Attachment camera

Digital imaging

1. What does digital imaging mean? Describe the advantages and attributes of digital cameras.
2. Describe any entry-level digital photomicrographic unit known to you.
3. Describe any advanced-level digital photomicrography unit known to you.
4. Write notes on:
    i. Software used in digital cameras
    ii. Nature of output in a digital camera
    iii. Transference of digital signals to a computer

Micrometry

1. Give an account of ocular micrometer (eyepiece reticle).
2. Give an account of stage micrometer.
3. Describe the method of calibrating the ocular scale and the microscope.
4. Write notes on:
    i. Measurement of cell dimensions
    ii. Marking the scale of magnification on camera lucida drawings and photomicrographs.

4

MICROTECHNIQUE

INTRODUCTION

In the previous chapters we learnt about 'seeing' and 'seeing microscopic objects' and the methods of documenting the images obtained out of such observations using microscopes. This final chapter aims at giving an outline of the series of technical steps involved in 'making slides for observation under the microscope'. These steps are collectively called **microtechnique**.

PURPOSE OF MICROSCOPIC EXAMINATION

The aim of microscopic observation of biological materials is manyfold.

- ☉ Understanding the anatomy of the structure.
- ☉ Studying the distribution of the constituent cell types in relation to each other.
- ☉ Studying the development of the organs (ontogeny).
- ☉ Studying the cell contents and cell division process (cytological investigations).
- ☉ Studying the chromosomes, their structure and number, behaviour during cell division, and structural and behavioural peculiarities if any found in the chromosomes.
- ☉ Studying the development of various types of cells including the reproductive cells (gametogenesis and sporogenesis).
- ☉ Studying the chemistry of different cell constituents (histochemistry) and cytochemical localization of materials.

In order to achieve any one or many of the aforesaid aims, the biological material (specimen) is to be subjected to the various treatments listed, by way of preparing a suitable micropreparation that aids in achieving the desired aim.

The type of microscope slide that is to be prepared depends on the following two aspects.

⊙   The user's requirement

⊙   The nature of the biological material or specimen.

The user may require the slide for one of the following purposes.

1.   for one-time observation (temporary preparation),

2.   for a short period of time, say a week or a fortnight, (semi-permanent preparation),

3.   for posterity, for use for several years (permanent preparation).

Depending on the nature of the biological specimen, the following four types of microslides are generally prepared.

1.   Whole mounts

2.   Smears

3.   Squashes

4.   Sections

Microtechnique is a series of technical steps involved in preparing the biological objects (organisms, organs, parts of organs, or tissues) for microscopic observation. The processed biological objects are mounted on thin glass slides called microslides in a resinous medium and sealed with a cover glass. Such a preparation is called a **permanent microslide**.

The aforesaid exercises comprising microtechnique can be serialized under the following technical heads.

1.   Fixation

2.   Dehydration

3.   De-alcoholization and clearing

4.   Embedding

5.   Microtoming

6.   Fixing the microsections onto the slide

7.   Staining

8.   Covering with coverslips

9.   Storing/keeping the micropreparations safely

KINDS OF PREPARATIONS FOR MICROSCOPIC OBSERVATION

Whole Mounts

Specimens such as unicellular algae, filamentous forms, colonial forms, mycelia of fungi, prothalli of ferns, small and transparent gametothalli of liverworts, etc. do not require being tampered with (teasing, sectioning, etc.) for microscopic observation. Such specimens can be mounted as such in a suitable mounting medium on a clean plain microslide, covered with coverslip and readied for microscopic observation. Such micropreparations are called whole mounts.

Smears

Loose cells such as pollen grains, spores, bacterial cells and blood cells are smeared as a thin layer on a clean microslide and prepared for observation. Such preparations are called smears.

Squashes

In prosenchymatous and plectenchymatous structures, the shape of the organ or the cell-to-cell relationship in the structure may not be of importance in the observation. Similarly in the study of the process of cell division, it is desirable to loosen the dividing cells so that the cell division process can be observed clearly. In such cases the given tissue (piece of algal thallus, fungal thallus, young anthers, root tips, testes, etc.) is mounted in a few drops of the chosen stain and enough pressure is applied on the tissue with the help of a section lifter or handle of a dissecting needle, covered with a coverslip and used for observation.

Sections

Sectioning of biological materials is an important exercise. Certain materials can be observed as such and do not require being sectioned. On the other hand, many biological materials need to be sectioned in order to understand their anatomy and the ontogeny of their parts.

- ⊙ The image that we see of the biological materials with the aid of a microscope should be a true representation of what existed in living condition.

- ⊙ The only way to ascertain this is by comparison of the image with the living cell. But many kinds of cells cannot be isolated for study while still alive. Such cells can best be examined in permanent preparations.

⊙ The relations of the cells to one another and to intercellular matter are shown much better in sections than while cells are teased apart for direct study while still alive. This is the greatest advantage of sectioning biological materials for microscopic observation.

However, the following are the difficulties in slicing tissues.

⊙ Living cells of a multicellular organism cannot be cut/sectioned effectively.

⊙ Even if sections could be effectively cut, the cells would not remain alive or retain their form.

To overcome these difficulties, the structure of the tissues and cells needs to be stabilized and the tissues should be able to be held firmly while being sectioned.

The tissue has to be 'fixed' more or less in its living form and then embedded in some soft-solid material before it can be sectioned. When sectioning has been carried out, all the parts can be dyed in contrasting colours to make observation much easier.

For these reasons it is usual to follow the steps listed below in the preparation of microscope sections.

⊙ Treat a piece of tissue with a fluid called fixative.

⊙ Embed it after fixation in some soft-solid medium such as paraffin wax that will hold its constituent parts in right relation to one another during sectioning.

⊙ Section it.

⊙ Dye the sections, often in two or more contrasting colours.

⊙ Mount the dyed sections in a medium that renders them transparent.

MATERIALS AND EQUIPMENT

An introduction to the basic materials and equipment that are used in preparing microslides is necessary before proceeding to learn the various steps involved in microtechnique. This unit aims at giving an account of the various glassware items and equipment that are used in microtechnique.

An account of the various sectioning devices if given in the section on sectioning will disturb the continuity of the steps and therefore it is thought fit to include it in this unit.

GLASSWARE

The glassware used for mounting the specimens for observation under microscope are the following.

Plain Microslides

A plain microslide is a piece of thin glass usually of size 3" × 1" × 1 mm. Rarely, slides of size 3 × 1½" or even 3" × 2" are used to accommodate a series of more number of sections of big specimens such as fossils.

It is very important that the microslide has a flat surface and perfectly ground edges. It is equally important that the slide is made of stable non-corrosive glass.

The thickness of the microslide is a very important consideration as it decides the working distance of the objective lens while working with microscopes (Refer Chapter 1). The optimum thickness for a good microslide is 1 mm. For critical cytological studies and observation of cleared diatom frustules 1-mm thick slides are most suitable. These may be a little costly. However, slides of thickness up to 1¼ mm are found to be satisfactory. Slides thicker than this effectively reduce the working distance and will result in breaking under high-power observation.

It is generally felt that microslides should appear perfectly white. These are more resistant to corrosion. Some brands appear greenish when viewed at the edges. This need not be taken as a discredit as greenish-looking slides are more resistant to corrosion than are perfect white slides!

Coverslips or Cover Glass

Very thin glass circles, squares or rectangles used for covering the biological material mounted on the slide in a suitable medium are called coverslips or cover glasses. Like microslides, these also should have flat surfaces.

Thickness, shape and size are the important criteria to be kept in mind while choosing the coverslip for use.

Coverslips are available in four thicknesses marked as No. 0 to No. 3 indicating the increment in thickness in the same order. Table 4.1 indicates the attributes of the coverslips and their specifications.

Table 4.1   Coverslips of various thicknesses and their uses

Number	Thickness	Specific use
0	0.09 mm	To be used for micropreparations that require observation under oil-immersion objective.
1	0.15–0.17 mm	Preferred for general use with all kinds of micropreparations.
2	0.20 mm	Meant for use in micropreparations that do not require high-power observation, e.g. whole mounts.
3	0.30–0.35 mm	Meant for covering dry whole mounts. If used for preparations that require high-power observation, will lead to breakage of the slide! (Refer working distance of the objective, chapter 1.)

As for the size, both circular and square coverslips come in the same size range namely 3/8" to 7/8". The most commonly used size is 3/4" (18 mm) while 1/2" coverslips are sufficient for routine classwork purposes.

The choice between square and circular coverslips depends on the requirement of the technician. Square coverslips are a little easier to handle. But circular coverslips are ideal if 'ringing and sealing of fluid or dry mounts' are attempted.

Rectangular coverslips are always 22 mm broad and are available in different lengths such as 30, 40, or 50 mm. These are used to cover serial sections and larger sections such as fossil sections. While using rectangular coverslips, care should be taken to leave enough space on one side of the slide for labelling. Table 4.2 indicates the coverslips of different shapes and sizes and their recommended uses.

Table 4.2   Coverslips of different shapes and dimensions and their uses

Category	Size/Dimension	Recommended uses
Square and circular	3/4" (18 mm)	Commonly employed for all kinds of preparations
	1/2"	Suitable for general classwork purposes
Rectangular	30 mm × 22 mm	For use with 3" × 1" slide
	40 mm × 22 mm	For use with 3" × 1" slide
	50 mm × 22 mm	For use with 3" × 1" slide
	50 mm × 35 mm	For use with slides of 1½" width
	50 mm × 43 mm	For use with slides of 2" width

Cavity Slides/Depression Slides/Culture Slides

Cavity slides are plain microslides with one or two hollow cavities to hold bulky specimens. These are more expensive. In olden days, factory-made cavity slides were not available and therefore, the microtechnician had to grind cavities in plain slides using dental drills.

More often, cavity slides are used to make cultures of microorganisms and therefore, are also known as culture slides.

The biological material/specimen intended for microscopic observation is subjected to the various processes outlined in the introductory unit of this chapter. In some cases the specimen is put through these steps and then mounted on the slide and in others, the specimen is stuck to the slide first and the slide is put through the steps. The following are the various types of containers/glassware available for handling the specimens and for handling slides.

Specimen-Transferring Tools

The specimen is to be transferred between various reagents during the different steps of microtechnique/slide making. Very small specimens can be transferred with the help of a pipette (Figure 4.1a) preferably fitted with a rubber teat. Section lifters (Figure 4.1b) are employed in the case of slightly larger specimens such as hand sections. Camel-hair brush of size No.1, comes in very handy to transfer very small delicate sections.

(a)   (b)

Figure 4.1   Tools for transferring the specimen (a) Pipette with rubber teat (b) Section lifter

Containers for Handling Specimens/Sections Stuck to Slides

Processing of the specimen may require it to stay in reagents of different grades either for a short time or for a longer time depending on the schedule followed. Watch glass, embryo cup, Stender dish, specimen tube and Coplin jar are the various containers in use (Figure 4.2).

Watch glass   These are very shallow circular containers made of glass of about 2 mm thickness. They are available in different diameters (5 mm to 10 mm). Conventional types of watch glasses require careful handling as they are easily upset.

Syracuse watch glass, also called Syracuse dish is an improvement over the conventional type. It is more stable on the worktable than is the conventional watch glass.

Embryo cup   This is also called embryological watch glass. An embryo cup is a solid block of good quality glass with a hollow cavity in it. The advantage over watch glass is that the embryo cup is provided with a glass lid to prevent evaporation of the liquid contained in it.

Stender dish   This is a circular tublike container made of quality glass. The greater advantage in Stender dish is its ground edge and the round ground-on cover. Smeared with a little petroleum jelly, this cover keeps the dish air-tight. It is possible to keep alcohol in the dish for several days without evaporation.

Specimen tube/specimen phial   Specimen tubes also called specimen phials are used to store specimens for any length of time. These are available in a variety of sizes. Bark-corked specimen tubes are less expensive. Specimen tubes with screw caps made of bakelite are more expensive.

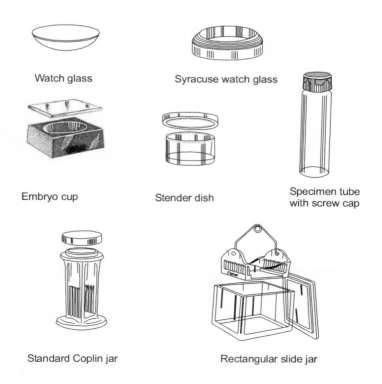

Watch glass   Syracuse watch glass

Embryo cup   Stender dish   Specimen tube with screw cap

Standard Coplin jar   Rectangular slide jar

Figure 4.2   Various types of containers for handling specimens

Coplin jar Coplin jar is meant for use when many slides with sections stuck to them are to be transferred between solutions simultaneously. If only one slide is being handled, one can use specimen tubes of a diameter greater than 1 inch.

Coplin jar is a rectangular glass jar furnished with a series of vertical grooves that hold a number of slides apart. Coplin jars may have six grooves and hold six slides, one in each groove.

The number may be doubled by placing two slides back-to-back and sliding this pair into a groove. This way, twelve slides can be held in a Coplin jar. However this has two disadvantages.

⊙ Reagents diffuse very slowly from between the slides.

⊙ After dewaxing is over, when the individual slide is lifted and wiped to remove the xylol, very frequently the ribbon side is wiped resulting in the loss of the sections.

Though the Coplin jar is basically rectangular, its base and mouth are rendered circular in outline. The base is quite heavy to render stability to the jar. The lid is designed to fit accurately to the jar so that evaporation of fluids is checked.

There are two kinds of Coplin jars, namely, vertical type and horizontal type.

In the vertical type, the slides are held vertically. In the horizontal type, the slides are held horizontally. The latter is supposed to have an advantage of economizing on the fluids used.

Coplin jars are made to handle 3" × 1" slides. When slides of larger dimensions are in use, the rectangular slide jar with a slide rack is to be used. The rack has vertical grooves in the opposite sides. Slides can be inserted horizontally in the grooves. Since the rack is provided with a handle, the entire set of slides can be transferred from one jar to another without handling individual slides during the operation.

Square petri dish Square petri dishes are ideal for processing the smear micropreparations. The size of the square petri dish is such that two slides can be placed conveniently side by side and handled. Coplin jars are not recommended for transferring the smear micropreparations.

Giant pipette A giant pipette is a makeshift arrangement which may be very useful for collecting microalgae from water bodies, making changes of dehydrating fluids on materials to be mounted entirely and for many other purposes.

It is nothing but a thick glass tubing of a suitable diameter and at least 25 cm length to which a large rubber bulb of about 8.5 cm diameter is attached.

Cleaning Slides and Glassware

All manufacturers claim their glassware to be ready to use. However, it is always desirable to clean the slides, coverslips and other glassware in an acid cleaning fluid before putting them to use in making micropreparations. Slides on which paraffin sections are to be mounted, or specimens are to be smeared or whole-mounted are to be chemically clean.

For routine classwork use

⊙ Cleaning fluids such as teepol or lysol can be used.
⊙ Immerse the microslides, coverslips or glassware in aqueous solution of a cleaning fluid for a few hours to overnight.
⊙ Wash off the cleaning fluid thoroughly in running water.
⊙ Wipe to dry using fibre-free cotton cloth.
⊙ Store the cleaned glassware in dust-free enclosures.

For making permanent micropreparations Slides on which paraffin sections are to be mounted or specimens are to be smeared or mounted as a whole are to be chemically clean for the specimen to stick firmly, resisting rigours of changing fluids. Presence of extraneous matter on slides may present undesirable artefacts in the micropreparations. Therefore, for special kinds of use the slides and coverslips are to be acid-cleaned thoroughly before use.

Potassium dichromate–sulphuric acid solution generally used for this purpose can be prepared as follows:

Potassium dichromate	20 g
Water	100 cc
Conc. Sulphuric acid	100 cc

Dissolve the dichromate in water and add the acid in small quantities. Allow the mixture to cool in between each addition of the acid. This mixture is to be stored in glass containers. It has long shelf life. (It can be re-used until it becomes too dark.) Immerse the glassware or slides and coverslips in this solution for a few hours.

Wash off the cleaning fluid from the glassware thoroughly in tap water and finally in distilled water. Wipe to dry using fibre-free cotton cloth. Store the cleaned glassware in a dust-free container or enclosure.

Nitric acid (one part)–hydrochloric acid (four parts) mixture is also recommended for cleaning glassware and slides. It can be used in the same manner as described earlier.

The disadvantages with this mixture include the following.

1. It has a very short shelf life.
2. The acid fumes may irritate the user.

Note It will be time-saving to clean one or two boxes of slides at a time and keep them handy in a clean air-tight container.

Slide Containers

The prepared slides/micropreparations are to be stored properly for varying length of time to serve different purposes. Slides can be stored either flat or vertically on their edges in the grooves provided on the lateral sides of the tray. Two types of containers available are 1. containers for flat storage and 2. containers for vertical storage of slides. Both have advantages and disadvantages of their own. The various types of slide containers available are shown in Figures 4.3, 4.4 and 4.5.

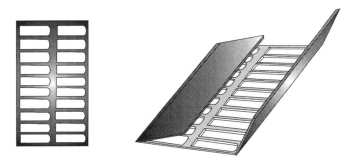

Figure 4.3 Slide submission tray

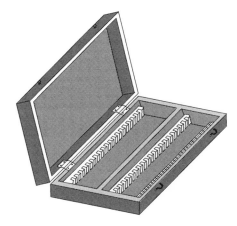

Figure 4.4 Slidebox

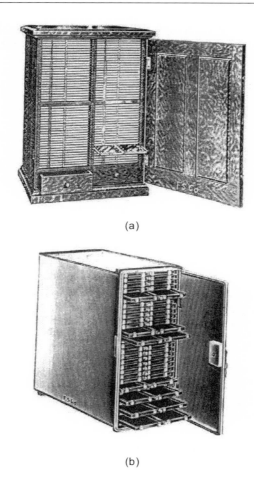

(a)

(b)

Figure 4.5   Slide storage cabinets (a) Vertical storage cabinet (b) Flat storage cabinet

EQUIPMENT

Hot-Air Oven

Hot-air oven is indispensable for carrying out the paraffin-embedding exercises in microtechnique. The various steps of embedding the specimen in paraffin wax take considerable time. These steps are discussed in detail under embedding of the specimen for micropreparations in the latter sections. The paraffin wax is to be kept in a molten state all through these steps.

An electrically operated, hot-air oven with a thermostatic control (Figure 4.6) is very useful for this purpose. The glass door permits viewing the contents, with the door remaining closed. The removable nickel-plated shelf facilitates keeping the specimen tubes/beakers containing wax at different distances from the source of heat.

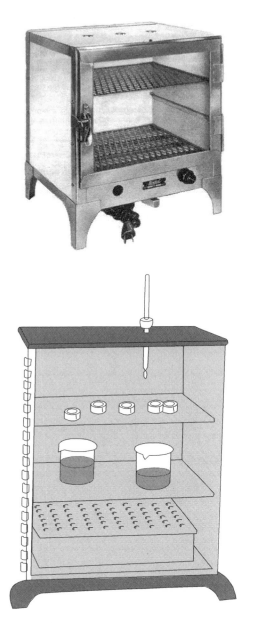

Figure 4.6   Electrically operated hot-air oven

When an electrically operated hot-air oven is not available, a simple radiant-heat embedding oven can be fabricated (Figure 4.7). The height of the hood should be adjusted until the wax is melted for about one half of its depth.

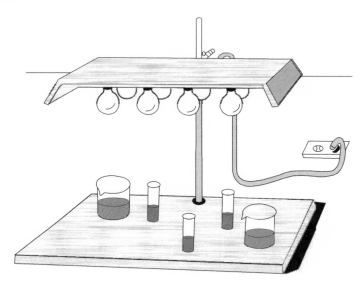

Figure 4.7   Radiant-heat embedding oven

Slide-Warming Table

Serial sections of paraffin-embedded specimens obtained in the form of ribbons are to be stretched a little before being stuck to the microslide. To achieve this, the ribbon taken on the microslide is flooded with formalin water. By slightly warming the slide with the ribbon afloat in formalin water over the flame of a spirit lamp, the ribbon expands. Kept undisturbed and covered free from dust, the formalin water evaporates slowly allowing the expanded ribbons to get stuck to the slide.

If many slides are to be processed successively, the formalin water may be drained from the slide and the same with the ribbon can be kept covered until the slide becomes dry.

An electrically operated, thermostatic slide-warming table serves these purposes when several slides are being processed in succession (Figure 4.8). The temperature-control device is of continuous variation type (stepless control) and the in-built automatic cut-off helps to keep the plate warm at the set temperature.

Figure 4.8   Electrical slide-warming table

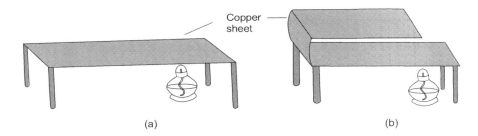

(a)   (b)

Figure 4.9   Manual slide-warming table

When an electrically operated slide-warming table is not available, makeshift slide-warming tables can be fabricated using copper plate as shown in Figure 4.9a and b. The plate can be kept warm with the help of a spirit lamp.

Section Cutting Devices (Microtomes)

Microtome is an instrument used for taking microsections of plant and animal tissues (Gr. *micro* = small; *tamein* = to cut). A detailed account of microtomes is given in the following section.

MICROTOME

The first microtome was designed by Cunning in 1790. This is at present called hand microtome. In 1735, Prichard designed a table type microtome. In 1839, Chavelier christened such instruments as microtome. Sliding microtome was introduced in 1798. Rotary microtomes were introduced in the years 1783 and 1786.

Spencer Lens Company introduced the first medical microtome in 1901. In the year 1910, large-sized rotary microtomes were introduced by Spencer company.

The following types of microtomes are at present available for routine use.

1. *Hand microtome*

2. *Mechanical microtomes* In the mechanical microtomes, mechanical devices are involved in moving the specimen against the cutting edge of the knife and for other manipulations. These are of the following types.

    a. Rotary microtomes, ideal for cutting specimens embedded in paraffin wax.

    b. Sliding microtome, meant for cutting specimens embedded in celloidin and plastic.

    c. Freezing microtome, meant for cutting frozen materials that are not embedded.

    d. Sledge microtome, meant for cutting very hard materials such as wood or bone.

    e. Ultramicrotome, meant for cutting microsections for electron microscopy.

Based on the mechanism involved in moving the object, two types are recognized.

1. Rocking type of microtome

2. Rotary type of microtome

HAND MICROTOME

Hand microtome was designed by Cunning in the year 1790. It consists of a cylindrical tubular specimen holder to hold the tissue. There is a tonguelike catch in the hollow of the specimen holder tube running through the length. The flap can be pushed against the specimen held in the holder with the help of a screw. On the lower end, the flap terminates on a micrometer screw (Figure 4.10).

There is a horizontal circular tablelike platform around the upper end of the specimen holder. The knife can be rested horizontally on the platform and be moved forward and back over the specimen to take sections.

When this micrometer screw is turned, the object held in the holder is pushed above the surface of the platform. The collar of the micrometer screw is graduated, usually in hundredths of a millimetre. Hand sections are normally cut in 20 μ to 30 μ.

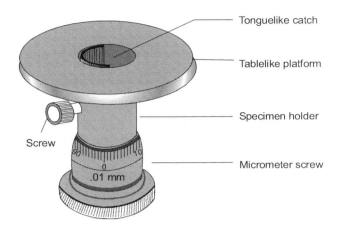

Tonguelike catch

Tablelike platform

Specimen holder

Screw

Micrometer screw

.01 mm

Figure 4.10   Hand microtome

ROTARY MICROTOME

Rotary microtome is the most widely used microtome among the paraffin microtomes (Figure 4.11). It gets its name from the circular drive wheel which is rotated in a circular motion to move the specimen holder up and down against the cutting edge of the knife. There is also a ratchet wheel which helps in moving the specimen holder forward by a definite distance (in microns) for every vertical movement of the specimen holder.

The microtome has a heavy steel base at the front end of which is a knife holder. The knife is mounted horizontally with its cutting edge facing upwards. There are bolt nuts to fix the knife firmly in the knife holder. The knife can be moved sidewards to the left or right so that any part of the cutting edge can be used for cutting. There is also arrangement to change the angle of the knife.

The knife holder is mounted on a strong sledge made of steel. The knife holder can be moved forwards and backwards along the sledge and can be firmly fixed at any given point with the help of a bolt.

The specimen holder is a hollow cylindrical heavy metallic arrangement. It has two metallic plate catches in its hollow. One of these catches can be moved towards the opposite one with the help of a screw so that the two grooved inner surfaces will firmly catch the wooden or metal piece mount supporting the paraffin block. There is also an arrangement to rotate the paraffin block mount in any angle along its axis.

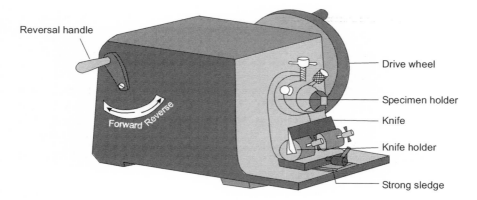

Figure 4.11   Rotary microtome

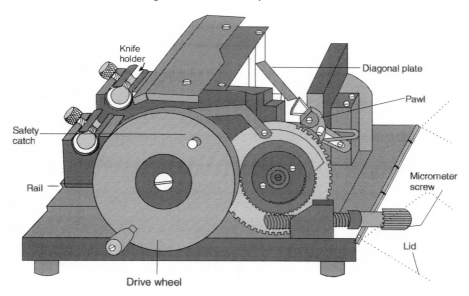

Figure 4.12   Arrangement to decide thickness of the section cut

There is a ratchet wheel attached to a micrometer screw. The ratchet is a toothed wheel. The ratchet is made of brass and teeth are sloped on one direction so that a pawl working on it can catch and prevent movement in the opposite direction. As the drive wheel is rotated, the pawl works against the ratchet to move the micrometer screw and thus the knob connected with it through a given distance for each rotation. As the knob moves forward, it bears on a diagonal plate, which moves the block the required distance forward at each revolution. This arrangement is very costly and is likely to be damaged by defective operation due to inexperience.

There is also an arrangement to move the specimen holder backwards. This is made possible by rotating the reversal handle which moves the diagonal plate backwards easing the specimen holder so that the latter moves backwards.

An important precaution is that, the knob which controls the section thickness is so moved that an exact number of microns is indicated. If for example, the knob is moved in such a way that the indicator line lies between 10 and 11 μ, the pawl will not engage the ratchet perfectly. A few weeks of careless operation under this condition will destroy the ratchet wheel which will have to be replaced.

There is a safety catch to prevent the movement of the drive wheel and hence the movement of the specimen holder.

Operating the Microtome

The following are the steps to be followed in operating a microtome.

⊙ Rotate the drive wheel slightly to move the specimen holder up.

⊙ Move the safety catch to the lock position so that the specimen holder does not move down.

⊙ Now rotate the reversal handle so that the specimen holder is moved back to the fullest extent.

⊙ Fix the wooden or metallic mount with paraffin block in the specimen holder.

⊙ Check if the plane of the material in paraffin block is as desired. If not, set it by rotating the mount and screw it firmly.

⊙ Check if all the screws in the specimen holder are firm.

⊙ Move the knife holder to a desired position towards the specimen holder.

⊙ Slide the knife into the knife holder and tighten the screws.

⊙ Move the knife holder on the sledge forward and backward so that the upper cutting edge is just in line with the front edge of the paraffin block.

⊙ Viewing from the side, adjust the angle of the knife leaving just enough clearance angle.

⊙ Tighten the screws of the knife holder so that the desired clearance angle is maintained and the cutting edge of the knife just meets the paraffin block.

⊙ Now carefully release the safety catch while holding the drive wheel handle to prevent sudden sliding of the specimen holder.

⊙ Move the drive wheel in a controlled manner so that the specimen holder moves gently up and down. All the while watch carefully if the paraffin block just passes past the cutting edge of the knife.

⊙ Leave the specimen holder down in the resting position.

⊙ Recheck if the screws of the knife holder are firm.

⊙ Decide the thickness of the section by rotating the micrometer screw (Figure 4.12). Check if the indicator line in the dial is pointing a particular division and not in between divisions.

⊙ Start rotating the drive wheel, first slowly and then a little fast at constant rhythmic circular movement.

⊙ One can notice the paraffin block advancing with every vertical movement of the specimen holder.

⊙ When the paraffin block strikes against the cutting edge of the knife, paraffin-embedded sections are cut from the block.

⊙ The successive sections remain attached to the cutting edge pushing the previous sections forward which form a ribbon.

⊙ As sectioning continues, the ribbon grows in length.

⊙ Lift the farther end of the ribbon with the help of a needle wetted with formalin water so that a continuous ribbon of sections is possible.

A length of continuous ribbon is possible when the following conditions are satisfied.

⊙ Proper infiltration of the material is achieved.

⊙ Paraffin block is of right consistency.

⊙ Right clearance angle.

⊙ Knife is in firm grip on the knife holder.

⊙ The knife edge is sharp without nicks.

⊙ There is no draught of air.

SLEDGE MICROTOME

Sledge microtome is useful for sectioning very hard materials such as wood or bones. In a sledge microtome, the specimen remains fixed and the knife is movable.

The sledge microtome (Figure 4.13) has a strong and heavy base. There is a heavy sledge rail made of heavy steel over which the knife holder slides back and forth. The knife is fixed horizontally in the knife holder. The cutting angle of the knife can be altered as desired. The knife can be so arranged as to meet the material at right angles or at an angle in the horizontal plane.

The specimen holder is opposite to the knife holder in the path of the movement of knife. The specimen holder can be raised and lowered so that the cutting edge of the knife will exactly meet the specimen and cut it.

At the lower end the specimen holder ends in a ratchet wheel which is positioned horizontally (in rotary microtome, the ratchet wheel is positioned in vertical plane). There is a micrometer screw which can be used to set the thickness of the section in microns. When the screw is fixed with the reference indicator pointing exactly to a particular reading in the scale (say 15 μ), the specimen holder is raised by 15 μ up with every movement of the Naples clamp.

The knife of sledge microtome is about 9" long and about 1.5 to 2" broad. The back of the knife is quite thick and the cutting edge is 'V' shaped.

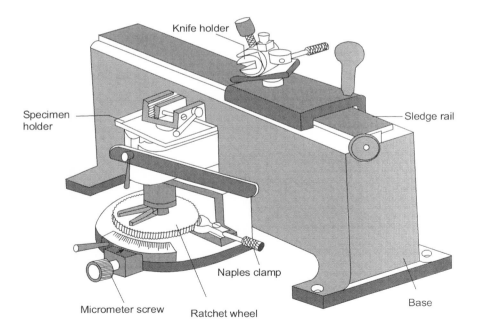

Figure 4.13 Sledge microtome

Sectioning Procedure

⊙ The specimen is to be firmly held in a supporting material. A small cube of wood in which a circular hole of suitable diameter is drilled is used. This cube is cut into two pieces exactly in the middle of the circular hole. The wood specimen is held between the wedges of two pieces of wood. The specimen to be sectioned just projects out by a few millimetres (Figure 4.13).

⊙ Many such wooden cubes with wedges of different diameter can be prepared and kept handy for use.

⊙ Materials such as cork or cork linoleum also can be used to make such holders.

⊙ The depth of the wedge or groove should be smaller than the radius of the specimen. Only then, the support would afford a firm grip to the specimen.

⊙ The specimen holder is lowered.

⊙ The knife holder is drawn back on the sledge rail.

⊙ The knife is fixed in the holder with just enough clearance angle.

⊙ The knife should be oriented at a wide oblique angle so that as much of the length of the cutting edge as possible is used for cutting.

⊙ The knife holder is carefully moved forward to the place where the cutting edge will meet the specimen.

⊙ Raise the specimen holder by rocking the Naples clamp so that the specimen is raised just to the level of the edge of the knife.

⊙ Move the knife holder backwards and push it forwards with a powerful stroke.

⊙ The cutting edge of the knife takes a section.

⊙ The section is carefully removed from the knife with the help of a wet brush.

⊙ Move the knife holder back.

⊙ Operate the Naples clamp once again to raise the specimen by the set distance.

⊙ Take another section by moving the knife holder forward.

⊙ Paraffin-embedded materials can also be sectioned in a sledge microtome.

⊙ Only individual sections are possible in a sledge microtome.

⊙ The sections are saved in 70% alcohol. They can be gradually dehydrated, cleared, stained and mounted in some resinous medium to make permanent slides.

MICROTOME KNIVES AND THEIR MAINTENANCE

Obtaining good sections in microtechnique almost totally depends on the microtome knife. All the time and efforts spent in specimen preparation and block making will go waste if the "cutting edge of the knife" is not perfect.

Razor blades and safety razor blades which are useful in making hand sections are useless in microtomy. Special microtome knives are designed and manufactured for use with microtomes. Blade holders that are available as optional accessories to microtome knifes have their own limitations in use.

Microtome knives are made of solid steel. The body or the main portion of the knife is called **blade**. The solid thick lower margin is called **back of the knife**. The sharp upper edge used for cutting is called **cutting edge**. The microtome knife is always supplied with a **handle** (Figure 4.14a) that can be screwed on to the blade through the hollow provided on either edge of the back. A **split cylinder** (Figure 4.14b) of steel is also always provided with the knife.

The split cylinder slips on the back of the knife and provides a temporary enlarged back. When the knife is placed back in the wooden box, it is always to be kept with its split cylinder slipped on its back so that the knife actually hangs in its wedge in the box with the cutting edge safe without getting damaged. The split cylinder is also useful in 'setting the cutting facet'.

The following three types of solid blades are available.

1. Square ground blade in which the main portion of the blade is a straight wedge (Figure 4.14c(1)).
2. Hollow ground blade in which the two sides of the blade have been ground away to yield concave surfaces (Figure 4.14c(2)) .
3. Half ground blade in which one side is flat or square ground and the other side is ground to an angle (Figure 4.14c(3)).

Irrespective of its grinding, the knife should have a cutting tip of relatively obtuse angle ground on the cutting edge. The process of providing this cutting facet to the tip is known as **setting**. The cutting facet should be set at least once a day if the knife is in continual use.

The nature and importance of the cutting facet is illustrated in Figure 4.14d. The knife blade itself must be inclined at such an angle to the block that the cutting facet is not parallel to the face of the block. A slight **clearance angle** should be allowed in between the cutting facet and the face of the block so that the knife will actually cut the section.

If the clearance angle is too large, the section is scrapped from the block instead of being cut. The section will be wrinkled and will roll up into a cylinder eventually!

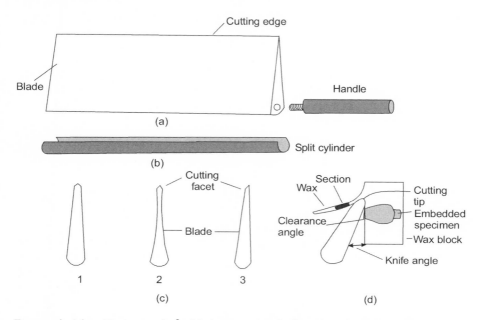

Figure 4.14   Microtome knife (a) A microtome knife with its handle (b) Split cylinder
(c) Types of cutting edges (d) Cutting facet and clearance angle

If the clearance angle is too small, the lower angle of the cutting facet scraps the block. The whole ribbon of sections will be picked up on the top of the block. Eventually the block itself cracks!

Therefore, maintaining the cutting facet at as uniform an angle as possible is an important exercise in microtomy. This is called **setting the cutting facet**. The split cylinder of steel provided with the microtome knife serves in setting the cutting facet. When the knife with the split cylinder is rested flat on a honing stone, the cylinder as well as the blade lies flat on the stone. When the knife is gently pushed forward, the cutting facet is produced as an angle between the cutting edge lying on the stone and the enlarged temporary back that has been placed on the knife.

A perfectly maintained knife will present a nick-free smooth edge when observed under a dissection microscope. In such a knife, about three strokes on either side are enough to produce a perfect cutting facet. Further strokes have no more effect than to diminish the lifespan of the knife (Figure 4.15a).

On the other hand, a carelessly handled knife will present an edge with nicks when observed under a dissection microscope. In such a case, if the nick is shallow, it can be removed by giving more number of strokes and the cutting facet can be set. If the nick is deeper than ¼ mm, the knife has to be returned to the manufacturer for setting the cutting facet.

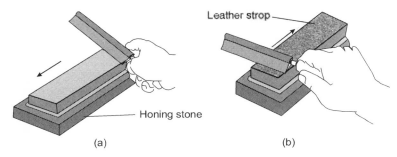

Figure 4.15   Honing stone and strop (a) Setting the cutting facet (b) Stropping a microtome knife

The purpose of 'setting' is to produce a cutting facet and not removal of 'knife imperfections'. For the latter, grinding is recommended which cannot be attempted in the laboratory. Electrically operated automatic grinding machines are available. But all laboratories may not be able to afford such facilities. Therefore the only alternative left is to send the knife to the manufacturer for grinding to remove the imperfections.

Stropping the knife using leather strops, only polishes the facet and does not improve the sharpness. Hence it is quite unnecessary for knives with properly set cutting facets. Stropping is to be performed with back strokes of the knife and never with forward strokes (Figure 4.15b).

The honing stones used in microtomy have the following considerations.

- Honing stones of very fine grain alone are to be used.
- The stone should be perfectly flat with smooth surface.
- The surface of the stone should be flooded with the recommended lubricant before starting the 'setting exercise'.
- While drawing the knife forward, no pressure is to be applied on the blade from above.

Tips on Use and Maintenance of Microtome Knives

- Microtome knives are very sharp and it is always safe not to meddle with their cutting edge. Always handle knife with its handle fixed to it. This minimizes the chances of getting fingers cut.

⊙ After use every time the knife is to be kept back in its box with the split cylinder on.

⊙ In the case of continual use, the cutting facet is to be 'set' at least once daily.

⊙ Follow the precautions while using the honing stone.

⊙ Wipe the surface of the knife along its blade sides and the cutting edge carefully with cotton soaked in xylol. This helps to remove the wax that gets stuck to the edge of the knife and sides of the blade.

⊙ Never attempt to sharpen the knife using a grinding wheel.

FIXATION AND FIXATIVES

INTRODUCTION

The following is an account of the fate of a piece of tissue cut out of a living or recently dead organism when no special care is taken to keep it or maintain its structure.

⊙ Left in air, it is likely to undergo osmotic swelling or shrinkage.

⊙ Even if these distortions are prevented, it is vulnerable to fungal or bacterial attack.

⊙ Even if microbial attack is prevented by asepsis, the tissue will gradually fall to pieces by self-digestion or 'autolysis' by the activity of the enzymes present in the cells.

So, what do we do to preserve a piece of tissue?

Therefore, to preserve a piece of tissue, it has to be treated either with physical agents or chemical agents. Subjecting the tissue to temperature treatments is one approach (e.g. cryopreservation). Treating the tissue with some chemical is yet another approach.

Any fluid with the following attributes is capable of preserving tissues.

⊙ A fluid that will not shrink, swell, dissolve or distort the tissue.

⊙ A fluid that will kill bacteria and moulds (fungi).

⊙ A fluid that will render autolytic enzymes inactive.

A fluid that combines all the aforesaid three attributes is called a preservative.

Then what is a fixative?

⊙ Fixative is a fluid that, in addition to being a preservative, also modifies the tissues in such a way that they become capable of resisting subsequent treatments of various kinds. It protects the tissue against damages that are likely to be caused by embedding and sectioning.

- ◉ Apart from this protective role, fixation also makes many tissue constituents, especially chromatin, readily colourable by suitable dyes.
- ◉ The essential function of a fixative is the stabilization of the protein part of the framework of the cell. This is particularly very useful in animal cells where a cell wall is absent.

Do all kinds of cells/tissues/cell constituents require fixation?

- ◉ Not every kind of tissue constituent requires fixation. Some are not capable of being fixed, e.g. hard tissues such as wood, stony endocarp, bone tissue, etc.
- ◉ However, all other kinds of soft tissues and organs are to be fixed before being processed for microscopic observation.
- ◉ There are certain substances of biological origin that are not subject to decay or distortion, e.g. chitin, cellulose, starch grains, scleroproteins, amorphous silica and certain inorganic crystals.
- ◉ Soluble sugars cannot be retained in their natural sites in the tissues by any fixative.

FIXATION—AIM AND ADVANTAGES

Fixation is the first and most important step in microtechnique. It is nothing but inactivating or immobilizing the organism, organ or tissues, killing them instantly.

The aim of fixation is to fix the biological object in the same state in which it is collected or to fix with least damage or change to its structure.

The following are the advantages of fixation.

- ◉ The protoplasm of the cells becomes dead.
- ◉ Changes in the external morphology is prevented.
- ◉ The internal degradation of the cell or tissue is stopped and so the object is fixed in the same stage in which it is to be examined.

AGENTS EMPLOYED IN FIXING
BIOLOGICAL MATERIALS

Based on the agents employed, two types of fixation are known.

1. Fixation by using physical factors
2. Fixation by chemical factors

Fixation by Using Physical Factors

By implementing sudden and drastic changes in the temperature, the biological objects can be fixed. This is achieved by increasing the temperature suddenly or by freeze-drying.

However, fixation by using sudden changes in temperature is not ideal for many kinds of tissues. Therefore, fixation by using chemical agents is widely used.

Fixation by Using Chemical Factors

Several chemicals are known to have the property of killing the tissues instantly. Such chemicals are known as chemical fixatives.

A chemical should satisfy the following conditions to be used as a fixative.

1. It should be capable of invading the cell or the tissue very rapidly and instantly. This will enable killing of all the parts of the tissue instantly.
2. It should be capable of stopping the entire cellular metabolism at once.
3. It should not alter the basic structure or chemistry of the cells.
4. It should be capable of preventing autodegradation of the tissue.
5. It should harden the tissue moderately.

The essential function of a fixative is the stabilization of the protein part of the framework of the cell. Most fixatives are solids used in aqueous solution. Some are organic liquids that can be used as such. A very small number of chemical compounds are useful as fixatives.

Most fixatives render tissues more basic or more acidic than they were in the unfixed state. This is because they react with and block the acidic or basic side groups of certain amino acids. As a result, the affinity of the protein for basic and acidic dyes is changed.

All fixatives fall into two groups according to their obvious reactions with soluble proteins.

   i. Coagulant
  ii. Non-coagulant

COAGULANT FIXATIVES

These are fixatives that produce a coagulum when mixed with a solution of albumin. They transform protoplasm into a microscopic sponge work. Table 4.3 lists some of the coagulant fixatives and their properties.

Table 4.3   Some coagulant fixatives and their properties

Examples	Properties	Standard concentration used
Ethanol (C_2H_5OH)	A colourless fluid miscible with water in all proportions	Undiluted (absolute)
Mercuric chloride ($HgCl_2$)	Colourless crystals soluble in water at 7%	Saturated aqueous solution
Chromium trioxide (CrO_3)	Brownish red crystals	As 0.5% aqueous solution

NON-COAGULANT FIXATIVES

These are fixatives that do not produce a coagulum when mixed with albumin. Table 4.4 lists some of the non-coagulant fixatives.

Table 4.4   Some non-coagulant fixatives and their properties

Examples	Properties	Standard concentration used
Formaldehyde (HCHO)	Colourless gas, highly soluble in water	As 4% aqueous solution
Osmium tetroxide (OSO_4)	Pale yellow crystals soluble in water @7%	As 1% aqueous solution
Potassium dichromate ($K_2Cr_2O_7$)	Orange-red crystals soluble in water @10% giving a weakly acid solution	As 1.5% aqueous solution
Acetic acid (CH_3COOH)	Colourless liquid miscible with water in all proportions	As 5% aqueous solution

⊙ Each of the primary fixative has its virtues and defects. Therefore, it has been found that a mixture of two or more fixatives (fixative mixtures) yield better results.

⊙ The coagulating property does not necessarily destroy structure at the microscopical level since the meshes of the sponge work may be very fine.

⊙ But non-coagulant fixatives are nearly always used in electron microscopy.

⊙ The production of a sponge work is helpful in the penetration of embedding media, especially paraffin.

In actual practice, there is no single fixative that has all these characteristics. Some fixatives may preserve certain types of cells and destroy the other types of cells. Some fixatives may interfere with the staining procedure at a later stage. Therefore, all these facts are to be borne in mind before choosing a suitable fixative for use.

The following chemicals are used widely as fixatives in biological microtechnique.

1. Methanol, ethanol, acetone
2. Hydrochloric acid, nitric acid, sulphuric acid
3. Trichloroacetic acid, picric acid
4. Chloroplastinic acid
5. Mercuric acid
6. Acetic-mercuric acid
7. Chromium trioxide
8. Osmium tetroxide
9. Formaldehyde and other aldehydes
10. Potassium dichromate

Of these chemicals, formaldehyde, methanol and ethanol can be used individually and directly as fixatives. These are called simple fixatives. (An account of widely used fixatives is given in Appendix.)

In most microtechnical processes, depending on the types of object and our requirement, two or more fixative chemicals are used in combinations. These are called chemical fixative mixtures.

CHEMICAL FIXATIVE MIXTURES

The following chemical fixative mixtures are in wide use.

Acetic Acid–Alcohol Mixtures (AA Mixtures)

Acetic acid invades the cells or tissues very rapidly and kills them instantly. Alcohol is not only a fixative, but also a preservative. Therefore, these two are used in various combinations as a fixative mixture.

The following are some of the most important formulations in use.

Farmer's fixative

Acetic acid and 100% alcohol are used in a proportion of 1:3 (V/V) on volume basis.

Acetic acid	5 ml
100% Alcohol	15 ml

Farmer's acetic–alcohol fixative mixture is very ideal for root tips and anthers. The root tips are to be left in this mixture for 15 minutes. Anthers are to be left for 1 hour.

After fixation, the object is to be washed several times in 70% alcohol, until the smell of acetic acid is removed. This ensures removal of acetic acid from the fixed tissues.

Carnoy's acetic acid–alcohol fixative

Acetic acid, alcohol and chloroform are mixed in a proportion of 1:2:3 (V/V) to prepare Carnoy's fixative. Chloroform stops the cellular metabolism instantly.

Glacial acetic acid	5 ml
100% alcohol	10 ml
Chloroform	15 ml

Carnoy's fixative is very ideal for fixing root tips and anthers. Fixation time is 10 to 15 minutes. After fixation is over, the objects are to be washed in 85% alcohol several times. The objects can be finally preserved in 85% alcohol for any length of time.

Formalin–Acetic Acid–Alcohol Mixtures (FAA mixtures)

FAA mixtures are more suited as fixatives. They are superior to AA mixtures. The formalin present in the FAA mixtures performs two functions, namely, preservation and hardening of the tissues. Though several formulations are available, the following two are very widely used.

Ralinin's FAA

95% Ethyl alcohol	50 ml
Glacial acetic acid	5 ml
Formalin	10 ml
Distilled water	35 ml

This is an ideal fixative for soft-bodied algae, and plant tissues. It hardens the object considerably. Biological objects can be kept in this fixative for several years. Fixing time is 18 hours. After fixation is over, the object is to be washed thoroughly in alcohol and preserved in alcohol.

Chicago FAA

70% Ethyl alcohol	100 ml
Formalin	6 ml

This is an ideal fixative for very small fragments of tissues. Even though acetic acid is absent, this is considered as a type of FAA mixture.

The strength of the alcohol used can be altered according to the tissue fixed. Very soft tissues can be fixed in FAA containing 30% alcohol or even that of weaker strength.

Chrome–Acetic Acid Mixtures (CA Mixtures)

Chromic acid (actually chromic oxide) is widely used in fixative mixtures, usually with the addition of acetic acid.

These mixtures are prepared without using alcohol. Soft tissues and soft-bodied organisms such as filamentous algae lose water very rapidly when fixed in fixatives containing alcohol. To avoid shrinkage due to rapid loss of water, fixation in chrome–acetic acid mixtures is recommended for such soft specimens.

Based on the strength of the chromic acid used, three types of CA mixtures are in use namely, weak CA mixtures, moderate CA mixtures and strong CA mixtures.

Weak chrome–acetic acid mixture

1% Chromic acid	50 ml
1% Acetic acid	50 ml

Moderate chrome–acetic acid mixture

1% Chromic acid	70 ml
1% Acetic acid	20 ml
Distilled water	10 ml

Strong chrome–acetic acid mixture

1% Chromic acid	97 ml
1% Acetic acid	3 ml

Gate's fluid is another chrome–acetic acid mixture where glacial acetic acid is used.

Gate's fluid

Chromic acid	0.7 g
Glacial acetic acid	0.5 g
Water	100 ml

This is found to be an excellent fixative for plant chromosomes in root tips. Fixing time is overnight.

Chrome–acetic acid mixtures (CA mixtures) are ideal fixatives for fixing filamentous algae, thalloid bryophytes, soft tissues, soft parts of flowers, leaf bits, soft stems, etc.

Time of fixation varies with types of organisms or tissues. Algae can be left in CA mixtures for a few minutes; leaf bits and root tips can be left for 12 hours; large bits of tissues can be left for 24 hours.

After fixation, the object is to be washed in running tap water for 24 hours followed by a distilled water wash for 12 hours.

CA mixtures are fixatives and not preservatives. Therefore, washed materials have to be preserved in some preservative solution such as FAA containing 20% or 30% alcohol.

Chrome–Acetic–Formalin Mixtures (Craf Mixtures)

Preservative property can be imparted to the CA mixtures by adding formalin. Addition of formalin to CA mixtures is a common practice in botanical microtechnique and these solutions are called **Craf** mixtures (Cr = chromic acid; a = acetic acid; f = formalin). The most widely used Craf mixture is Navaschin's fixative.

Navaschin's fixative

Navaschin's recipe contains two stock solutions. They have to be prepared and kept separate. They can be mixed in the prescribed proportion just before use.

Navaschin Stock Solution A

1% Chromic acid	15 ml
Glacial acetic acid	10 ml
Distilled water	90 ml

Navaschin Stock Solution B

Formalin*	40 ml
Distilled water	60 ml

The two stock solutions can be mixed in equal quantities just prior to use. Fixation time is 12 hours. After fixation there is no need to wash the object in water.

Some improvements were made in this recipe of Navaschin and these modifications are called Craf concoctions. Though there are about five different Craf concoctions, the following two are widely used.

Craf-1 fixative

1% Chromic acid	20 ml
1% Acetic acid	75 ml
Formalin*	5 ml

Craf-2 fixative

1% Chromic acid	20 ml
10% Acetic acid	10 ml
Formalin*	5 ml
Distilled water	65 ml

(*has to be kept separate; to be added just prior to use)

In the aforesaid formulations, formalin is to be added only just prior to use. Within a few hours after adding formalin, the mixture turns olive green. Fixation time is 12 hours.

Craf mixtures are also capable of preserving the material. After fixation, materials are not to be washed in water.

Picric Acid Fixative Mixtures (PA Mixtures)

Picric acid (trinitrophenol) has been widely used as a component of fixatives. Picric acid as a fixative is ideal for micropreparations made for cytological observations. Two formulations of PA mixtures are available, of which Bouin's fluid is the best known.

Bouin's picric acid fixative mixture

Saturated aqueous solution of picric acid	75 ml
40% Formaldehyde	25 ml
Glacial acetic acid	5 ml

This is used as a fixative for root tips and embryo sac studies. Fixation time is 12 hours. After fixation, the material is to be washed in 20% alcohol or acetone.

Bouin's fluid became very popular in zoological microtechnique. However, Peter Grey (1964) opines that the only advantage of this fluid is that the materials can be left in it for a long time without becoming unduly hard. The disadvantages are that, picric acid forms water-soluble compounds with many substances found in the cell, so that sections cut from materials fixed in Bouin's fluid show large vacuoles. It is also very difficult to wash the fluid from the tissues. Even small traces of picric acid left in the sections interfere with staining.

Allen's modifications of Bouin's fluid

Bouin's fluid was recommended by its inventor for the fixation of meiotic figures. However, it has been replaced largely by Allen's modification.

Picric acid	1 g
Chromic acid	1 g
Urea	1 g
Glacial acetic acid	10 ml
40% Formaldehyde	15 ml
Water	75 ml

Small pieces of tissues can be fixed overnight and then washed in 70% alcohol until no more colour comes away.

Johansen (1940) gives the following formula for the same.

1% Chromic acid	50 ml
10% Acetic acid	20 ml
Formalin*	10 ml
Saturated aqueous solution of picric acid*	20 ml

(* to be added just prior to use)

It is better to have stock solutions of the components and to mix them in the recommended proportion as and when required.

Allen's modification of Bouin's fixatives is very ideal for cytological preparations, particularly for metaphase and anaphase studies. The materials can be kept in this fixative mixture safely for several months.

Potassium Chromate Mixtures (PC mixtures)

Zirkle–Ehrlich's formula is notable and widely used.

Potassium bichromate	1.25 g
Ammonium bichromate	1.25 g
Cupric sulphate	1.0 g
Distilled water	200 ml

Fixation time is 24 hours to 48 hours. After fixation is over, the materials are to be washed in water.

This is very ideal for studying mitochondria, nucleoplasm, vacuoles, etc. The disadvantage is that spindle fibres dissolve in this mixture. Therefore, it is not suitable for studying the stages of cell division.

VARIOUS PLANT GROUPS OR PLANT PARTS AND FIXATIVES IDEAL FOR THEM

Tissues containing bacterial growth   Zenker's fluid is used to fix tissues infected with bacteria. This is prepared as follows:

Potassium dichromate	2.5 g
Sodium sulphate	1.0 g
Mercuric chloride	5.0 g
Glacial acetic acid	5.0 ml
Distilled water	100 ml

Chlorophyceae   Weak chrome–acetic acid mixture and FAA are suitable fixatives for this group of algae.

For marine algae, filtered seawater should be used in the fixative in the place of distilled water.

Phaeophyceae   10% formalin in filtered seawater is ideal for fixing. Craf-2 solution is also found to be suitable.

Cyanophyceae   3% or 5% formalin solution or Bouin's solution are suitable fixatives for the members of Cyanophyceae. For marine Cyanophyceae, the fixative should be prepared using filtered seawater.

Rhodophyceae   8% to 10% formalin as well as Craf-2 solution prepared out of filtered seawater are ideal fixatives.

Fleshy and parasitic fungi   Navaschin's fixative and Craf-1 solution are ideal fixatives.

Lichens   Formalin–propionoalcohol (FPA) mixture is ideal for lichens.

Bryophyta   FAA–FPA mixtures are ideal.

Pteridophyta, Cycadophyta and Coniferophyta   FAA fixative is ideal.

Angiosperms   The ideal fixatives for various plant parts are listed in Table 4.5.

Table 4.5   Fixatives for various plant parts

Plant parts	Fixatives
Root tip	Farmer's fixative or Carnoy's fixative
Roots	Craf-1
Shoot tip	FPA
Stems	FAA
Leaves	FPA
Flowers	FAA
Fruits	FPA

POINTS TO BE KEPT IN MIND WHILE FIXING BIOLOGICAL MATERIALS FOR MICROTECHNIQUE

1. Plants or animals or their parts or organs are to be fixed immediately after collection. Therefore, it is important to carry fixative solutions to the field itself while going on collection trips.

2. As far as possible, fixatives recommended for the particular materials are to be used, particularly for cytological preparations.

3. For anatomical preparations, the plant parts or tissues are to be cut into small pieces, say of size (1 cm × 1 cm × 0.5 cm).

4. While cutting plant parts into pieces, care should be taken to cause the least damage to the internal tissues. Sharp and heavy knives are to be used for this.

5. Certain plants or plant parts or tissues may have air in the intercellular spaces. Therefore, they will keep afloat in the fixative mixture. In such cases, the air can be removed by using an aspirator. If an aspirator is not available, the specimen tube with specimen(s) in the fixative can be tightly closed with the lid, and shaken vigorously to remove air from the intercellular spaces. The materials will then sink to the bottom in the specimen tube. While shaking, care is to be taken that the material does not break and fragment.

6. While transferring the material from the fixative to the next stage, it should be washed thoroughly to remove the fixative. Washing away the fixative from the material is a very important step. The acids present in the fixative, if left behind in the material, may interfere with staining at a later stage.

STAINS AND STAINING

The role of stains and staining procedures in microtechnique is to obtain clear images of the microsections examined. The clarity of the images of microsections viewed in microscopes depends on the degree by which the microsections deviate the light rays passing through them (i.e., contrast).

Some biological materials (specimens such as microalgae, etc.) have coloured parts such as chloroplasts and so can efficiently deviate light rays passing through them. The deviated light rays form a clear image against the bright background of undeviated rays passing away from the structural details of the material.

Unfortunately, several biological materials do not have natural colours. Moreover, many biological objects become transparent after passing through dehydration and clearing operations. They are not distinguished from the bright background as they allow most of the light passing through them and hence are unable to produce a clear image.

If microsections or micropreparations of such materials are to be seen clearly, the different parts of the cells in them are to be given the ability to deviate the light rays passing through them. Such objects are to be stained to overcome this difficulty. In other words they are to be impregnated with colour which renders them more visible. Therefore, staining is a very important step in microtechnique.

PRINCIPLES OF STAINING

Stain is a dye or a substance in solution that impregnates the object imparting colour to it.

A dye, whether it is derived from natural sources or synthesized, owes its colour to the presence of a chemical group known as chromophore. Azo group found in methyl orange and many other dyes and indamine group found in methylene blue and celestine blue are the typical chromophores.

Compounds containing chromophores are called chromogens. The chromogens derive their ability to stain materials only in the presence of auxochromes which have either acidic or basic components.

The mere presence of chromophore does not impart colour but makes it possible for the colour to appear when an ionizing group known as auxochrome is attached. These ionizing groups carry either a positive charge or a negative charge.

Dyes are used as solutions. The ions in solution must be balanced. Cationic dyes like methylene blue require addition of a free anion such as chloride. Anionic dyes are balanced by a sodium cation.

The staining process is based on the concept that the dye must adhere to the structure which is being stained and remain attached to it through the various stages of staining, destaining, counterstaining and mounting.

A dye is permanently attached to a structure when the charge on the dye becomes balanced by the charge on the particle dyed. This explains why basic dyes like methylene blue or haematoxylin become attached to cellular structures rich in nucleic acid that retain a negative charge through fixation and sectioning. Hence these stains are called nuclear stains.

Most of the cytoplasmic structures are rich in protein. The proteins found in the cytoplasm retain a positive charge. Acid dyes such as eosin, erythosine, etc. attach themselves permanently to the cytoplasm. Hence these are called cytoplasmic stains.

The terms acidity or basicity of stains has nothing to do with the pH of the solutions used in staining. They refer to the charge carried by the auxochrome ion. The degree of acidity or basicity depends on the number of charged auxochromes and chromophores that enter into the composition of the dye molecule.

Some dyes are weakly charged and therefore, are not able to remain permanently attached to the structure which is dyed through the stages of staining and mounting. The degree of adhesion can be enhanced by using some intermediary substances that are called mordants. Sulphates, particularly the double sulphates called alums are most widely used as mordants in microtechnique.

PRINCIPLE OF DIFFERENTIAL STAINING

Many micropreparations (microsections) present an assortment of component tissues or organelles. The different tissues or cell organelles differ in their chemical nature and therefore, have different abilities to retain dyes of contrasting colours. Differential staining techniques take advantage of this principle.

Staining microsections with two or more different stains of contrasting colours is called differential staining.

The stain that is used first in differential staining process is a general stain which attaches to all the structures. This is called primary stain.

The stain that is used in the second and a subsequent step is called counterstain.

Prior to counterstaining, the excess of primary stain is to be removed from the microsection and this stage is called destaining. The solutions which reduce the affinity between the primary stain and the structures stained are used for destaining.

Different types of tissues differ in their permeability to different substances. Similarly different dyes (stains) differ in their solubility characteristics. These form the basis for differential staining. For example, Sudan III is soluble in oil but insoluble in water. Thus a colloidal dispersion of the dye in water is picked up by oil droplets in contrast to other tissues present.

DIRECT AND INDIRECT STAINING

Theoretically, two types of staining are recognized, namely, direct staining and indirect staining. Table 4.6 traces out the differences between direct and indirect staining.

Table 4.6   Differences between direct and indirect staining

Direct staining	Indirect staining
The dye is applied to the tissue or the object and is stopped when sufficient dye has been absorbed.	The tissue or object is soaked in the dye solution and then differentiated usually in an acid or a mordant until the dye has been removed from unwanted regions.
Direct staining particularly from weak solutions is preferred in the case of large whole mounts.	Indirect staining is more usually employed on sections or small objects.

USE OF MORDANTS

Mordant is an intermediary substance used to increase the degree of adhesion of dyes that are weakly charged. The double sulphates called alums are the most widely used mordants in microtechnique.

The dye attaches itself to the mordant and the mordant "eats into" or grips the tissue.

The greatest advantage of mordanting is that the colour is not removed by neutral fluids whether aqueous or alcoholic. One may therefore stain progressively or regressively until the tissue is properly displayed and then dehydrate at leisure or counterstain as desired.

Sometimes, the mordant becomes attached to the tissue by a covalent bond and under such circumstances the dye attached to the tissue is not removed by the neutral solutions used for dehydrating in the following stages. The use of ionized solutions, usually acid, or solutions of the mordant itself removed the dye. This is the basis of differentiation used with haematoxylin and carmine.

The fastness of the mordant dyes makes them suitable for use in aqueous mounts, provided that acidity is avoided, e.g. carminic acid (carmine) and haematin used with salts of aluminium and of ferric ions as mordants.

It is not always necessary to prepare a mordant/dye complex first and subsequently to allow it to come into contact with the tissues. Instead, one may first soak the tissues in a solution of the mordant and then in a solution of the dye. The basiphil (base-loving) tissue constituents will take up the positively hydrated aluminium ions and the dye will displace water from the attached aluminium complex when given the chance to do so. It might, indeed, be said that the dye is being used as a reagent for the detection of aluminium.

The mordanting regimens commonly used in microtechnique fall under two categories.

Single-bath method Dye is mixed with the solvent. Either progressive or regressive dyeing can be followed in this method.

Two-bath method The tissue is first placed in the mordant and then in the dye. Only regressive method is to be followed in this method.

There are two ways of differentiating mordant dyes after deliberate overdyeing.

1. *Place the tissue in an acid (often a weak solution of HCl).* When a mordanted dye is differentiated by acid, the tissue–mordant link is attacked. This is proved by the following procedure.

    i. Take two sections/slides (with sections mounted on them).

    ii. Treat both with mordant (aluminium sulphate).

    iii. Place one slide/section into acid used for differentiation (weak H_2SO_4).

    iv. Wash off the acid in water.

    v. Now place both the slides/sections in the dye for the same length of time.

The acid-treated section/slide stains very feebly in comparison with the other.

2. Place the tissue/section in the mordant itself. The mordant, the very substance that attaches the dye to the tissue, can also be used to remove the dye from it. The two-way action of mordant depends upon the relative abundance of the mordant and dye. For example, when a section has been dyed/stained, the total amount of dye in it is very small. If the section is now placed in a solution of the mordant, the latter is present in enormous excess. The mordant solution extracts the dye from the section.

Thus whether a mordant/mordant–dye solution dyes or extracts depends on the relative abundance of the dye and mordant, i.e., on the mordant quotient. The mordant quotient of a mordant/dye solution (e.g. aluminium purpurate solution) that neither increases nor decreases the intensity of colouring of such a section is called the critical mordant quotient (CMQ).

If sufficient time is allowed, destaining is complete and no visible trace of the dye will remain in the tissue.

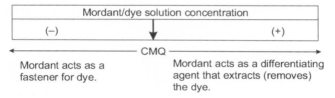

If an undyed/unstained section is placed in an aluminium purpurate solution in which the MQ is at the critical figure, dyeing will take place very slowly until chromatin is strongly and cytoplasm is feebly coloured. No further increase of colour will occur however long the section may remain in the dye.

Solutions at critical mordant quotient strength do not overdye and therefore are easy to use. Standard purpural (MQ = 8) is an example. It can be recommended to the beginners as a routine dye for chromatin and other positively charged tissue constituents. It is to be used progressively. The period of dyeing varies according to the fixative used. Half an hour to one hour usually suffices. The section is then simply washed in 50% or 70% ethanol.

The coal-tar dyes generally do not require mordants. However, many microtechnicians have obtained desirable improvement in the performance of many of the coal-tar dyes by using some chemicals as mordant. For example,

- ⊙ Eosin and erythrosin is improved by the addition of traces of acetic acid.

⊙ Barium chloride (2 to 4% solution) has been used as a mordant for the acid dyes.

⊙ Addition of traces of lithium carbonate is claimed to improve the action of basic dyes.

⊙ Iodine and picric acid are employed as mordants for the various violet dyes after the stains have been allowed to react on the tissues.

The following are used as mordants for various staining schemes. All these are best used for 5 to 10 minutes on the slide after they have been brought down to water.

⊙ Silicotungstic acid (4% aqueous solution) for basic dyes

⊙ Potassium permanganate (1% solution)

⊙ Ammonium chromate (4% solution)

⊙ Ammonium dichromate (3% solution)

⊙ Aluminium hydroxide or aluminium potassium sulphate (potash alum) 3 or 4% solution

The following are to be noted in using a mordant solution.

1. Excess mordant should always be washed off the slide thoroughly.

2. The pH of the fluid used for washing out and differentiating determines the selective retention of the stain. Basic dyes should as a rule be washed out with solutions which are acid in reaction. Most acid dyes which are all used as counterstains, should be differentiated in solutions which are slightly alkaline.

SOLVENTS FOR THE STAINS

Knowledge on the solubility of the stains used and the nature of the most appropriate solvent for the stain is essential for attaining desired results in micropreparations. The following are useful notes on the solvents for various stains.

⊙ Basic dyes used in botanical microtechnique are dissolved in either water or 50% ethyl alcohol.

⊙ The acid dyes employed as cytoplasmic counterstains are usually dissolved in an alcohol of high percentage or in clove oil, because they ordinarily wash out very easily.

⊙ Haematoxylin may be dissolved in water or absolute alcohol but is never used without mordanting.

⊙ The carmines are always in aqueous solutions with the customary addition of various salts or acids.

- ⊙ Under certain circumstances, it may be desirable to dissolve a dye in a solvent other than that specified. But the effects of such solvents on the performance of the stains are to be ascertained by trial and error.

- ⊙ The basic coal-tar dyes are often dissolved in acetin (glycerine monoacetate) and the acid dyes in an alcohol–ether such as methyl cellosolve or in beechwood creosote.

- ⊙ Lactic acid or leolinic acid is a good solvent for indulins, the "alcohol-soluble indulin" and nigrosin. (Dissolve the colourless crystals of lactic acid in either water or alcohol.)

STRENGTH OF STAIN SOLUTIONS

When a dye is purchased, the total amount of dye contained in each batch is indicated. If the dye content amounts to 80% or more, it may be considered sufficiently high for practical purposes.

It is a general rule to overstain tissues and then to differentiate the stain until the desired intensity or depth of staining is reached and therefore one need not worry too much on this.

For example, a dye certified as having 80% or higher dye content may be used in the proportion of 1 g to 100 cc of the solvent to give a 1% solution.

If the dye content is below 80%, appropriate adjustments in the weight of the dye are to be made to make a solution of specific percentage. For example, if the dye content is given as 50%, 2 g of such dye to 100 cc of solvent would be required to make a 1% solution.

If a saturated solution is indicated, there is no need to determine the amount of the dye to be dissolved.

The solubility of certain dyes is accelerated by the application of heat. But in some cases, such as the violets, heating the solutions whether filtered or not, leaves irremovable precipitates in the tissues.

Many dyes have long shelf life. But some get spoilt whatever be the solvent. Spoilt stain solution should never be used.

BLEACHING

Some specimens become excessively darkened by the fixing fluids. Sections cut from such specimens require to be bleached before a proper staining effect can be obtained.

While bleaching, always watch the progress of action and stop it as soon as complete or else the continued action will hydrolyse or macerate the tissues. The following bleaching agents are commonly used.

Hydrogen peroxide   Usually hydrogen peroxide comes in strength of 2 to 3%. It may be used in full strength or diluted to as high as 50% with either water or 50 or 70% alcohol.

Superoxol marketed by Merck's is a peroxide of 30% strength. It may be used where a powerful oxidizing bleacher is required.

Ammonia peroxide   Addition of ammonia water accelerates the bleaching action of hydrogen peroxide.

Hydrogen peroxide (10% strength)	10 cc
Water	200 cc
Ammonia water	1 cc

The material or mounted slide is transferred from water to the bleaching agent. Wash thoroughly in water after bleaching has been accomplished.

Chromic acid   Presence of too much of phlobaphene renders certain tissues too dark to microscopy. Such specimens should be bleached before subjecting them to stains.

The following bleaching reagent mixture is recommended.

Water	90 cc
Potassium bichromate	1 g
Glacial acetic acid	10 cc
Chromic acid	1 g

Permanganate   If the sections appear to have suffered from too much chromate fixation, immerse the sections for 1 minute in a 1% aqueous solution of potassium permanganate, rinse, remove the permanganate in a 1% aqueous solution of oxalic acid, wash again, and proceed to staining.

Chlorine gas   Chlorine gas fumes have been found to be an excellent bleaching agent. Place crystals of potassium chlorate of approximately the size of a wheat grain in a Coplin jar. Pour a little dilute HCl. As soon as green-yellow fumes become apparent, fill the jar quickly with 50% alcohol. Immerse the slides containing sections for about 20 minutes to complete bleaching.

Caution   Sections cannot be stained if commercial bleaching fluids containing chlorine are used!

The blackening caused by osmic acid may be removed by dissolved chlorine gas or by immersing the sections in hydrogen peroxide diluted with water to one-half of the strength. The process may be hastened by placing the container in sunlight.

Boric acid solution and aqueous solution (2%) of ammonium persulphate are also commonly used as bleaching agents. The latter is a powerful oxidizer and therefore should be used with caution.

Note Sometimes preserved materials lose their staining capacity. The following schedule is recommended for restoration of staining capacity of tissues.

⊙ Bleach if necessary.

⊙ Soak for 15 minutes in a 10% solution of benzoyl peroxide in acetone.

⊙ Wash out in a solution of 2 parts of xylol to 3 parts of acetone followed by absolute alcohol.

PROGRESSIVE AND REGRESSIVE STAINING

The main aim of staining is to obtain sharp differentiation between different tissues in the micropreparations. A micropreparation is considered excellent if its tissue elements after staining present sufficient contrast by differential intensity of stains. The desired intensity in staining schedule is attained purely by personal judgement of the microtechnician and there are two ways to attain this.

Progressive Staining

By observing the staining under the microscope from time to time, any desired colour intensity may be attained. The staining reaction is stopped once this is achieved. This method is called progressive staining.

However, a satisfactory differentiation is usually not obtained by this method. Either the staining progresses a little too much or stops a little short of sharp differentiation.

Regressive Staining

The section or micropreparation is overstained deliberately to a considerable extent and then destained until a satisfactory optimum is reached. This is the most commonly followed method.

Most of the schedules described in the following pages follow regressive staining.

DIFFERENTIAL ACIDIFICATION

In some cases the tissue elements do not present sufficient contrast in their relative degree of acidic or basic reactions. Under such circumstances, the hydrolysis phase of Feulgen's reaction is employed to render the nuclei more acid, giving them a greater affinity for nuclear stains.

⊙ Bring the slide or fixed material down to water.

⊙ Treat it in cold 1N HCl for exactly 1 hour. (Heating the acid will dissociate the material.)

⊙ Rinse once with distilled water.

⊙ Place in nuclear stain.

This is the most suitable schedule for thick materials mounted as a whole, e.g. fern prothalli, *Ectocarpus*, root tips, *Elodea* leaves and other similar objects.

GENERAL AND SPECIFIC STAINS

General Stains

Stains that impart colour to everything simultaneously are called general stains. *In toto* staining of sections during classwork represents this type of stain.

Though there is no selective differentiation, such an effect may be achieved to a slight extent by regressive destaining! What differentiation occurs is usually produced by the dehydrating fluids and not by the stain!

Specific Stains

Stains that have affinity with specific structures based on the chemical nature of the structures are called specific stains. For example,

⊙ Sudan IV stains only fats or fat-containing elements such as suberin.

⊙ Congo red is specific for plant mucin.

⊙ Alkanet gives a bright red colour to oils.

STAINS USED IN PLANT MICROTECHNIQUE

The dyes used in botanical microtechnique to stain plant specimens and sections fall under two broad categories, namely, natural dyes and coal-tar dyes.

NATURAL DYES

The three natural dyes that are still used in plant microtechnique have not been manufactured synthetically. All the three are important cytological stains. One of them namely cochineal is obtained from an insect and other two are from plants belonging to the angiosperm family Caesalpineaceae.

Brazilin

Though many different trees collectively known as 'brazilwood' form the source, Brazilin is obtained mainly from *Caesalpinia cristata* or *C. echinata*. The dye is chemically related to haematoxylin but is less active and weaker than the other.

Brazilin	0.5 g
70% alcohol	100 ml

Dissolve and keep the container well-stoppered and away from light and air. Allow a ripening period of about a week.

Brazilin by itself does not have any colour. It reacts and imparts colour only after mordanting with ferric ammonium sulphate (iron alum).

Haematoxylin

Haematoxylin is a chromogen derived from logwood, *Hematoxylin campechianum* L. It is a homologue of Brazilin possessing one or more hydroxyl groups in its chemical constitution.

The dye itself has no affinity for tissues and so it is very much essential to use some mordanting. The stain is made up in combination with the metallic salts of iron (ferric form), aluminium or copper.

Many staining schedules are available for this stain some of which are progressive and others regressive.

The colour effects of haematoxylin vary with the character of the medium in which it is dissolved and according to the after-treatment. For example,

- ⊙ in the presence of acid solutions, the colour is red
- ⊙ in the presence of alkaline solutions, it is blue
- ⊙ exposure to ammonia fumes turns the colour to blue
- ⊙ Heidenhain's iron alum schedule renders chromosomes and pyrenoids black and the cytoplasm grey

Heidenhain's iron haematoxylin

Reagents required

Stock solution

Haematoxylin	10 g
Absolute ethyl alcohol	100 ml

Keep the stock solution for a few days to ripen. The process of ripening may be hastened by placing the solution in a wide beaker and exposing it to quartz mercury-vapour arc lamp for about 45 minutes.

Working solution

Dilute a portion of the stock solution with distilled water to 0.5% strength as and when required.

 ⊙ At high temperatures haematoxylin solutions undergo hydrolysis forming a metallic scum on the surface. Such solutions are not to be used.

⊙ Spoilage is also indicated when the solution starts to turn brown.

Preparation of a stable haematoxylin solution

Reagents required

Stock solution	5 ml
Methyl cellosolve	100 ml
Distilled water	50 ml
Tap water containing some calcium compound	50 ml

Shake the solution well. The solution should acquire a rich wine-red colour. If otherwise, add a pinch of sodium bicarbonate and shake vigorously. Ripening occurs usually at once and the solution can be used at once.

This solution is not spoiled at high temperatures. It also retains its staining capability for longer periods than do simple aqueous solutions of haematoxylin.

Most of the difficulties with haematoxylin arise during destaining and differentiation. While using haematoxylin, the same solution should not be used for both mordanting and destaining. Johansen recommends solutions of reagents other than ferric ammonium sulphate on the grounds that ugly precipitates are avoided, thicker sections are clearly stained and disagreeable tan or brownish colour does not result.

Ferric chloride acts both as a mordant and as a differentiator. A 2% to 5% solution of ferric chloride can be used as a mordant allowing 30 minutes reaction time. After rinsing, the stain can be differentiated in a 1 to 3% solution of the staining reagent. The stain is more blue than black and differentiation is more precise.

The following three different recipes are available for using haematoxylin as a stain in botanical microtechnique.

Delafield's haematoxylin

Solution A (Alcoholic solution of haematoxylin)

Haematoxylin crystals   4 g
95% Ethyl alcohol   25 ml

Solution B

Ammonium aluminum sulphate (aqueous solution)   400 ml

Procedure

1. Add 25 ml of solution A drop by drop to solution B.
2. Expose to light and air for 4 days.
3. Add glycerine c.p. 10 ml and methyl alcohol 100 ml.
4. Allow the mixture to stand for 2 months until the colour is sufficiently dark.
5. Ripening time is reduced by exposure of the solution to mercury vapour arc lamp for 2 hours.
6. The ripened undiluted solution is a powerful stain.
7. The stain is differentiated either with distilled water or with 70% ethyl alcohol acidified with HCl.

Harris' haematoxylin

This recipe gives a totally superior stain.

Reagents required

Haematoxylin crystals   5 g
Aluminium ammonium sulphate   3 g
50% Ethyl alcohol   1000 ml

Procedure

1. Heat-dissolve the dye and alum.

2. Then add 6 g mercuric oxide (red powder only) and boil for 30 minutes.

3. Filter the solution.

4. Bring the volume up to the original volume with 50% alcohol.

5. Acidify with HCl in a proportion of 1 drop of acid to every 100 ml of stain solution.

Improved Mayer's haemalum

This recipe is recommended for the nuclei of filamentous algae and fungi. It does not stain plastids or cell walls.

Reagents required

Haematoxylin crystals	1 g
Distilled water	1000 ml

(dissolve in a few ml and then add to make up volume)

Sodium iodate	2 g
Aluminium potassium sulphate	50 g

Add a crystal of thymol to prevent the growth of fungi.

Experience has shown that the stain gives very good results in dilutions of 10 times its strength and on being allowed to react overnight.

Ehrlich's haematoxylin

This recipe is recommended and used extensively with safranin on woody tissues.

Reagents required

Haematoxylin crystals	1 g
Glacial acetic acid	5 ml
Glycerine	50 ml
Absolute ethyl alcohol	50 ml
Distilled water	50 ml
Aluminium potassium sulphate	To excess

Procedure

1. Keep the solution in a dark place until it becomes dark red.

2. Exposure of the solution to mercury vapour arc lamp for 2 hours reduces ripening time to 3 or 4 hours.

3. Sections may be transferred from water or 30% alcohol to the stain. Allow 5 to 30 minutes of reaction time. Wash off the excess stain with water or with 35% alcohol and dehydrate.

4. Orange G or erythrosin may be used as a counterstain.

5. If safranin is used along with Ehrlich's haematoxylin, the section is first stained in safranin.

Haematein

Haematein is preferred over haematoxylin because

  i. it is easy to prepare and to use,

 ii. it saves time and

iii. it gives good results.

Procedure

1. Grind 0.5 g haematein in a glass mortar with 100 ml of 95% ethyl alcohol.

2. Add the concentrate to 500 ml of 5% aqueous aluminium potassium sulphate.

3. Transfer the slides to the stain from water. The stain is progressive. So the slide is to be watched frequently for 5 minutes or so which is the average time required.

4. Rinse in tap water for 1–3 seconds.

5. If desired, the slides may be counterstained for 1 to 3 seconds with eosin bluish—1 part of stock solution (0.5% solution in 20% alcohol) to 2 parts of distilled water.

6. Wash in several changes of tap water, dehydrate and mount.

Cochineal and its Derivatives

Cochineal is a yellowish red dye obtained by grinding the fried bodies of the female cochineal insect and extracting the colouring matter. Cochineal and its derivatives are some of the most important bulk stains available. They are all progressive stains but may be used regressively also. Cochineal itself is not used much in botanical microtechnique.

Carmine is a bright red powder obtained by adding alum to cochineal. It is the mixture of several compounds of which carmine is the chief colouring matter.

Carmine and carminic acid are so easy-to-use and give excellent effects—in botanical microtechnique it is used much as a cytological stain.

Carmine is only slightly soluble in water at a neutral reaction. Therefore, solutions must be either acid or alkaline.

Carminic acid is the active dye principle of cochineal and carmine. It is fairly a strong dibasic acid. It is best known to botanists as the principal ingredient of Mayer's carmalum.

Indigocarmin

It is included under natural dyes because it is based upon one. It is not to be confused with carmine. It is a sodium salt of indigosulphonic acid and has acid properties. It is bluish in colour and when mixed with picric acid (picro-indigocarmin) it becomes green. Indigocarmin is used in staining algae. Solubility is 1.68% in water at 25°C and 0.01% in 95% alcohol.

COAL-TAR DYES

Based on similarity in chemical structure, coal-tar dyes are grouped under the following six groups.

1. Nitro dyes, e.g. picric acid
2. Azo dyes, e.g. orange G, bismarck brown, Sudan IV
3. Anthoquinone dyes, e.g. alizarin
4. Quinine-imide group dyes which include
   a. Indamines*
   b. Thiazins, e.g. methylene blue, thionin
   c. Oxazins*
   d. Azines which include
      ⊙ Amido-azines, e.g. neutral red
      ⊙ Safranins, e.g. safranin O, magdala red
      ⊙ Indulins, e.g. nigrosin
5. Phenyl methane group of dyes which include
   a. Diphenyl methane*

   b.   Diamino triphenyl methane, e.g. fast green, light green,
        malachite green

   c.   Triamino triphenyl methanes, e.g. acid fuchsin, crystal violet,
        aniline blue

   d.   Hydroxy-triphenyl methanes*

6.   Xanthene group of dyes which include

   a.   Pyronins*

   b.   Rhodamines*

   c.   Fluorane derivatives, e.g. eosin, erythrosin

   (* none in common use generally or in botanical microtechnique)

A general account of some of the most important stains frequently
used in botanical microtechnique is given in the following pages.

ACID FUCHSIN

Chemically known as triaminotriphenyl methane (rosaniline), acid fuchsins
are a complex mixture of sulphonated derivatives of basic fuchsin. This
is used to stain cortex, pith parenchyma, cellulose walls and also widely
used as a mitochondrial stain. This is an acid dye belonging to phenyl
methane group.

   It is used as a 1% solution in 70% alcohol. 0.5% to 1% solution in
distilled water works equally well.

   ⊙   A staining reaction time of 2 hours is required.

   ⊙   When the stain is used in 70% alcohol, differentiate in saturated
       solution of picric acid in 70% alcohol for 1 minute and then rinse
       in 70% alcohol until the colour turns from yellow to reddish
       magenta.

   ⊙   Complete dehydration quickly as the stain is easily extracted by
       higher alcohols.

   ⊙   Mount at once.

   Acid fuchsin must not be confused with basic fuchsin. When the name
fuchsin alone is mentioned, it is usually the basic form which is meant.

ANILINE BLUE WATER-SOLUBLE
(SYN. COTTON BLUE; WATER BLUE; CHINA BLUE)

It is a strong acid belonging to triaminotriphenyl methane group. The dye
is a mixture of several compounds. During the manufacture the exact

nature of its components cannot be controlled and therefore no two lots will be the same.

Aniline blue is very valuable as a counterstain especially to safranin used on plant tissues. It stains cellulose walls and achromatic figures. In combination with erythrosin, it is said to be excellent for filamentous Chlorophyta.

The dye is supposed to be soluble in water only but an aqueous solution is practically useless. 1% solution in 90% ethyl alcohol serves well. After a brief differentiation in 95% alcohol, the aniline blue should be fixed and intensified in 95% alcohol slightly acidified with HCl.

Johansen's recipe is as follows:

⊙ Dissolve as much stain as possible in methyl cellosolve.

⊙ Add clove oil and a little absolute alcohol.

⊙ Use this solution from a drop bottle. Clear in clove oil or synthetic oil of wintergreen (methyl salicylate).

⊙ Wash in xylol and mount in balsam.

CRYSTAL VIOLET (SYN. GENTIAN VIOLET)

This basic dye belongs to triaminotriphenyl methane group with a solubility of 1.68% in water and 13.87% in alcohol.

Crystal violet is the most important cytological stain. In many cases it gives results not obtainable with safranin, iron haematoxylin, or other nuclear stains.

All the violets wash out so quickly in the dehydrating alcohols that one should mordant the stain, use one of the special methods, or dissolve the stain in clove oil. The clove oil solution may be kept in a dropping bottle.

Alternatively, make a saturated solution of CV in clove oil and add a few drops of this solution to a dish full of xylol. This mixture is very unstable and therefore, when in use needs to be brought up to desired strength by the addition of more stain from time to time.

The problem with violets is that they frequently overstain the cytoplasm making chromosome counts difficult. This can be avoided by acidifying the sections with dilute acetic acid before staining. Transfer the sections from water to 2% aqueous acetic acid for about 30 minutes. Then wash twice the length of time in running water and then proceed with staining.

ERYTHROSIN BLUISH

This acid dye is a fluorine derivative belonging to xanthene group with a solubility of 0.15 to 11.10% in water and 0.04 to 1.87% in alcohol.

Botanists use erythrosin in the place of eosin. It is found to be an excellent counterstain to crystal violet in cytological methods. It stains the gelatinous sheath of algae, e.g. *Nostoc*.

1% solution in 95% alcohol or clove oil is recommended. Staining time required is very short, no longer than 3 minutes. Clove oil solution stains well in 10 seconds.

FAST GREEN FCF

Acid in reaction, fast green FCF belongs to diaminotriphenyl methane group. It has a solubility of 16.04% in water and 0.33% in alcohol. It is far superior to light green SF as it never fades.

Fast green stains more intensely in a short time. Solutions of this stain should be prepared several days in advance as it requires ripening time. The solution should be alcoholic and weak not over 1% or 0.1%.

Methyl cellosolve	33.3 ml
Absolute alcohol	33.3 ml
Clove oil	33.3 ml
Fast green FCF	0.5 g

Try the solution on a sample slide. If the colour appears too strong, dilute it with enough clove oil until the desired shade is reached.

Fast green is recommended for differentiating safranin. But experience shows that it turns blue in alkaline solutions. When used on the stems and leaves of aquatic plants and with most gymnosperm materials, it is generally bluish to bluish green and rarely a bright green.

LIGHT GREEN SF

Light green SF is an acid dye belonging to diaminotriphenyl methane group with a solubility of 20.35% in water and 0.82% in alcohol. It is an excellent cytoplasmic stain. The disadvantage is that it fades within a short time.

Fast green FCF appears to be a good substitute to light green. However, on some filamentous algae light green gives better results and fast green overstains them even in high dilutions.

Light green SF solution should not be stronger than 0.5%. A 0.2% solution is found to be strong enough. The staining reaction is rapid with light green.

A solution in 95% alcohol is commonly used. Many prefer to dissolve the dye in alcohol and dilute it with clove oil and keep the stain in drop bottles. The stain reduces other coal-tar dyes, especially safranin. Therefore, it should not be allowed to react too long.

An acidified saturated solution of light green with HCl or acetic acid is an excellent differentiating stain for lignified tissues. A simple washing with water removes the stain from all except lignified cell walls.

Suberized and cutinized tissues are differentiated from lignified tissues by combining light green with Sudan IV.

Light green is not to be confused with malachite green, acid green, fast green and methyl green.

SAFRANIN O

If a safranin stain is specified, the dye known as safranin O (orange) is always meant; if a safranin of any other type is meant, it is indicated by the letter Y (yellowish) or B (bluish) as the case may be.

Safranin is a basic dye belonging to azine group with a solubility of 5.45% in water and 3.41% in alcohol. In spite of this solubility indication by the manufacturer, it dissolves better in strong alcohol than in water.

Safranin O is the most important morphological and cytological stain in botanical microtechnique. It stains lignified, cutinized, suberized and chitinized structures as well as chromosomes, nucleoli and centrosomes.

The following is a commonly used recipe.

Stock solution

Safranin O   2.25 g

95% ethyl alcohol   225 ml

Working solution

Take a part of the stock solution and dilute it with equal volume of distilled water when needed for use. If this solution is too strong, dilute the same with 50% alcohol.

Johansen's recipe

Safranin O   4.0 g (dissolve in)

Methyl cellosolve   200 ml (after dissolution is complete, add)

95% alcohol	100 ml
Distilled water	100 ml
Sodium acetate	4.0 g (intensifies the stain)
Formalin	8.0 ml (as a mordant)

Slides are left in this solution for 24 to 48 hours. Differentiation is exceptionally easy giving sharp and brilliant contrasts.

The problem with safranin is that it overstains indiscriminately and therefore requires differentiation. A much sharp differentiation is obtained by adding picric acid to the 95% dehydrating alcohol. After staining with safranin, the excess stain should always be removed by washing with water. Otherwise ugly precipitates are deposited in the tissues.

SUDAN IV (SYN. SCHARLACH R/FAT PONCEAU R)

Sudan IV is a weakly acid dye belonging to azo group. It is insoluble in water and has a solubility of 0.09% in alcohol.

Sudan IV is a specific stain for fat. Use a saturated alcoholic solution for about 10 minutes and wash rapidly in alcohol (alcohol dissolves fat and therefore avoid leaving the slide longer than necessary). Lecithin, resins, latex, wax and cuticles are stained by Sudan IV. Chloroplasts are stained a dull red.

STAINING SCHEDULES

The staining schedules most commonly used in botanical microtechnique are presented hereunder. Since safranin is the most important and valuable of the coal-tar dyes in botanical microtechnique, schedules involving safranin combinations in double, triple and quadruple staining are discussed in detail.

SAFRANIN AND FAST GREEN

This combination proves to be very dependable on sections of almost every type of plant material except the algae. The schedule is as follows:

- ⊙ Bring the slide down to 70% alcohol (free-hand sections up to 35% alcohol).

- ⊙ Give any special treatment required for the fixative used.

- ⊙ Stain in a 1% solution of safranin in methyl cellosolve–alcohol (Johansen's recipe) for 2 to 24 hours (allow only minimum period for gymnosperms).

⊙ Wash off the excess stain in running water (a few minutes).

⊙ Differentiate and dehydrate simultaneously with 95% alcohol to which 0.5% picric acid crystals have been added for 10 seconds. If the slide has been left in the stain for too long, a longer washing in picro-alcohol may be warranted.

⊙ Stop the action of the acid by immersing the slide in 95% alcohol ammonified at the rate of 4 or 5 drops per 100 cc (excess ammonia must be avoided). Less than 2 minutes is sufficient. The alcohol at this stage extracts some of the stain and therefore do not leave the slide for longer than necessary.

⊙ Bring the slide to 100% alcohol to complete the process of dehydration for 10 seconds (for single slides) to as long as 10 minutes (if too many slides are to be processed simultaneously).

⊙ Counterstain with fast green. Use the stain from drop bottle. It is a powerful stain and therefore the stain should not be allowed on the sections for more than 15 seconds.

⊙ After staining, drain the stain drops back into the drop bottle. The stain may be used over and over again for hundreds of slides.

⊙ Rinse off the excess counterstain with used clove oil. After the clove oil has become too saturated with green colour, it can be diluted to one-half of the intensity with equal parts of absolute alcohol and xylol and can be reused for washing off the counterstain into a waste jar.

⊙ Clear the sections in a mixture of 50 parts clove oil, 25 parts absolute alcohol and 25 parts xylol for a few moments.

⊙ Remove clearing agent by washing the slide a few seconds in xylol. Appearance of any cloudiness in the section or slide indicates that moisture has been accidentally picked up. In such an event pour a few drops of alcohol over the section ensuring complete dehydration.

⊙ Give two changes in pure xylol.

⊙ Mount in balsam.

The safranin should appear a brilliant red in nuclei, chromosomes, and lignified and cutinized cell walls. Fast green should be equally brilliant in the cytoplasm and on cellulose cell walls. Safranin and fast green are durable dyes and should not show any sign of fading even after about 6 years.

SAFRANIN AND HAEMATOXYLIN

This schedule is recommended for both free-hand sections and paraffin-embedded sections and is very ideal for semi-woody tissues and the protocol is as follows:

- ⊙ Bring free-hand sections up to 35% alcohol and paraffin sections to 70% alcohol.

- ⊙ Stain in safranin solution in 1% methyl cellosolve + alcohol (Johansen's recipe) for 18 hours.

- ⊙ Wash out excess stain in water.

- ⊙ Differentiate carefully in 50% alcohol acidified with HCl. When xylem appears bright red and cellulose walls are a deep pinkish colour, the stain is about right. Avoid too much destaining, as more of safranin will be removed during subsequent steps.

- ⊙ Wash thoroughly in water for 5 minutes.

- ⊙ Counterstain with haematoxylin for 15 to 20 minutes. The sections should appear deep purple when removed from the counterstain.

- ⊙ Now treat each slide individually, with water slightly acidified with HCl for a few seconds. As soon the sections appear reddish, transfer to tap water and wash thoroughly for about 20 minutes. If the haematoxylin is not turned blue by tap water, dip the slide momentarily in a beaker of water containing a few drops of ammonia.

- ⊙ In the case of paraffin sections, run up through 50 and 70% alcohols to 95%, allowing 3 to 5 minutes in each.

- ⊙ Mounting may be done in euparol straight from 95% alcohol.

- ⊙ Or one may proceed to absolute alcohol and pass through xylol to balsam.

- ⊙ In case of free-hand sections, dehydrate by gradually substituting hygrobutol for water, finally infiltrate with balsam and mount.

SAFRANIN, CRYSTAL VIOLET AND ORANGE G (FLEMMING'S TRIPLE STAIN)

Though there are differences of opinion about the merits of this combination, the contrasting colours are a pronounced advantage. The third stain orange G used does not impart a third colour but differentiates between the primary stain and the counterstain.

A properly stained preparation should present the following colour effects:

Cell components	Colour
Chromatin of metaphase and anaphase	Safranin
Chromatin of prophase	Violet
Condensed parts of chromosome	Red
Chromosome with little or no chromatin	Violet
Chromonemata	Red
Chromosome matrix	Purple
Nucleoli	Red
Spindle fibres and plastids	Violet
Cytoplasm	Buff-grey

Only tissues fixed in mixtures containing chromic acid and osmic acid can be successfully stained by this schedule. Specimens fixed in other fluids should be first washed in water and mordanted for a day or so in a 1% solution of osmic acid in 2% chromic acid or as directed in Stockwell's variation (given in the next section).

Typical Schedule

⊙ Bring the slide to 70% alcohol. If mordanted, first place in 35% alcohol for 5 minutes and then gradually to 70% alcohol.

⊙ Stain in standard safranin solution. The reaction time varies according to the material. It should not be less than 2 hours. For most plant specimens, 6 hours is sufficient while there is no harm in leaving the sections in the stain for 24 hours.

⊙ Rinse thoroughly in water.

⊙ Counterstain in a 1% aqueous solution of crystal violet for 15 minutes to 1 hour or more as required. The reaction time is to be determined by trial and error.

⊙ Remove surplus stain by washing in water.

⊙ Treat/dehydrate twice in 95% alcohol and three or four times in absolute alcohol.

⊙ Wipe the underside of the slide clean. Add a few drops of orange G solution (saturated in clove oil) to cover the section for not more than 10 seconds.

⊙ Drain off the orange G back into the drop bottle. Wash off the excess stain first with diluted clove oil and then dip the slide in pure clove oil in a container. Allow a few moments. Now place the slide on a glass plate and observe under the microscope. If the violet is satisfactory, wash in xylol to stop the action of clove oil.

- ⊙ Give two changes in xylol.
- ⊙ Mount in balsam.

Stockwell's Variation

Some sections appear too dark due to the presence of phlobaphene (e.g. root tips of *Quercus*, buds of *Dudleya* and other Crassulaceae). Such sections are to be first brought to water from the fixative and bleached overnight in the following solution:

Water	90 cc
Potassium bichromate	1 g
Glacial acetic acid	10 cc
Chromic acid	1 g

Chromic acid renders the precipitated tannins soluble; the acetic acid then removes them. Dichromate thereupon catalyses the tissue.

If the specimen was not fixed in a solution containing chromic acid to mordant it, the slides should first be mordanted in a 1% aqueous chromic solution for at least 1 hour (preferably overnight). Wash out the acid thoroughly before proceeding to the stain.

- ⊙ Stain for about 1 to 24 hours in the following stain solution:

1% aqueous solution of Gentian violet	1 part
1% aqueous solution of safranin	1 part
Distilled water	1–4 parts

A staining time of 1 hour is sufficiently long for most plant tissues. A dilute stain acting over a period of 24 hours gives superior results.

- ⊙ Wash off the excess stain in tap water.
- ⊙ Treat in 1% potassium iodide + 1% iodine in 70% alcohol for 30 seconds.
- ⊙ Treat the slide in the following series allowing a few seconds in each:
  1. 50% alcohol
  2. 70% alcohol
  3. 95% alcohol + picric acid (about 1 g per 100 cc)

4. 95% alcohol + ammonia (8 to 10 drops per 100 cc)
5. Pure 95% alcohol
6. Absolute alcohol
7. Clove oil + orange G (0.2 g per 100 cc)
8. Pure clove oil
9. Xylol—three changes* (make sure all traces of clove oil are removed)

⊙ Mount in balsam.

*After the first xylol, examine the slide under a microscope. If there is too much safranin, return the slide to absolute alcohol, then back to xylol. Excess violet may be reduced by returning the slide to clove oil, then back to xylol.

A well-stained preparation should show the following final colour effects.

Cell components	Colour
Chromosome	Light to dark purple
Spindle fibres	Purplish
Nucleoli	Red
Cytoplasm	Orange

With morphological and anatomical preparations, the final effect is the same as with other triple combinations.

QUADRUPLE STAINING

Tissues in which there is either a variety of cell types or a considerable chemical difference in the structure of cells are best studied in quadruple stained preparations. In this method, safranin, crystal violet, fast green and orange G are used in combination.

Quadruple staining is redundant in the case of tissues with little differentiation such as meristematic tissues.

Johansen's quadruple staining schedule is intended to correlate stain affinity with specific structures. Newer stain solvents are recommended in this schedule. Though the mixtures appear to be complicated, differentiation is automatic and does not depend on personal judgement. The following is a simple procedure.

1. Bring the slides down to 70% alcohol.
2. Stain in methyl cellosolve + 50% alcohol safranin solution for 24 to 48 hours.

3. Rinse in tap water.

4. Stain in 1% aqueous methyl violet 2B for 10 to 15 minutes.

5. Rinse in tap water.

6. Leave the slides in fast green FCF solution* for 10 to 15 minutes.

   *Fast green FCF saturated stock solution (A)

Clove oil	1 part
Methyl cellosolve	1 part

   Dissolve enough stain powder to obtain a saturated solution.

   *Fast green working solution

Solution (A)	1 part
95% alcohol	3 parts
Tertiary butyl alcohol	3 parts
Glacial acetic acid	to 1% of total volume

7. Rinse briefly in a washing solution consisting of equal parts of 95% alcohol and tertiary butyl alcohol plus about 0.5% glacial acetic acid.

8. Immerse for about 3 minutes in orange G solution*.

   *Orange G solution

Methyl cellosolve	1 part
95% alcohol	1 part

   Dissolve enough orange G powder to make a saturated solution.

9. Wash in a mixture** of equal parts of clove oil, methyl cellosolve and 95% alcohol.

10. Wash in a mixture** of equal parts of clove oil, absolute alcohol and xylol.

11. Rinse twice in xylol.

12. Mount in balsam.

    (*The stain working solutions can be used to stain a large number of slides before replacement is required.

    ** The washing solution will need frequent replacements.)

The following are the colour effects presented in a properly stained preparation.

Cell components	Colour
Dividing chromatin	Red
Resting chromatin	Purplish
Nucleoli	Red and occasionally violet
Nucleoplasm	Colourless or greenish
Lignified cell walls	Bright red
Cutinized cell walls	Reddish purple
Suberized cell walls	Red
Cellulose cell walls	Greenish orange
Cytoplasm	Bright orange
Middle lamella	Green
Starch grains	Purple with green or orange halos
Plastids	Purplish to greenish
Invading fungal mycelium	Green
Guard cells of stomata	
Callose portion	Bright red
Remaining parts	Purple
Root sections	
Casparian strips of endodermis	Red
Remainder of endodermis	Yellow
Cytoplasm of lateral roots (if present)	Green

OTHER USEFUL SCHEDULES

CRYSTAL VIOLET AND ERYTHROSIN COMBINATION

When a sharp differentiation is desired between lignified and non-lignified cells, crystal violet–erythrosin combination is employed in staining. Crystal violet stains the lignified walls violet and erythrosin stains the non-lignified walls bluish red.

In some specimens xylem elements stain satisfactorily in a few minutes. In others it may require 30 minutes or longer in which case, the action of erythrosin is to be watched as it tends to replace the violet in lignified cells!

Procedure

⊙ Bring the slide down to water.

⊙ Stain in a 1% aqueous solution of crystal violet for 15 minutes on a trial basis. If not satisfied, prolong the reaction time.

⊙ Rinse quickly in tap water.

⊙ Dehydrate quickly but thoroughly in 95% alcohol and then in absolute alcohol.

⊙ Counterstain in a saturated solution of erythrosin B in clove oil for 1 to 5 minutes.

⊙ Treat in a mixture of equal parts of absolute alcohol and xylol for 2 minutes or less.

⊙ Wash in xylol.

⊙ Mount in balsam or DPX.

JOHANSEN'S METHYL VIOLET–ERYTHROSIN SCHEDULE

Johansen's methyl violet–erythrosin combination gives excellent results for studying the stages of cell division in root tips. The schedule is as follows:

⊙ Bring the slides down to water.

⊙ Stain in of 1% solution of methyl violet 2B in distilled water.

⊙ Rinse off excess stain with water.

⊙ Differentiate and dehydrate simultaneously for 10 to 15 minutes in 95% alcohol saturated with picric acid.

⊙ Stop the action of the acid by transferring the slide to 95% alcohol ammonified at the rate of 2 or 3 drops of ammonia per 100 cc.

⊙ Wash in pure 95% alcohol for 15 seconds.

⊙ Counterstain with a nearly saturated solution of erythrosin in equal parts of absolute alcohol and clove oil for 5 to 10 seconds.

⊙ Clear in clove oil for about 30 seconds.

⊙ Wash thoroughly twice in xylol.

⊙ Mount in balsam.

The colour effects presented by the cell components are as follows:

Cell components	Colour
Resting and dividing chromatin	Brilliant purple
Plastid	Dark red
Cell wall	Red
Cytoplasm	Pinkish

FOSTER'S TANNIC ACID–IRON CHLORIDE STAINING SCHEDULE

More often ontogenetic studies require staining of the meristematic cells that are distinct from the surrounding mature cells. Foster's tannic acid–iron chloride staining schedule is primarily designed for this purpose. It has other wider applications also.

- Bring the slides down to water.
- Mordant in 1% aqueous solution of tannic acid for 10 minutes.
- The tannic acid solution is susceptible to fungal attack. Therefore, add sodium salicylate at the rate of 1 g to 100 cc of the solution to prevent fungal attack.
- Wash thoroughly in water.
- Remove the excess stain by placing the slides in 3% aqueous ferric chloride for several minutes.
- Examine the slide under microscope.
- If the cell walls of meristematic cells appear black or dark blue and the nuclei and cytoplasm grey, the stain is correct.
- If the stain is too weak, wash the slide thoroughly in water and return to tannic acid solution.
- Repeat this process until satisfactory staining effect is obtained.
- Leave the slide in 50% alcohol for a few minutes.
- Counterstain for 48 hours in 1% alcoholic solution of safranin.
- Rinse in water.
- Destain cautiously in 70% alcohol very weakly acidified with HCl.
- Progress with dehydration (70%, 80%, 90%, 95% and absolute alcohol).

⊙ Substitute alcohol with xylol by gradual displacement method (alcohol 3: xylol 1; 1:1; 1:3; pure xylol).

⊙ Mount in balsam or DPX.

The final colour effects are as follows:

Cell components	Colour
Cell walls	Intense black
Cytoplasm	Violet or pink
Plastid	Blue
Nucleoli and chromosomes	Red

DEHYDRATION

Dehydration is the most important step in permanent micropreparations. This follows fixation as a second step.

After fixation is over, the fixative is to be thoroughly washed and removed from the material. If the fixative is an aqueous solution, washing of the material is to be done in running tap water followed by distilled water. If on the other hand, the fixative is an alcoholic solution, washing is to be done in the same percentage of alcohol which is used in the fixative. Only after thoroughly removing the fixative, the material is to be subjected to dehydration.

Dehydration in microtechnique is "the removal of water from the fixed/preserved tissue not only from the surface of the tissue, but also from the interior of the tissue" as the term implies literally.

Dehydration is essential because of the following reasons.

⊙ Materials are to be embedded in paraffin to facilitate microtomy. Paraffin wax is soluble in organic solvents such as xylol. These solvents are hydrophobic. Therefore, while embedding the material in paraffin wax, bubbles of water get locked in the tissue if dehydration is not complete. This will interfere in microtomy.

⊙ Most of the mounting media in which the prepared specimen or section is finally mounted are not miscible with water and therefore, in the series of steps followed in the preparation of biological specimens for microscopic observation, dehydration is the most important step.

⊙ Most of the stains are used as alcoholic solutions. If there is water in the tissue, it will interfere with the staining process.

In order to be a perfect dehydrating fluid, the reagent should possess the following attributes.

⊙ It should possess hygroscopic properties.

⊙ It should be miscible equally well with water, ethyl alcohol, balsam and paraffin.

⊙ It should not cause desiccation of the tissue.

Dehydration is to be done gradually and the reagents (dehydrants) used for this purpose are of two types.

1. Dehydrants that cannot dissolve paraffin wax, e.g. ethyl alcohol, acetone, glycerine, etc.

2. Dehydrants that can dissolve paraffin wax, e.g. butyl alcohol, tertiary butyl alcohol, diaxon, xylol, etc.

As per the requirement and based on the type of dehydrant used, several dilutions such as 5%, 10%, 15%, 20%, 25%, ..., 95% can be prepared and kept in glass-stoppered reagent bottles.

After washing, the fixed material is to be transferred to the grade of alcohol next higher to that used in the fixative. When a non-alcoholic fixative has been used, the material is transferred to a fairly weak alcoholic grade which can be decided considering the nature of the tissue.

The material is to be left in each grade for a specific time. The nature of the tissue decides the time to be allowed for dehydration in each grade. For example, soft parts such as root tips and leaves can be left in each grade for ½ an hour or one hour. Woody parts can be left in each grade for 12 hours.

Beyond 70% grade, the material is to be left in each grade for a longer time (say 1 to 24 hours). Finally the material is changed thrice in 100% alcohol to ensure complete dehydration.

At the end of dehydration, the tissue (material) is in 100% dehydrant. The intercellular spaces and the cell interior are filled with the dehydrating agent. If the dehydrant is left in the material, it may interfere with infiltration of paraffin and also with staining in later stages. Therefore, after dehydration, the material is to be cleared of the dehydrant before being embedded in paraffin wax. Dehydrants such as xylol combine two functions, namely clearing and dissolving paraffin wax.

DEHYDRATING AGENTS

Several reagents are used for dehydration of biological materials of which the following are important.

Ethyl Alcohol (Ethanol)

Ethyl alcohol which is used as a killing and fixing fluid is a dehydrating agent also. This is the most commonly used dehydrant in microtechnique in most laboratories.

Ethyl alcohol is a fast-acting dehydrant. Violent diffusion currents are set up when a biological specimen is introduced into the ethyl alcohol causing severe shrinkage of cells and cell contents. Therefore it is customary to use alcohol as a graded series, of say, 15%, 30%, 50%, 70%, 90%, 95%, and finally, 100%.

It is to be understood that there would be a much greater and more violent diffusion current when a specimen is transferred from water than when it is transferred from 70% to 90% alcohol. Therefore, the microtechnician should understand that the intention is to subject the specimen to a graded series of stresses rather than to a graded series of alcohols!

Ethyl alcohol is available as 95% alcohol (neutral grain spirit) and absolute (100%) alcohol.

It is difficult to acquire the latter which is also expensive, forcing most laboratories to resort to 95% alcohol for microtechnique. Complete dehydration is imperative for good results to be obtained in microtechnique. Therefore, to achieve this end, the following points are to be borne in mind.

⊙ The lowest concentration at which dehydration should commence is to be determined keeping in mind the nature (softness/hardness) of the tissue.

⊙ Using the same criterion of the nature of the tissue, determine the concentration intervals.

⊙ Allow specimens in each grade for sufficient time. This has to be learnt by personal experience or from published literature.

As ethyl alcohol, particularly absolute alcohol, is hard to obtain, many other substitutes have been recommended, tried and found to yield equally good results. Any universal solvent which mixes alike with water, wax and resins such as balsam will serve the purpose.

Isopropyl Alcohol (Isopropanol)

Ethyl alcohol (ethanol) is recommended as a desirable dehydrant in plant microtechnique. But ethanol is expensive. Moreover, it is not easily available. Therefore, isopropyl alcohol (isopropanol) which is almost equivalent to ethanol is used in most laboratories as a dehydrating agent.

Advantages

1. Easily available and comparatively inexpensive.
2. Equally good as a dehydrating agent.
3. Does not harden tissues as does ethyl alcohol.

Disadvantage

Isopropanol cannot be used as a killing agent as ethyl alcohol is used.

Methyl Alcohol (Methylal or Methanol)

Several books on plant microtechnique recommend the use of methanol as dehydrant. However, methanol is a potent poison and dehydrates tissue very vigorously leading to tissue damage. Therefore, if methanol alone is available for use, it has to be handled with extreme care and in closer grades to avoid tissue damage.

Methanol also shares most characteristics of dioxan(e) when used in microtechnique. It is costlier than dioxan(e).

Butyl Alcohol (Butanol)

Several concentration grades of butyl alcohol can be prepared using ethyl alcohol. The material is removed from the aqueous fixative, washed in water and then transferred through ethyl alcoholic grades up to 30%. From ethyl alcohol, the material is gradually shifted to butyl alcohol as shown in Table 4.7.

Table 4.7   Ethyl alcohol–butyl alcohol series as suggested by Sass (1964)

Total volume	95% Ethyl alcohol (ml)	Butyl alcohol (ml)	Distilled water (ml)
100	20	10	70
100	25	15	60
100	30	20	50
100	30	40	30
100	25	55	20
100	20	70	10
100	15	85	0
100	0	100	0

The material is to be left in each concentration for 20 minutes to 2 hours and finally it is to be given three changes in 100% butyl alcohol.

Tertiary Butyl Alcohol

Though it resembles dioxan(e) in most properties, it is superior to the latter in that it is lighter than melted wax.

Advantages

1. It mixes with all reagents very well.
2. The greatest advantage is that it is the least expensive.
3. The safest dehydrating fluid that a beginner can use.

Tertiary Butyl Alcohol Series

Sass (1964) suggested ethyl alcohol–tertiary butyl alcohol series also. The fixed material is to be washed and is to be brought up to 50% alcohol through the concentration series. Thereafter, the material is to be transferred through the ethyl alcohol–tertiary butyl alcohol series as shown in Table 4.8.

Table 4.8   Ethyl alcohol–tertiary butyl alcohol series (Sass, 1964)

Total volume (ml)	95% Ethyl alcohol (ml)	Tertiary butyl alcohol (ml)	Distilled water (ml)
100	50	10	40
100	50	20	30
100	50	30	20
100	50	50	0
100	25	75	0
100	0	100	0

Finally, the material is to be given three changes in 100% tertiary butyl alcohol.

Both butyl alcohol and tertiary butyl alcohol are good dehydrating agents. They are also capable of dissolving paraffin wax. Therefore, paraffin infiltration can follow immediately after dehydration.

Hygrobutol

This special type of tertiary butyl alcohol is prepared especially for dehydration of materials intended for mounting entire in balsam. It is more expensive.

Acetone

Acetone is a highly volatile organic solvent. It is a safe reagent giving satisfactory results as a dehydrant. Several concentration grades of acetone can be prepared using distilled water (7.5%, 15%, 25%, 30%, 40%, 45%, 50%, 60%,..., 100%). It is enough to allow the material in each concentration for less than one hour. Other aspects of fixation are the same as for ethyl alcohol.

Disadvantages

1. Paraffin wax does not dissolve in acetone. Therefore, secondary or tertiary butyl alcohol, chloroform or benzene has to be used after acetone prior to infiltration.
2. As it is highly volatile, one has to work fast while using it.
3. It is not recommended as a dehydrating agent by many microtechnicians as it dissolves fats, resins, waxes and oils present in the cells and also precipitates albumin.

Cellosolve (Ethylene Glycol Monoethyl Ether)

Cellosolve is strongly recommended for tissues that are intended to be embedded in paraffin. It has certain advantages and disadvantages.

Advantages

1. Less volatile compared to alcohol.
2. Less hygroscopic and therefore, does not lose its strength under normal circumstances.

Disadvantage

It is more viscous than alcohol and creates a greater diffusion stress. Therefore, a more extended series of graded concentrations is to be employed for delicate materials.

Dioxan(e) (Diethylene Dioxide or Dehydrated Diethylene Glycol or Dioxon)

Dioxan(e) mixes readily with water but only slightly less with molten wax. The materials can be transferred directly from water to dioxan(e).

A graded series is recommended for delicate tissues. After thorough impregnation with the dioxan(e), the material can be transferred direct to the mounting medium in the case of whole mounts or to a bath of molten wax for infiltration.

The material fixed in aqueous fixative is to be transferred to the following series (Table 4.9) of dioxan.

Table 4.9   Series to be followed for materials fixed in aqueous fixative

Dioxan (ml)	Distilled water (ml)	Duration in hours
35	65	4–12
65	35	4–12
100	0	4–12

Finally, the material is to be changed thrice in 100% dioxan.

The materials fixed in alcoholic fixatives are to be changed to 50% dioxan and then through the following series (Table 4.10) to 100% dioxan.

Table 4.10   Series to be followed for materials fixed in alcoholic fixative

Dioxan (ml)	Distilled water (ml)	Duration in hours
50	50	4–12
65	35	4–12
100	0	4–12

Advantages
1. Use of dioxan(e) as a dehydrant is very simple.
2. Dioxan(e) is a very efficient dehydrating agent.
3. This is capable of dissolving paraffin wax also.
4. Unlike tertiary butyl alcohol, dioxan can be used directly and separately.

Disadvantages

1. Dioxan(e) vapour is highly toxic. Its toxicity is cumulative, seriously affecting the functioning of liver and kidney. Therefore, dioxane is to be used with extreme caution. Peacock (1966) cautions that dioxan(e) stays in the human body system for a very long period and causes adverse effects.
2. Heavy diffusion stresses are created when the material is transferred from dioxan(e) to molten wax.
3. It is considerably heavier than melted paraffin. Therefore, it is important to remove dioxan(e) completely before embedding.

Reagents such as chloroform, benzol or butyl alcohol can be used to wash traces of dioxan(e) before proceeding to infiltration with paraffin.

In spite of these disadvantages, dioxan(e) has found general acceptance as a dehydrant.

Glycerine

This is a colourless, dense, sweet liquid. Glycerine is an ideal dehydrating agent for soft filamentous algae. The boiling point of glycerine is 290°C. Therefore, by heating glycerine, the material can be dehydrated. As dehydration is very gradual, plasmolysis is averted.

The fixed and washed plant material (tissue) can be put in a wide-mouthed jar containing 5% glycerine. This jar can be kept open until the material becomes dehydrated. Care should be taken to prevent dust falling into glycerine. Dehydration can be hastened by placing this jar in a hot-air oven at 35°C. After dehydration is over, the material is to be changed over to fresh glycerine.

POINTS TO BE KEPT IN MIND WHILE DEHYDRATING MATERIALS FOR MICROTECHNIQUE

1. Most of the dehydrating and clearing agents in use cause a considerable shrinkage of tissues. This may not matter in the case of animal tissues where shrinkage is uniform and the appearance is not distorted. Shrinkages in plant tissues do matter, because, the cellulose cell wall does not shrink as much as do the cell contents resulting in distortion of appearance. Incompletely dehydrated plant tissues therefore, will present cell contents pulled away from the cell wall which may not be the actual situation in live cells.

2. Most dehydrating agents used are hygroscopic. These will dehydrate the air as readily as they do the specimen. Therefore, it is advisable to keep a layer of an efficient dehydrating agent at the bottom of the bottle. Anhydrous copper sulphate is recommended for this as it not only readily absorbs moisture in the air but also indicates—by changing from white to blue—that it is exhausted.

CLEARING OR REMOVAL OF DEHYDRATING AGENT

At the end of dehydration, the material is filled with 100% dehydrant which fills the intercellular spaces and the cell interior. Dehydrated material is to be brought to a condition fit either for mounting in balsam (in the case of whole mounts) or for embedding in paraffin if microtomy is desired. To achieve this, the dehydrating agent is to be removed completely from the tissue.

Most reagents used for clearing/de-alcoholization have a high refraction index and render the biological materials saturated with them more transparent or clearer. Therefore, the term clearing can also be taken to mean "rendering the material transparent (clearer)" and the reagents which are capable of removing the dehydrating agents from the fixed biological materials are called clearing agents.

In most microtechnique schedules, alcohol is used as a dehydrating agent. It is necessary to remove alcohol from the material after the process of dehydration is over. This is because the resins used as mounting media and waxes used for embedding are as immiscible with alcohol as they are with water. The removal of alcohol from the dehydrated materials is often called de-alcoholization and this term has become synonymous with clearing.

Choice of a suitable clearing agent depends on whether the material is being processed for whole mount in balsam or for embedding in wax for microtomy. The following essential oils and reagents (Table 4.11) are widely used as clearing agents for various purposes in botanical microtechnique.

Table 4.11   Clearing agents in botanical microtechnique

Purpose	Agents used
Whole mounts	Terpineol
	Clove oil
	Bergamot oil
	Cedarwood oil
	Beechwood creosote
Embedding in wax	Benzol
	Toluol
	Chloroform
	Trichloroethylene
	Xylol

PROCEDURE FOR USING CLEARING AGENT (REMOVAL OF DEHYDRANT)

Removal of dehydrant from the material is a very important step in microtechnique. The exact procedure adopted varies for hard and soft tissues.

Procedure for Hard Tissues

Hard tissues are to be transferred from 100% dehydrant to the 3:1 mixture of dehydrant and clearing agent (e.g. xylol). After the first step, the material is transferred to 1:1 mixture and then to 1:3 mixture. Finally, the material is changed in 100% clearing agent twice or thrice.

Procedure for Soft Tissues

Very soft tissues such as algal thalli, soft fungal fructifications, etc. should not be transferred to the clearing agent suddenly. The transfer should be very gradual. It can be done as follows:

- ⊙ Material is in 100% dehydrant.
- ⊙ Two-thirds of the total volume of the dehydrant is decanted from the specimen tube.
- ⊙ Five or ten drops of clearing agent is added to the specimen tube at fixed intervals.
- ⊙ Once the specimen tube is full, the mixture of fluids is decanted totally. 100% clearing agent is poured into the specimen tube.
- ⊙ The material is to be changed to pure clearing agent two or three times.

In the final stage, if the clearing agent is not foggy, dehydration is complete. The cleared material will be transparent.

On the other hand, if the clearing agent is foggy, dehydration is not complete. In such a situation, the material is to be transferred to 100% dehydrant. Only after dehydration is complete, should the material be brought to clearing agent.

An account of some important clearing agents are discussed in the following sections.

CLEARING AGENTS USED FOR WHOLE MOUNT

If the dehydrated material is to be mounted as such in a resinous medium like balsam, such a preparation is called "whole mount". Essential oils or their synthetic equivalents are used as clearing agents for materials intended for whole mounting in balsam. These readily mix very well with 90 to 95% alcohol and thus remove the traces of water that may be left in the specimen due to imperfect dehydration.

Terpineol

This is a synthetic oil of lilac. It is a natural constituent of many essential oils. It is preferred as a clearing agent for zoological materials to be embedded in celloidin than for botanical materials. It may be used as a substitute for ethyl alcohol as the latter is difficult to acquire.

Advantages

1. Readily miscible with 90% alcohol.
2. Does not possess unpleasant odour.
3. Does not harden materials.
4. Materials or slides cleared with terpineol can be transferred from water direct to xylol without using alcohol.
5. Harmless to most stains.

Disadvantage

Shrinks tissues extremely.

Clove Oil

Clove oil is distilled out of the dried flower buds of *Schyzygium aromaticum*. This an excellent clearing agent for specimens or sections before mounting in balsam. About 82% of clove oil is eugenol.

Advantages

1. More fluid than terpineol.
2. It is hydrophilic in nature. Therefore, it acts as an efficient dehydrant.
3. It also clears the tissue very efficiently and renders the material transparent.
4. It has a very high refraction index.

Disadvantages

1. Clove oil has a pungent odour.
2. Renders tissues brittle if left in it for a long time.
3. All traces of clove oil are to be removed after clearing process is over because most stains fade out in its presence.
4. It causes yellow colouration in the tissues.
5. It hardens the material.
6. It is very expensive.

Bergamot Oil

Though not in use in the present days, bergamot oil was widely used in botanical microtechnique by botanists of early 20th century.

Advantages

1. Clearing schedule with bergamot oil is very simple. One can safely start with the material in 95% alcohol. Bergamot oil can be added drop by drop gradually until the alcohol is replaced with the oil.
2. Complete removal of the oil is not a compulsory requirement.
3. In clearing stained preparations, bergamot oil does not destain coal-tar dyes.

Cedar Wood Oil

Cedar wood oil is distilled from the wood of a gymnosperm called *Juniperus virginiana*. It is yellow in colour. Two types of cedar wood oil are available, one meant for use with oil immersion lenses and the other meant for clearing. Commercial-grade cedar wood oils are frequently adulterated with solvents like xylol. It is widely used as a clearing agent in plant microtechnique on account of its advantageous properties.

Advantages

1. It does not harden tissues.
2. It has a very high refraction index.
3. It is a deodorant.
4. It protects the microsections from the attack of insects.
5. Tissues may be left in this oil for long without any appreciable damage to it.
6. It can be used like xylol, but at a less close series of concentration.

Disadvantage

Clearing is very slow.

Beechwood Creosote

Beechwood creosote is the most favoured clearing agent for certain plant materials such as prothalli of ferns, gametothalli of certain liverworts, etc., which are very fragile and become too brittle with dehydration. Such materials can be passed through alcohol series of up to 80% and then to beechwood creosote to complete the process of dehydration. Two changes with creosote will complete the process of dehydration.

Advantages

1. Removal of clearing agent from the material is easy. Creosote dissolves in balsam-solvents such as dioxan, hygrobutol, benzol or toluol. Therefore, one of these can be used to remove the clearing agent from the material before mounting in balsam.

2. Some counterstains such as fast green are soluble in beechwood creosote. Fern prothalli, for example, may be primarily stained with Harris' haematoxylin, run up to 80% alcohol, transferred to clear creosote, placed in creosote containing 0.5% fast green dye, cleared with another change of creosote and finally infiltrated with balsam.

CLEARING AGENTS USED FOR MATERIALS TO BE EMBEDDED IN WAX

For materials intended for embedding in paraffin wax, hydrocarbons are used for clearing or de-alcoholization. Benzene, xylene, toluene and trichloroethylene are some of the hydrocarbons extensively used for this purpose. Apart from these hydrocarbons, chloroform is also used as an effective clearing agent.

Benzene, xylene and toluene are equally miscible with molten paraffin. But chloroform has a greater advantage of dissolving even solid paraffin.

Benzol (Benzene)

Hoffman distilled benzene from coal tar. Benzol is the commercial name of benzene. Benzene is also distilled from petroleum products. It is also separated from toluene by hydro-deoxidation.

It behaves in the same manner as does xylene. It is highly inflammable and therefore has to be handled with care.

Advantages

1. It infiltrates into the tissues very rapidly.
2. Solubility in ethyl alcohol is very high.

Because of these properties, benzene acts as a very efficient de-alcoholizing agent. However, there are disadvantages in using benzene also.

Disadvantages

1. Benzene hardens the tissues rendering them brittle. Because of this property, the microsections break while microtoming.
2. When paraffin-embedded materials processed with benzene are microtomed, the ribbons of serial sections become interrupted.
3. It is a very harmful poisonous chemical.

Toluol (Toluene; Methyl Benzene)

Toluene or toluol is very similar to benzene and xylene as far as its clearing property is concerned. This reagent also is highly explosive and therefore has to be handled with extreme care.

Xylol (Xylene)

Xylene is a dimethyl benzene. In most microtechnical procedures involving alcoholic mixtures as fixatives, xylene is used as a de-alcoholizing agent and a clearing agent. Its dual function has rendered it the most sought-after agent in microtechnique.

Some prefer to use dichloroethylene in the place of xylene.

Transference of the plant material from dehydrant to the clearing agent should be very gradual. The following series (Table 4.12) can be used to transfer hard and large pieces of tissues.

Table 4.12   Series to be followed for hard and large tissues

Ethyl alcohol (ml)	Xylol/dichloroethylene (ml)	Duration in hours
75	25	3
50	50	3
25	75	3
0	100	3

In the case of softer tissues or parts such as floral parts, flower buds, root tips, embryo sacs, young seeds, etc. transference to the clearing agent should be very gradual. The following series (Table 4.13) can be used for such materials.

Table 4.13   Series to be followed for softer tissues

Ethyl alcohol (ml)	Xylol/dichloro ethylene (ml)	Duration (min.)
90	10	30
80	20	30
70	30	30
60	40	30
50	50	30

(Contd.)

Table 4.13   (Continued)

Ethyl alcohol (ml)	Xylol/dichloro ethylene (ml)	Duration (min.)
40	60	30
30	70	30
20	80	30
10	90	30
0	100	30

Advantages

1. Xylol is more efficient than any other clearing agent.
2. It removes alcohol very rapidly.
3. Solubility of paraffin wax in xylol is very high. Because of this reason, the dissolved wax infiltrates into the tissue very rapidly.
4. Xylol does not create unwanted chromatic effects in the tissues.
5. The material does not become brittle in xylol.

Disadvantages

1. The specimen/material is to be kept for several hours in each grade.
2. Several changes in pure xylene are required.
3. Transfer of material from xylene to paraffin wax also must be very gradual.
4. Every trace of xylene is to be removed from the material before it is embedded in paraffin. If not, the xylene present in the material will crystallize the wax.
5. Tissues tend to be excessively hardened if left too long in xylene.
6. Balsam dissolved in xylene dries very slowly.
7. Xylene should always be free from water and acids. A small test for the presence of water in xylene is given below.

Add some xylene to paraffin oil. Appearance of cloudiness indicates presence of water.

In spite of all these disadvantages, xylene is the most widely used clearing agent for materials intended to be embedded in wax and for clearing sections previous to mounting in balsam or some other resinous medium.

Trichloroethylene

Trichloroethylene is a very good substitute for xylene.

Advantages

1. It does not destain the sections or materials.
2. Paraffin and balsam dissolve completely in trichloroethylene.
3. Slides cleared in trichloroethylene and mounted in balsam dissolved in trichloroethylene dry more quickly than those mounted in balsam dissolved in xylene.

Chloroform

Chloroform is extensively used in zoological microtechnique and occasionally in botanical microtechnique.

Chloroform is expensive. It is very volatile. It is also harmful to our body. Therefore, all these points should be considered during use of chloroform in microtechnique.

Advantages

1. The advantage of this reagent is that it is easily removed from the material in the final stages of infiltration than xylene.
2. A mixture of chloroform and carbon disulphide is recommended as an excellent clearing agent by some microtechnicians.

Disadvantages

1. Chloroform hardens celloidin.
2. As it spoils delicate stain combinations, it has to be avoided for use on stained slides.

Note The hydrocarbons and chloroform are very sensitive to water. Therefore, it is imperative that the material is completely dehydrated before being transferred to one of these clearing agents. Very often it is found that perfect dehydration is not attainable so easily. Under such circumstances, phenol can be used as an adjunct with the clearing agent on account of its coupling property. The following is an example for such a phenolic mixture recommended for such a use.

Carbolxylene

Xylene   70 ml

Phenol   30 g

Specimens may be transferred directly from 50% alcohol into this reagent mixture. It is very important to remove this mixture thoroughly off the specimen by washing in pure xylene before transferring it to paraffin wax.

Direct contact with skin is to be avoided while handling phenol and carbolxylene mixture because phenol causes very unpleasant burns in the skin.

POINTS TO BE KEPT IN MIND WHILE CLEARING MATERIAL FOR MICROTECHNIQUE

1. Dehydrating and clearing are the most important steps in preparing microscopic preparations (slides) for observation.

2. Proceeding to further steps with imperfectly dehydrated and imperfectly cleared materials is a waste of time and resources.

3. The exact time schedule suitable for any particular material can only be determined by trial and error. Personal experience is the best guide.

4. It is easy to see whether the material has been completely dehydrated or not. A perfectly dehydrated material does not produce milkiness when transferred to clearing agent such as xylene. If the clearing agent becomes foggy when the material is transferred to it, it denotes that dehydration is not complete. Under such conditions, the material is to be again kept in 100% dehydrant twice or thrice to ensure complete dehydration. Only then, should the material be transferred to the clearing agent.

5. As for clearing agents, there is no simple method to verify if it has been completely removed before transferring the material to paraffin. Two or three changes in balsam/any other resin or paraffin allowing ample time in each are the only way to ensure that the clearing agent has been completely removed.

6. The technique of clearing biological specimens in a clearing agent is the same as that for dehydration.

7. In the case of delicate materials such as filamentous algae, fern prothalli, etc. it is essential to pass through a gradient between alcohol and the clearing agent to avoid distortion/shrinkage. The following methodology is recommended.

Floatation Method

⊙ The simplest way to do this is through floatation method.

⊙ Pour a layer of the oil (clearing agent) in the specimen tube.

- ⊙ When the oil has settled at the bottom, pour alcohol very carefully over this so that the latter forms a layer over the former without mixing.
- ⊙ Now transfer the specimen which has been brought up to 100% alcohol to the upper layer of alcohol in this tube.
- ⊙ The specimen sinks to the junction of the two layers in this tube.
- ⊙ Once it comes into contact with the clearing agent layer, impregnation of the oil commences and the specimen becomes heavier and starts to sink to the bottom of the oil layer.
- ⊙ One can watch columns of alcohol rising from the specimen as it lies at the bottom of the tube.
- ⊙ Stoppage of release of alcohol denotes that the specimen is de-alcoholized completely.
- ⊙ Now pipette out the upper layer of alcohol carefully.
- ⊙ The specimen can be extracted from the bottom of the remaining oil layer and transferred to a tube containing 100% clearing agent (oil) where clearing will be completed in a few minutes.

8. It is quite possible that the hydrocarbons and the essential oils purchased from scientific suppliers, especially repacked consignments, will be saturated with water. Therefore, it is necessary to dehydrate them using Drierite before using them for microtechnique.

However, as they do not have a tendency to absorb moisture from the air, it is not necessary to keep them in bottles containing demoisturisers as recommended for dehydrating agents.

MOUNTING AND MOUNTANTS

Mounting is the last process to which the section/tissue/biological material is subjected to in the making of microscopic preparation, be it a section or a whole mount.

The medium in which the section/whole mount is mounted on a slide is called mounting medium.

Solid, unshrinkable objects such as frustules of diatoms may be mounted dry. In such cases air is the mounting medium.

In electron microscopy, sections are examined dry in a vacuum. The embedding medium is removed and the tissue constituents are exposed directly to the electron beam.

Excepting for the aforesaid examples, tissues/sections are always mounted in media that are fluid at the outset, though many solidify later.

The liquid mounting medium may be a single pure substance, a mixture of liquids, or a solution of one or more solids in a liquid.

ATTRIBUTES OF A LIQUID MOUNTING MEDIUM

⊙   It must be stable and optically homogeneous.

⊙   It must be transparent and colourless.

⊙   The mounting medium must fill even the minutest spaces formed within the cells by coagulant fixatives. Otherwise, different parts of the specimen would be permeated by fluids of different refraction indices rendering the image a confused one.

⊙   The medium must be capable of wetting the various tissue constituents, especially proteins. In other words, it must be able to lie against them without leaving any intervening spaces.

⊙   It must not dissolve or corrode the tissue constituents. However, solvents of particular cell constituents (such as lipids) are permissible, if the intention is to study the insoluble remainder of the tissue.

⊙   It must not support the growth of moulds or bacteria.

⊙   The refraction index of the medium must be related to the means adopted to obtain contrast in the image produced by the microscope.

The following example illustrates this relationship:

•   Let us say, that a piece of tissue has been fixed in formaldehyde and that all lipids, carbohydrates and nucleic acids have been dissolved out of it by special treatment.

•   The specimen will consist mainly of protein.

•   Such a specimen in its fixed condition will have a refraction index of about 1.536.

•   If the fixed tissue is now permeated by a colourless transparent fluid of the same or very nearly the same refraction index, such as methyl salicylate, the object will not be seen as there is no contrast between the object and the medium in which it has been mounted. (Recall what has been learnt in Chapter I on "How things are seen".)

•   This kind of transparency of the specimen can be overcome by dyeing the tissue and then mounting in the same medium as before.

•   Light of certain wavelengths is reduced in intensity (deviated) by the dye attached to the proteins but passes freely through the mounting medium. The complete homogeneity of the medium and the protein in this example is favourable to the production of an optically perfect image. It should be remembered that in this case the image is not produced by the protein itself, but by the dye attached to it!

- Alternatively, the undyed object of this example, may be rendered visible by mounting it in a fluid that differs slightly from the proteins in refraction index. The specimen should then be examined in phase-contrast microscope. In order to get the best effect, the difference in refraction indices should be small. The retardation or advancement of the light that passes through the object in relation to that which passes only through the mounting medium should not greatly exceed a quarter of the wavelength (1/4 of λ) of the light used for examination, if effective phase-contrast effect is desired.

- On the other hand, in the case of light microscopy, such a transparent object of the above example may be mounted in a medium of much lower or higher refraction index than its own. "Becke lines" are formed in the image in areas where the object meets the medium. Images obtained by higher power magnifications present exaggerated "Becke line" artefacts.

⊙ The mounting medium should preferably be of adhesive nature. This helps in holding/binding the coverslip to the slide rendering permanence to the preparation. If the medium is non-adhesive, the coverslip is sealed with gelatine/nail polish/varnish.

TYPES OF MOUNTING MEDIA

The mounting media available for slide preparation in microtechnique are categorized on the basis of the following two properties.

1. Affinity to water
2. Property of adhesion

Mounting media fall under two categories, namely hydrophil and hydrophobe based on their affinity to water.

Hydrophil Media

Media that contain water or are miscible with water fall under this category. The sections or whole mounts may be transferred direct from water to the mounting medium. However, it is advisable to effect this transfer gradually, i.e., to introduce the medium very gradually to the tissue.

Hydrophobe Media

Media that are not miscible with water and therefore require dehydration of the specimen are called hydrophobe media. This is achieved by passing tissues through a graded series of ethanol (70%, 80%, 90% and absolute alcohol). The dehydrated section is usually transferred to the solvent, if any, contained in the mounting medium, and from this solvent to the mounting medium itself.

Some hydrophobe media such as methyl salicylate contain no solvent. The tissue is transferred directly from the absolute ethanol to such media.

Most hydrophobe media have high refraction indices, approximating those of proteins that have been fixed by formaldehyde or by coagulant fixatives. These generally give more transparent preparations than do hydrophil ones.

Since high refraction index and firm adhesion of the coverslip are desirable in most cases, adhesive hydrophobe media are more often used than the others. Table 4.14 lists the differences between hydrophobe and hydrophil mounting media.

In hydrophobe media, the essential constituent is a 'resin' in the wider sense of the term, i.e., a solid, amorphous organic compound, insoluble in water, and have no melting point as it is composed of molecules of varying lengths.

In recent years, the term resin includes synthetic plastics besides the natural resins.

Natural resins are exudates from barks of certain trees (gum arabic) or roots of certain plants (asafoetida). These are oxidation products of terpenes.

Plastics having similar physical characters are also referred to as resins in the recent years. Distrene 80 (a polystyrene used in DPX), acrylic acid, etc. are examples.

Table 4.14   Differences between hydrophobe and hydrophil mounting media

Hydrophil media	Hydrophobe media
Contain water or are miscible with water	Do not contain water nor are miscible with water
Do not require dehydration of objects	Require dehydration of objects
Low refraction index	High or rather high refraction index

Adhesive and Non-adhesive Mounting Media

⊙ Some mounting media adhere to the surfaces and thus bind the coverslip to the slide, e.g. Canada balsam (hydrophobe), DPX (hydrophobe), etc.

⊙ Some mounting media are non-adhesive, e.g. glycerol (hydrophil), methyl salicylate (hydrophobe), etc. The differences between non-adhesive and adhesive media are presented in Table 4.15.

Table 4.15 Differences between non-adhesive and adhesive mounting media

Non-adhesive media	Adhesive media
Cannot bind coverslip to the slide. Hence sealing is required to make the preparation permanent.	Binds coverslip firmly to the slide on drying. Hence sealing is not an absolute necessity unless desired otherwise.
Final refraction index is known because there is no change in the composition if evaporation occurs.	The index of the complete medium ready for use changes as the medium dries up. Therefore, only the extreme limits of refraction indices can be stated, e.g. the index of the complete medium ready for use; the index of the medium from which the solvent has been driven off completely.

SOME IMPORTANT MOUNTING MEDIA

Glycerol (Glycerine) as a Mounting Medium

Glycerine is a non-adhesive hydrophil used as a mounting medium in micropreparations.

Some of the properties of glycerine are listed below.

⊙ Refraction index of pure glycerol is 1.474.

⊙ The refraction index varies with dilutions, for example,

1. 78 g glycerol + 22 ml distilled water = Ref. index 1.44
2. 65 g glycerol + 35 ml distilled water = Ref. index 1.42

⊙ Addition of cadmium chloride increases the refraction index to 1.54 at saturation. However, the salt imparts a pale yellow tint to the otherwise colourless medium.

Advantages

⊙ Glycerol is very valuable as a mounting medium for sections of tissues that have been embedded in butyl methacrylate and are intended for the study, without dyeing, by phase contrast microscopy.

⊙ It is used in studies of lipids as they are preserved whether fixed or not.

⊙ Also lysochromes maintain well in this medium.

Disadvantage

Certain dyes including mordanted haematin are not perfectly stable in preparations mounted in glycerine.

Ferrant's Medium

Ferrant's medium is a good example of an adhesive hydrophil mounting medium. The preparation of this fluid is given as follows:

Powdered gum arabic	40 g
Distilled water	40 ml

Dissolve and add 20 g of glycerol. A piece of camphor can be added as a disinfectant.

The pH of this fluid is 4.1 (addition of camphor does not alter it). The refraction index of the medium made up according to the formula given above is 1.423 or 1.424 if saturated with camphor.

After applying the coverslip, the slide can be left overnight in the paraffin oven. The coverslip adheres firmly.

The role of glycerine in the medium is as follows:

1. It prevents cracking of the medium when it dries up.
2. It readily penetrates the tissues through the minute spaces in them, while the larger molecules of the gum diffuse slowly.

Advantage

It is much used in the study of lipids.

Disadvantage

Phase contrast images of micropreparations mounted in Ferrant's medium are often imperfect. The uneven distribution of the two substances of high refraction index through the tissue is probably the cause for this.

Methyl Salicylate

It is a non-adhesive hydrophobe medium.

Non-adhesive hydrophobe media are not preferred generally because of the following reasons.

1. They are inconveniently volatile.
2. It is easy to prepare hydrophobe adhesive media that will stick to glass firmly.

However, methyl salicylate has the following advantages on account of which it is preferred in certain micropreparations as mounting medium.

⊙ It is colourless.

⊙ It is miscible in all proportions with absolute ethanol.

⊙ It gives excellent transparency to most preparations. Its refraction index (1.537) is very close to that of proteins fixed in the usual ways.

⊙ Since it is a single substance, there is no question of change of refraction index by differential evaporation of components.

⊙ Basic, acid and mordanted dyes seem to maintain their colours well in it.

DPX

DPX is the abbreviation for distrene-plasticizer-xylene. The commercial product marketed under the name DPX is a mixture of three isomeric dimethyl benzenes with ethyl benzene.

It has the following percentage composition whether derived from petroleum or coal.

o-Xylene	23%
m-Xylene	43 %
p-Xylene	19%
Ethyl benzene	15 %

DPX is a colourless liquid. Dyes maintain very well in this colourless medium.

Distrene 80 is the trade name of the polystyrene used in DPX. It is a colourless solid freely soluble in xylene. It has the same general characters as acrylic acid but differs in the substitution of a phenyl group for the carboxyl of the acid. This polymer retracts under the edges of the coverslip as the solvent evaporates.

The aforesaid defect is mitigated by addition of a plasticizer to the medium. The plasticizer used in DPX is tri-*p*-tolyl phosphate (often called tricresylphosphate). It is an ester of phosphoric acid, in which three *p*-tolyl have replaced three hydrogens. This plasticizer is a colourless, non-volatile liquid of high refraction index (about 1.56).

Xylene is chosen as a solvent for hydrophobe mounting media because it evaporates sufficiently slowly to allow the coverslip to be adjusted at leisure.

Preparation of DPX   If ready-to-use DPX is not available, it can be prepared thus:

- ⊙ To 100 ml of xylene add 18.75 ml of tri-*p*-tolyl phosphate and then 25 g of distrene 80. (The plasticizer is irritating to the skin and so avoid contact with the skin.)
- ⊙ The refraction index of DPX while it contains the original amount of xylene is 1.532. Since the refraction index of xylene is only about 1.496, that of the DPX mountant must increase as drying proceeds.
- ⊙ If all the xylene is driven out of the DPX, the resultant substance (distrene + plasticizer) is a solid, melting above 100°C. Although the plasticizer is a solvent for distrene, not nearly enough of it is present to make a solution.
- ⊙ In the case of whole mounts, there is some tendency to retraction under the coverslip, despite the presence of a plasticizer. This can be overcome by applying DPX to the mounts in excess quantity. This avoids formation of airspaces after retraction of the medium on drying. The excess of medium outer to the periphery of the coverslip can be peeled off after the coverslip has stuck firmly to the slide.

Gum Arabic

It is sticky water-soluble substance (gum) that exudes through cracks in the bark of species of *Acacia* especially *A. senegal*, a native of Sudan and other parts of tropical Africa. It was first imported in Europe from Arabian ports.

The gum is taken from both wild and cultivated trees. The gum consists of calcium salts and arabic acid. Hydrolysis of the gum yields arabinose, rhamnose, galactose and glucuronic acid. Molecular weight is about 240,000. Shape and size of the molecule determines its high viscosity in aqueous solution.

Dammar Balsam

This is also called gum dammar. This is not available in ready-to-use form. It is available only as crude gum in the form of lumps of different sizes mixed with powdered material and debris.

Lumps of the gum can be taken in a suitable container and melted over a flame. The melted balsam is poured into the chosen solvent. Benzol is preferred over xylol as it dries more quickly than does the latter. The mixture is filtered through a coarse filter paper placed in a ridged funnel. If the first filtrate shows cloudiness due to the presence of fine dust or debris, it is to be filtered again through a fine filter paper.

The preparations mounted in dammar balsam do not fade around the periphery as do the preparations mounted in Canada balsam. Because of this property it is considered to be superior to the latter.

Canada Balsam

It is a natural resin obtained from the gymnosperm plant *Abies balsamea*. It is available in a neutral filtered liquid form dissolved in xylol or benzol. The solution may be used as such or slightly diluted using xylol, dioxan or trichloroethylene as per requirement.

Balsam should never be heated to melt it. The ready-to-use solution should be neutral, clear to slightly yellowish tinge and of a consistency suitable to mount free-hand sections. Very dilute and darkly coloured solution indicates that it has been diluted too much and heat-spoiled.

On exposure to light, balsam turns acidic. Therefore, it is advisable to store the solution in dark amber-coloured bottle or black-painted bottle. Placing a piece of clean marble in the bottle and replacing it with a fresh one occasionally is said to prolong the shelf life of the solution.

While using Canada balsam as a mounting medium, always mount the sections from xylol, benzol or trichloroethylene.

Euparol

Euparol is a mixture of camsal, sandarac, eucalyptol and peraldehyde. The refraction index is higher than that of Canada balsam.

Euparol is popularly used as a mounting medium for preparations stained with haematoxylin as it has got the property of intensifying this stain. The sections can be mounted from 95% alcohol.

Euparol has a slight solvent action on celloidin. This property is taken advantage of to unroll and flatten out curled and too stiff sections before applying cover glass.

Euparol is a clear liquid. If it becomes cloudy before mounting could be completed, warm the slide gently over the flame of a spirit lamp until the cloudiness disappears.

Styrax

Styrax is a synthetic resin with a very high refraction index. This is very ideal for mounting cleared diatom frustules.

It can be diluted with benzol. Specimens or sections can be mounted in styrax from xylol or benzol.

Hyrax

Hyrax is very similar to styrax. This medium brings out the fine details of smears stained with brazilin. Sections can be transferred from xylol.

Cedar Wood Oil

Cedar wood oil used for immersion lenses can also be used as a mounting medium. It hardens only along the periphery of the coverslip remaining liquid inside. Sections can be mounted from xylol. Stains appear to keep preserved well in cedar wood oil.

Lactophenol

Lactophenol is a mixture of phenol, lactic acid, glycerine and distilled water as shown in Table 4.16.

Table 4.16   Composition of lactophenol

Ingredients	Quantity/proportion	
	General	Occasional
Phenol crystals	1 part	1 part
Lactic acid	1 part	1 part
Glycerine	1 part	2 parts
Distilled water	1 part	1 part

Sometimes stains are added to colour otherwise colourless specimens. Copper sulphate crystals are added to preserve green pigments in the specimen.

Clarite

It is a synthetic resin. It is also known by the name Nevillite V. It is colourless, strictly neutral, inert, homogeneous resin and dries quickly.

Plant specimens can be mounted in 80% solution in xylol. It is highly hydrophobic. Therefore, it cannot be used in mounting specimens passed through hygrobutol.

Glycerine Jelly

This is a suitable mounting medium for semi-permanent preparations. It can be prepared as follows:

- ⊙ Dissolve 10 g of high-quality gelatin in 60 ml of distilled water. It may take 2 hours or longer to dissolve.
- ⊙ Add 70 ml of glycerine and stir well.
- ⊙ To each 100 ml, add 1 g phenol crystals.
- ⊙ Warm the mixture for 15 minutes. Stir continuously until the flakes produced by the addition of phenol disappear.
- ⊙ While still warm filter the mixture through cheesecloth folded twice or thrice into a convenient bottle.
- ⊙ The mixture solidifies on cooling.

The whole can be re-melted by heating gently just before use. However, the mixture gets spoiled by continual re-melting. Therefore it is advisable to cut out small portions and melt these before use.

MICROSLIDE PREPARATION

The methods of preparing various kinds of micropreparations, also called microslides, are presented in this unit. For an introduction refer the section on Types of micropreparations in this chapter.

WHOLE MOUNTS

There are many specimens that are most satisfactorily mounted and observed as a whole. Though whole mounts do not require sectioning, some amount of trimming of excess tissue may be required. Filamentous algae, mycelia of fungi, prothalli of ferns, epidermal peelings, small and transparent gametothalli of liverworts, etc. are best mounted as such in a suitable mounting medium on a clean plain microslide, covered with coverslip and used for microscopic observation. Such micropreparations are called whole mounts. Smears of pollen grains and spores are in reality whole mounts, but are treated under a separate heading in that name.

Whole mounts can be temporary, semi-permanent or permanent depending on the purpose and length of use. Whatever the type of whole mount, the microslide and coverslip should be clean and dry.

TEMPORARY WHOLE MOUNTS

Temporary whole mounts are prepared for routine temporary and preliminary observation mostly for classwork purpose. The specimen is mounted in a few drops of water on a clean plain microslide and covered with a coverslip.

Procedure

⊙ Place just enough drops of water in the central point of the microslide.

⊙ Transfer the specimen to the water drop.

⊙ Take care not to trap any air bubble in the specimen.

⊙ Hold the clean coverslip gently and lower it horizontally over the water drop until the centre of the coverslip touches the water drop.

⊙ Release the coverslip so that the mounting medium (water) gently spreads reaching the edges of the coverslip.

⊙ Some have a tendency to bring the edge of the coverslip into contact with the edge of the water drop while supporting the coverslip with a dissecting needle. By drawing the needle slowly, the mounting medium is drawn to the other edge. This method has the disadvantage of drawing the specimen also to the edge of the coverslip. Therefore, this method is not preferred by many.

In order to mount the specimen exactly in the centre of the slide, the following steps are to be followed.

⊙ Draw the outline of a microslide (Figure 4.16) on a white hardboard (the blank reverse side of printed invitation cards should serve this purpose).

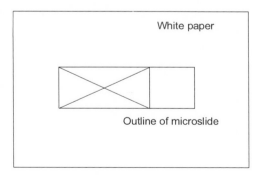

Figure 4.16   Outline drawing of microslide to guide mounting in the central point

⊙ Draw 1" × 1" outline for the label preferably on the left side.

⊙ Draw diagonals connecting the four corners in the remaining space.

⊙ Place the clean plain microslide on the outline drawn.

⊙ The specimen is to be mounted (Figure 4.17) in the point where the diagonal lines meet (in the outline already drawn on the hardboard).

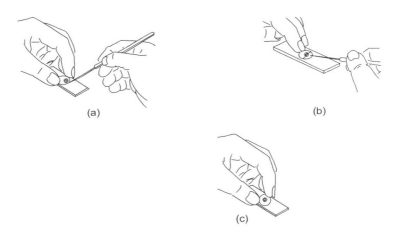

(a)   (b)

(c)

Figure 4.17   Applying the coverslip over the specimen (a) and (b) Correct methods of applying the coverslip (c) Incorrect way of applying the coverslip

SEMI-PERMANENT WHOLE MOUNTS

Whole mounts that require keeping for a little longer (a few hours to a fortnight) are mounted in glycerine medium. Pure glycerine or aqueous dilutions of glycerine or some form of glycerine jelly are used for making semi-permanent whole mounts.

Glycerine preserves the natural colours of the plant specimens. It has been found to be an ideal mounting medium for semi-permanent preparations of unicellular and colonial Chlorophyta, protonemata of mosses, fungal spores, prothalli of ferns, etc.

Procedure

Delicate specimens

⊙ Place delicate specimens that are likely to plasmolyse easily in one or two drops of 10% glycerine (aqueous) on a clean plain microslide.

⊙ Keep the slide undisturbed, covered under a petri dish.

⊙ This allows the glycerine to concentrate.

⊙ When the mounting medium has concentrated sufficiently, place a clean coverslip over the drop of glycerine cautiously taking care that glycerine does not ooze out of the coverslip.

⊙ The edge of the coverslip is sealed with a neutral nail polish or any other inexpensive resin.

Stained preparations in glycerine jelly

⊙ Kill and fix the specimen.

⊙ Stain the specimen in some aqueous stain. Only aqueous stain solutions are to be used for mounting in glycerine jelly.

⊙ Iron haematoxylin with or without counterstain has been found to be suitable.

⊙ Wash off the excess stain from the specimen before mounting.

⊙ Place the stained specimen in the 10% aqueous glycerine in a small dish that offers as much evaporating surface as possible.

⊙ Leave the dish covered and undisturbed. Keeping the dish on the upper shelf or cooler part of a thermostat may help in evaporation.

   Caution Rapid evaporation may lead to shrinkage.

⊙ Allow enough time for the 10% glycerine to reach the consistency of pure glycerine. Now the specimen is ready for mounting.

⊙ Using a section lifter, take enough of the specimen and remove excess of glycerine from the specimen using a blotting paper.

⊙ Place the specimen in one or two drops of warmed jelly, just enough to spread to the edge of the coverslip. If the jelly mixture oozes out of the edges of coverslip, it is impossible to seal the same.

⊙ Apply a clean coverslip, preferably a circular one.

⊙ Sealing of the coverslip can be performed either at once or after a week or ten days when the jelly has solidified.

⊙ Gold-size or Canada balsam is generally used for sealing.

⊙ Sealing may be done free hand or using a turn table.

   Preparation of Kaiser's glycerine jelly.

Pure gelatin	1 part by weight
Water	6 parts by weight

⊙ Allow the gelatin to soak for at least 2 hours.

- ⊙ Add glycerine 7 parts by weight.
- ⊙ Add phenol crystals 1 g for every 100 g of the mixture.
- ⊙ Warm for about 15 minutes, stirring constantly and vigorously until all the flakes produced by phenol have disappeared completely.
- ⊙ Filter through cotton while still warm.
- ⊙ Store the mixture in a small bottle that can be conveniently warmed in a hot-water bath.
- ⊙ Melt the jelly every time in hot-water bath prior to mounting.

PERMANENT WHOLE MOUNTS

It may be required to make whole mounts of some specimens as permanent preparations. The following two methods are the most commonly used of the several methods available.

Hygrobutol Method

This is the simplest method that can be attempted by even the beginners. It has been found to work well even with difficult specimens such as *Spirogyra*. It is important that each step be carried out in its logical sequence to obtain the desired result.

- ⊙ Kill and fix the specimen in a weak or medium chrome–acetic fixative which has been found to give very good staining effects especially the filamentous members of Chlorophyceae. FAA works out well for all kinds of materials except aquatic forms.
- ⊙ After fixation, place the specimen in a deep solid watch glass or low stender or petri dish and carry out all the further steps in it by pouring out the fluid every time and not transferring the specimen between containers.
- ⊙ Wash out the fixative thoroughly with running water to wash off CA fixative and with distilled water to wash off FAA.
- ⊙ Stain with an aqueous stain. Harris' haematoxylin, iron haematoxylin and Mayer's carmalum are recommended.
- ⊙ Differentiate the dye sharply. Take care not to destain too much since the further steps may remove some stain.
- ⊙ Wash out the differentiating agent thoroughly.
- ⊙ Dehydrate in 15%, 30%, 50% and 70% ethyl alcohol allowing at least 20 minutes in each concentration. Keep the container covered between changes of fluids to avoid evaporation.

⊙ Leave the specimen in 85% alcohol for at least 18 hours. The long immersion in 85% alcohol hardens the tissue without making it brittle. This is very important for the further handling of the specimen. Shortening of this step will result in the specimen becoming excessively brittle upon the addition of a stronger alcohol rendering it non-amenable to further treatment.

⊙ Counterstain with any desired cytoplasmic stain dissolved in equal parts of 95% alcohol and methyl cellosolve. As chances for overstaining are least, the counterstain used may be fairly strong. About 15 minutes should be enough for counterstaining. However, make sure that the stain has penetrated deeply. Table 4.17 will help in choosing the right counterstain.

Table 4.17   Primary stains and counterstains recommended for some specimens

Primary stain	Counterstain	Specimen
Haematoxylin	Erythrosin B	Rhodophyta
	Orange G	Phaeophyta
	Fast green	Chlorophyta
Carmine	Not required	For most specimens
	Aniline blue or fast green	Leaves or epidermal peels

⊙ Differentiation of the counterstain is not required since the hygrobutol to be used in the next step prevents the 95% alcohol from extracting too much of the stain.

⊙ Pour out the counterstain and immediately wash out the excess stain with 95% alcohol.

⊙ Give a change in 95% alcohol.

⊙ Start adding hygrobutol by gradual substitution method. (Add a small amount of hygrobutol every minute or so to avoid strong diffusion currents. Every time mix the fluids by gently tilting the container back and forth. Discard some of the mixture between every third or fourth addition. Continue until the mixture has reached an approximate proportion of 90 parts hygrobutol and 10 parts ethyl alcohol. It is not essential to remove alcohol completely.)

⊙ Pour out most of the butyl and ethyl alcohols replacing at once with thick balsam diluted at least ten times with hygrobutol. The specimen should be immersed in butyl balsam of volume ten times its own.

⊙ Keep the container aside in a dust-free warm place. Allow enough time until much of the solvent butanol has evaporated leaving the balsam to a consistency suitable for mounting.

⊙ Take care to add enough diluted balsam so that the specimen will not be exposed to air on evaporation.

⊙ The process of evaporation should be gradual. Therefore do not induce rapid evaporation by any artificial means. The safest minimum period for evaporation is said to be 2 hours.

⊙ Place a fairly large drop of balsam about the size of two grains of wheat in the centre of a clean microslide.

⊙ It may be necessary to manipulate the specimen transferred to the mounting medium. The specimens that are mounted singly, such as sections, prothalli, etc., can be manipulated with ease. Using fine scissors cut the mass of filamentous specimens into smaller bunches of 5 mm and less. It will be easier to mount the bunch and the individual filaments can then be separated and spread easily.

⊙ Leave the slide on a warming plate for a day or two to solidify the balsam.

⊙ Place a clean coverslip over the drop of balsam carefully and gently press on the coverslip with the handle of a dissecting needle which may help in spreading the balsam towards the edge of the coverslip. It also helps to flatten the specimen if it is slightly curved.

Glycerine–Xylol Method

This is another equally simple and inexpensive method of making permanent whole mounts. The procedure is as follows:

⊙ Kill and fix the specimen as described in the previous method.

⊙ Wash off the fixative thoroughly.

⊙ Stain with an aqueous basic stain, e.g. any haematoxylin solution.

⊙ Transfer the stained specimen in enough volume of 10% aqueous glycerine taken in a small container such as a stender dish or petri dish.

⊙ Keep the container undisturbed in a dust-free corner.

⊙ If at all the dish is to be covered to eliminate dust from settling, take care to leave airspace between the container and the lid/cover.

⊙ Leave the set-up for a few days until the diluted glycerine attains the consistency of pure glycerine.

- ⊙ If required, the container may be kept in a hot-air oven to accelerate the process of evaporation.

- ⊙ Remove the glycerine with several changes of 95% alcohol. If the specimen is in the form of thicker masses, it requires more number of changes.

- ⊙ It is always better to place the specimen in a wire strainer which is placed in the dish with about 1 cm of clear space left below the strainer. This helps the heavier glycerine to settle down free from the specimen.

- ⊙ If desired, the specimen in 95% alcohol may be counterstained with any suitable dye dissolved in 95% alcohol.

- ⊙ To complete the process of dehydration, replace 95% alcohol with absolute alcohol.

- ⊙ De-alcoholize the specimen by gradual replacement method (alcohol: xylol = 9:1, 8:2, 7:3, 6:4, 5:5, 4:6, 3:7, 2:8, 1:9, and finally pure xylol). Allow 5 to 10 minutes in each mixture.

- ⊙ Hygrobutol may also be used in the place of xylol as the specimen may not be so much hardened as with xylol.

- ⊙ Replace xylol (or hygrobutol as the case may be) with balsam highly diluted with xylol or hygrobutol.

- ⊙ Leave the dish undisturbed until the balsam evaporates to mounting consistency.

- ⊙ Mount the specimen in the same way described earlier.

SMEARS

Smear micropreparations are the most suitable for studying the stages of cell division. The smear method is limited to study of loose cells that are not held to each other by middle lamella. In plant materials, this refers to the microsporocytes after they have begun to separate from each other and round up.

Smear method is not suitable to study the pollen masses of *Acacia* and the pollinia of Orchidaceae and Asclepiadaceae. These have to be mounted as a whole!

The basic approach in smear technique is to spread the loose cells in a single layer on the surface of a clean microslide, kill and fix them all instantly without distortion.

Fortunately, all the cells that can be smeared will stick to the surface of the slide. Therefore, there is no need for using a cementing agent.

SMEARING TECHNIQUE

- The slides on which smears are to be applied should be chemically clean. Therefore, use acid-cleaned plain microslides and coverslips.
- Navaschin's fixative is recommended as the most suitable for smears. Mix just sufficient volumes of Navaschin A and Navaschin B and use the mixture at once. Recommended fixing time is 4 hours.
- Use paired square petri dish for making smears.
- Place glass rods of suitable lengths one each at the opposite ends of the lower half of the petri dish. The glass rods will keep the slide off the bottom.
- Pour the fixative mixture just more than enough to cover the glass rods.
- Place a clean microslide on the outline drawn in the white hardboard. Mark the upper surface of the slide in one corner with a glass marking pencil or by etching it with a diamond edge.
- Remove an anther from the bud and place it in the centre of the slide. If the anther is longer than 2 mm cut it into pieces of convenient length.
- Using a clean scalpel or section lifter, crush the piece(s) and spread the microsporocytes quickly and evenly on the surface of the slide around the central point. Remove the tissue remnants of the anther.
- Invert the slide at once and place it carefully in the petri dish in such a way that the entire smeared surface of the slide comes into instant contact with the fixative. Rest it on the glass rods immersed in the fixative about 2" away from each other.
- Any mishandling of the slide at this stage will wash off the smear completely.
- Complete the whole exercise of removing the anther from the bud, smearing and fixing the smear within 4 or 5 seconds.
- Leave the lower half of the dish covered with the upper half.
- Turn the slide smear side up after 10 minutes and leave it undisturbed for four hours.

Alternative Method

- Place the piece(s) of anther in the centre of a slide.
- Hold another clean slide crosswise on the first.
- Apply enough force to extrude and spread the microsporocytes.

⊙ Separate the slide and invert them at once in the petri dish containing the fixative.

⊙ Both the slides can be processed simultaneously.

STAINING THE SMEAR

⊙ Once fixation is over, turn the slide smear side up.

⊙ Using forceps remove any debris of anther tissue that may be present.

⊙ Place the slide on glass rods placed in the lower part of a petri dish and wash gently in running water for about 15 minutes.

⊙ Examine the slide under microscope and reject those from which cells have been washed off.

⊙ The slides are now ready for staining.

Several staining schedules are available, of which the following are simple and easy to follow.

Belling's Iron–Acetocarmine Method (Semi-permanent Preparation)

The following is the formula for Belling's iron–haematoxylin stain solution.

Glacial acetic acid	90 cc
Distilled water	110 cc (Heat to boiling and then add)
Carmine powder	1 g
Ferric sulphate aqueous solution	A few drops

The following are to be noted in the preparation of solution.

1. Carmine is to be added immediately after removing the beaker from the flame.
2. Cool the stain mixture in the refrigerator.
3. Decant after cooling.
4. Add a few drops of ferric ammonium sulphate until a dark wine red colour develops. Too much iron will precipitate carmine.
5. Keep the solution in a well-stoppered bottle.

Procedure

⊙ Take a few drops of acetocarmine solution on a clean microslide.

⊙ Place the freshly removed anther(s) or pieces of anther on the drop of the stain.

⊙ Allow a few minutes for the stain to penetrate the anther.

⊙ Remove the stain with the help of a blotting paper/absorbent paper.

⊙ Place a few drops of fresh stain.

⊙ Press out the microsporocytes using a clean scalpel.

⊙ Remove the debris of the anther tissues.

⊙ Place a coverslip over the smear.

⊙ Remove any excess fluid by placing absorbent paper at the edge of the coverslip.

⊙ Seal the coverslip immediately.

⊙ The preparation may require a few days for the stain to penetrate the sporocytes.

Johansen's Methyl Violet Method (Permanent Preparation)

Use freshly prepared 1% aqueous solution of methyl violet 2B.

1. Transfer the smears from water to the stain.

2. Recommended staining time is 15 minutes which can be increased if warranted.

3. Transfer the stained smear to water and leave for ½ an hour.

4. Hereafter handle the slides individually. Hold the slide edgewise and immerse in alcohol grades contained in a small beaker.

5. Differentiate in 70% and 90% alcohol acidified with picric acid to a strength of 0.5% (w/v or v/v). 10 seconds in each will suffice. Hold the slide and gently move it back and forth in the alcohol.

6. Discard the alcohol that has become saturated with the stain as a result of transferring several slides through them.

7. Bring the slide to 95% alcohol containing ammonia (4 drops to each 100 ml of alcohol).

8. Transfer the slide to absolute alcohol and complete the dehydration. 10 to 15 seconds will suffice.

9. Transfer the slide to pure clove oil. It completes differentiation. Keep gently moving the slide back and forth for up to 15 seconds. This ensures even differentiation.

10. Give a wash in xylol containing a trace of absolute alcohol.

11. Allow the slide in pure xylol for 2 to 3 hours. This improves the sharpness of the stain.

12. Examine the slide under microscope. Unsatisfactory slides may be rejected.

13. Mount in balsam or DPX mountant.

McClintock's Acetocarmine Method
(Permanent Preparation)

⊙ Take a mixture of 1 part glacial acetic acid to 3 parts of absolute alcohol in a specimen tube.

⊙ Fixation time is a minimum of 12 hours. Specimens may be left in the fixative mixture for several weeks. This only helps in improving the stainability of the chromosome.

⊙ If longer storage is required, store the specimen in 70% alcohol tightly closed in a specimen tube.

⊙ Place a few drops of acetocarmine on a plain microslide.

⊙ Transfer the specimen from the fixative (or from 70% alcohol), to the stain on the slide.

⊙ With the help of a clean scalpel, squash the specimen to separate the cells apart or to squeeze out the microsporocytes if it is anther.

⊙ Remove the tissue debris.

⊙ Place a coverslip over the squashed material.

⊙ Heat the slide over the flame of a spirit lamp for a second. Repeat this process for four to five times. The solution should not be heated to boiling.

⊙ Examine the slides under a microscope and reject useless ones.

⊙ Place the slide carefully coverslip side up on the glass rods placed opposite to each other in a petri dish containing 10% aqueous acetic acid.

⊙ One can see the coverslip gradually rising.

⊙ Using a dissecting needle, gently push the coverslip to the edge of the slide.

⊙ Soon the coverslip will begin to float freely and it will be easier to grasp it with a forceps.

⊙ The tissue or the microsporocytes stick to both the slide and the coverslip.

⊙ Both are to be passed through the following series allowing a few minutes in each.

   1. Acetic acid + Absolute alcohol = 1:3

   2.   Acetic acid + Absolute alcohol = 1:9

   3.   Absolute alcohol + Xylol   = 1:1

⊙ The slide and the coverslip are recombined directly from the last of the series in balsam dissolved in xylol.

SQUASHES

Some authors prefer to treat squash preparations under the method of preparing smears. There is a difference between the two. In smears, the cells which are already loose and not attached to each other are spread/ smeared over the surface of the slide. But in the case of squashes, soft tissues or organs are squashed on the slide to separate the constituent cells.

As the name literally means, the specimen placed on a clean slide is crushed under a coverslip and examined. This method is applicable to soft tissues/organs when it is desirable to tease or separate the cells to facilitate observation of individual cells.

In botanical microtechnique, specimens such as root tips, procarps and cystocarps of members of Rhodophyta, etc. are best studied by squashing.

The following two methods are generally followed.

WARMKE'S METHOD

This method has been found to yield very useful permanent micropreparations. It may also be applied on microsporocytes.

⊙ Fix the tissue using formalin (1 part) and absolute alcohol (3 parts) mixture for a minimum of 12 hours.

⊙ Leaving the specimen in the fixing solution helps increasing the affinity of the chromosomes for the stain.

⊙ Fixed specimens can be stored for long in 70% alcohol.

⊙ Transfer the specimen to a mixture of equal parts of 95% alcohol and concentrated hydrochloric acid.

⊙ Allow 5 to 10 minutes for the HCl to dissolve the middle lamella.

⊙ Acid treatment softens the tissue.

⊙ Treat the specimen in Carnoy's fluid containing chloroform for 5 minutes or longer. Carnoy's fluid hardens the tissue which has been softened by the acid.

- ⊙ Take a few drops (just enough to spread under the coverslip) of acetocarmine stain solution on a clean plain microslide.
- ⊙ Place a small piece of the specimen, preferably less than 0.5 mm long, in the drop of stain.
- ⊙ Press the specimen using a clean scalpel to squash and separate the cells.
- ⊙ The cells will separate and float free in the stain.
- ⊙ Place a coverslip over the stain and press gently. Small square coverslips are found to be more suitable.
- ⊙ Heat the slide cautiously by passing through the flame of spirit lamp. This helps in clearing the cytoplasm. Heating should not boil the stain solution.
- ⊙ The preparation can be made semi-permanent by sealing the edges of the coverslip with a suitable resin. Such preparations keep for about a week.
- ⊙ If desired, the preparation can be made permanent by placing the slide in 10% aqueous acetic acid following McClintock's method.

HILLARY'S METHOD

This method is found to be useful for root tips and anthers that are difficult to smear.

- ⊙ The root tip may be fixed using any fixative mixture.
- ⊙ Wash off the fixative thoroughly.
- ⊙ Apply Feulgen reaction technique.*
- ⊙ Allow sufficient time for the stain to penetrate the tissue.
- ⊙ Pass the specimen through dioxan three times.
- ⊙ Place a drop of balsam diluted with dioxan on a clean slide.
- ⊙ Place the specimen in the drop of balsam.
- ⊙ Divide the pieces into small longitudinal sections using a fine dissecting needle.
- ⊙ Add a few more drops of balsam if necessary.
- ⊙ Place a clean coverslip carefully by placing it horizontally on the drop of balsam.
- ⊙ Apply gentle pressure over the coverslip so that the cells will separate a little more.
- ⊙ Keep the slide aside until the balsam dries.

*Feulgen's Nuclear Staining Method

This staining method is recommended for preparation of squashes using Hillary's method. Feulgen and Rosenberg devised this method as a microchemical test to distinguish the particular nucleic acid found in the chromatin from similar types. Development of a specific purple or occasionally magenta colour when a reduced or colourless form of basic fuchsin is brought into contact with an aldehyde in the presence of the nucleic acid peculiar to chromatin is the basic feature of this method.

Preparation of the stain

- Take 0.5 g of basic fuchsin in a 250 ml beaker.
- Pour 100 ml of boiling distilled water and shake thoroughly.
- Cool to 50°C and filter the solution.
- Add 10 ml of 1N HCl to the filtrate.
- Add 0.5 g of potassium metabisulphite at once and shake thoroughly.
- Transfer the stain solution to a glass-stoppered bottle.
- Keep the stain in dark for 18 hours.

Procedure

- Bring the slide down to distilled water.
- Rinse in cold 1N HCl.
- Place the slide in fresh 1N HCl and heat the solution quickly to 60°C. Avoid overheating. Allow the slide at that temperature for 4 to 5 minutes.
- Transfer the slide to the staining solution which should be either colourless or of a light straw colour.
- Plant tissues require a staining time of 3 to 5 hours, while for animal tissues the optimum time is 2 hours.
- Remove the slide from the stain and gently tap the lower edge on absorbent paper. This will withdraw the excess stain.
- Keep the slide for 10 minutes in the following differentiating solution mixture:

1N HCl	5 cc
10% aqueous potassium metabisulphite	5 cc
Distilled water	100 cc

Give three changes in the differentiating solution, each of 10 minutes duration.

⊙ Plant materials may be counterstained quickly with 0.05% fast green in 95% alcohol.

⊙ Pass the slide to xylol by gradual displacement method.

⊙ Mount in balsam or DPX.

SECTIONING OF BIOLOGICAL SPECIMENS

In order to study the internal arrangement of cells, the given biological material is to be cut into very thin slices of say around 0.1 mm or less. Such thin slices of tissue are called microsections.

One can refer to the section on types of microscopic preparations in Introduction to Microtechnique for a comprehensive introduction on the importance and need of sectioning biological materials. The difficulties met with in sectioning and the methods of overcoming them are also outlined there.

In this unit, the methodology of sectioning biological specimens is dealt with in detail.

INTRODUCTION TO METHODS OF SECTIONING

Biological specimens that are to be subjected to microscopic observation are much varied in their nature. They may be hard and woody or soft. They may be brittle or pliable. In shape they may range from cylindrical (stem and roots), flat and thalloid (leaf, sepals, petals, liverwort thalli) or may be of irregular shape (coralloid roots of *Cycas*, fruit body of *Polyporus* etc.). In size they may be very small or very large.

There is more than one purpose for which the specimen is sectioned. The section may be taken for one-time observation in the class or practical examination which requires only temporary and semi-permanent micropreparations. Students of higher level and researchers may have to keep the sections as a documentary evidence for their research work and therefore make permanent microslides of such sections.

Depending on their nature, some specimens are sectioned directly without being subjected to prior treatment. For example, stiff specimens, which offer resistance to the cutting edge of the razor blade such as stems, roots, leaves, petioles of many tracheophytes, etc. can be sectioned as such with the help of a razor blade, while holding the specimen between the thumb and index finger.

Flat and pliable organs such as leaves, gametothalli of liverworts, sporophylls and cones of pteridophytes, fruit bodies of certain basidiomycetes, thalli of many macroalgae, etc. need to be supported in some kind of soft-solid material like pieces of carrot, pieces of potato tuber, petioles of *Colocasia* spp., the pith of pith-plants such as *Aeschynomene aspera**. Pieces of thermocol also come in handy for this purpose. The support that is used for sectioning should be soft enough that the razor blade cuts across it with ease.

(* *Aeschynomene aspera,* a member of Fabaceae, is the source of pith of commerce in South India. The stem on drying becomes crispy and can be worked very well with sharp blades. The stem is extensively used in making Tanjore dolls.

The elders mentioned in western text books are species of the genus *Sambucus*. The American elder is *Sambucus canadensis* and the European elder is *S. nigra*.)

In the examples cited above, the sections obtained are processed individually and finally mounted on the slide.

The biological material should be of such consistency that it will resist the sharp edge of the blade or knife passing through it while sectioning.

Some specimens may be too soft to section as such and these require some processing prior to sectioning so that they are rendered hard enough to stand against the cutting edge of the razor blade or knife. Such specimens are dehydrated, cleared and embedded in paraffin wax and the wax blocks are held and sectioned.

Hard and woody specimens do not require any treatment or processing prior to sectioning. If very hard, they may have to be softened a little so that the knife or razor blade can pass through it with ease. Attempting to section very woody specimens such as rhizomes and hard rachii of ferns and *Cycas*, woody stems, etc., holding them between fingers and using a razor blade very often results in the individual cutting his or her fingers. Therefore, it is advisable to hold such specimens in a hand microtome or in some sort of improvised device and attempt sectioning.

Manual sectioning has the following disadvantages.

⊙ Sections are of uneven thickness.
⊙ Very thin sections are not possible.
⊙ More often the specimen is cut obliquely.

In spite of these disadvantages, manual sectioning serves most purposes. With practice one should be able to take very good sections manually. In the case of manual sectioning, the section is subjected to the processing and staining schedule and finally mounted on the slide.

When micron-thin sections are desired, some sort of mechanical cutting device is to be used for sectioning. Mechanical devices employed for taking very thin sections are called microtomes. Various types of microtomes are available and their accessories have been discussed earlier in this chapter.

The various sectioning methods can be dealt under two broad heads, namely, free-hand sections and microtome sections.

FREE-HAND SECTIONS

Originally the term "free-hand sections" was applied to sections cut by means of razor blade from the specimen held free or with the support of a pith or any such support in the other hand.

Later the term included sections cut from live or fixed non-embedded specimens by means of a hand microtome as well as a sliding microtome (sledge microtome).

Johansen (1940) includes all kinds of sections, cut from both embedded and non-embedded specimens irrespective of the mode of the sectioning process, that are processed loosely without attaching them with a slide using an adhesive, in this category.

In the present book only non-embedded sections are treated as the free-hand sections.

Free-Hand Sections of Fresh Specimens
Using a Razor Blade

In regular classwork, free-hand sections are cut using a razor blade. This is a very useful, convenient and inexpensive technique serving most purposes.

The specimen is held firmly between the thumb and index finger in one hand.

The index finger should be horizontal and the thumb vertical.

The thumb will be pressing against the mid-phalanx of the index finger.

Hold the specimen in such a way that the specimen is a little above the surface of the horizontally held index finger and the thumb is well below.

Using the other hand, rest the razor blade or safety razor blade horizontally on the index finger with the cutting edge of the blade against the specimen.

Forward circular motions of the blade on the left towards the specimen will cut the specimen into thin sections (Figure 4.18).

The specimen can be raised every now and then so that it is cut in every circular motion of the blade.

With practice one can take very good sections worthy of preservation as a permanent slide.

Figure 4.18   Cutting a hand section. The razor is drawn across the specimen with gentle pressure, and the section is then washed into a stender dish.

As soon as a couple of sections are cut, immerse them in clean water in a petri dish or watch glass. Never allow the sections to become dry.

Pliable and soft specimens do not offer resistance to the cutting edge of the blade. Therefore they need to be held in some kind of soft and firm material through which the blade passes easily.

Note   The blade should be moved firmly and quickly, and the plane of cutting should be perfectly horizontal.

Free-Hand Sections Using a Hand Microtome

Hand microtome is a very useful device developed to aid in sectioning biological materials. It has certain definite advantages over taking sections holding the specimen as such with the fingers. A description of the instrument is provided in the section on microtomes in this chapter. The technique of sectioning specimens using a hand microtome is given below.

⊙   Most often the specimen that is to be sectioned is rarely of the shape and size suitable to be gripped in the specimen holder of the hand microtome. Therefore, the specimen is to be held in some substance that can be cut and shaped easily to support the specimen to be cut.

⊙ Cut out cylinders of suitable diameter from fresh carrot using a cork borer.

⊙ If the specimen is flat (e.g. leaf, gametothalli of liverworts, etc.), splice the cork and insert the specimen in between the cut halves.

⊙ Insert the cylinder of carrot along with the inserted leaf into the specimen holder of the hand microtome and tighten it.

⊙ To accommodate cylindrical organs such as stems, petioles, etc., a hollow cylinder has to be cut out. The outer diameter should fit the specimen holder and the inner diameter should be slightly less than that of the specimen to be cut.

⊙ Split the hollow cylinder, place the specimen in the hollow, reunite the cylinder (Figure 4.19a) and insert the same into the specimen holder and tighten.

⊙ Cut sections (Figure 4.19b) using a sharp razor blade.

⊙ The specimen can be raised by a desired height (say 5 μ or 10 μ) by turning the graduated sleeve.

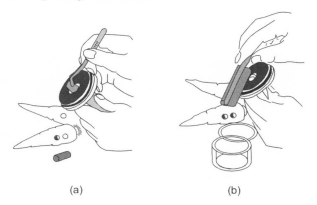

(a)   (b)

Figure 4.19   Sectioning specimens using hand microtome (a) Fixing the specimen (b) Cutting sections

Advantages

⊙ Sections of uniform thickness are possible.

⊙ The large platform supporting the razor prevents the cutting plane from becoming oblique.

⊙ Sections of desired thickness can be had.

Free-Hand Sections Using a Sliding Microtome/Sledge Microtome

Sliding microtome or sledge microtome, also called wood microtome, is used to cut thin sections out of hard and woody specimens. It is suitable for non-embedded specimens only. The specimen is to be supported in a suitable corky material and held firmly in the clamp. A description of sledge microtome and the method of operating it have been given in an earlier section on microtomes in this chapter.

Sectioning

⊙ If the specimen is fresh, moisten the knife and specimen with the help of a camel-hair brush.

⊙ If it is a preserved one, use the preservative or 50% alcohol for moistening.

⊙ A mixture of equal parts of 95% alcohol and glycerine affords a better lubrication.

⊙ Sections tend to curl if allowed to dry. In order to avoid this, transfer the section at once to watch glasses containing either FAA or any other fixative.

⊙ In the case of preserved specimens, the section can be transferred to 50% alcohol.

⊙ Cut twice as many sections as required, allowing the selection of best ones.

Processing and Staining Schedule

⊙ The staining and dehydration may be carried out in watch glasses or embryo cups.

⊙ Larger sections of tough specimens are transferred between solutions using section lifter or camel-hair brush.

⊙ In the case of smaller and less-firm sections, the liquids are removed using a pipette allowing the sections to remain in the same container.

The following stain combinations have been found to yield good results.

1. Safranin and Harris' haematoxylin
2. Safranin and fast green
3. Safranin and aniline blue

4. Safranin and crystal violet (most suitable for gymnosperm specimens)
5. Iodine and acid fuchsin
6. Iodine with iron haematoxylin
7. Iodine with orange G
8. Methyl green with acid fuchsin
9. Methyl green with iron haematoxylin
10. Methyl green with orange G

⊙   When staining is completed, commence rapid dehydration following the hygrobutol method for whole mounts as described earlier.

⊙   Give two changes in pure hygrobutol.

⊙   Transfer and leave the sections to diluted balsam to partially evaporate the solvent.

⊙   Mount in balsam.

MICROTOME SECTIONS

Paraffin Infiltration

If the biological material is to be sectioned using a microtome, it should be reinforced both externally and internally.

The substance which is used to reinforce the material should be capable of stabilizing simultaneously both internal and external to the tissue. It should also be fairly firm. Only then, the microtome knife can cut both the material and the embedding medium alike.

Paraffin wax is the most widely used infiltrating and embedding medium in biological microtechnique.

Advantages of embedding specimens in paraffin wax

⊙   Paraffin wax can be easily handled.

⊙   The microsections of paraffin-embedded materials are in a dry state.

⊙   Continuous serial microsections in the form of ribbons are possible.

⊙   Very thin microsections are possible only with materials embedded in paraffin wax than with any other embedding medium.

⊙   Any staining procedure can be followed to stain the microsections embedded in paraffin wax. In the case of sections embedded in other materials, only specific staining procedures are to be followed.

⊙ The ribbons containing the microsections can be kept for several years without spoilage.

⊙ Wax can be removed easily from the ribbon and the sections.

Quality requirement of paraffin wax for use in microtomy The paraffin wax that is used in microtechnique should possess the following qualities.

    ⊙ Paraffin wax having a melting point of 40–50°C or 50–60°C is ideal for our country's climate. Particularly the latter is very ideal. In western laboratories, paraffin wax having a melting point of 30–40°C is used. In most books on microtechnique, the same is recommended for use. But paraffin wax of very low melting point may not suit our tropical climate.

    ⊙ At the same time paraffin wax of very high melting point also will not serve the purpose. The material will get cooked at such temperatures.

    ⊙ The wax that is used should be sufficiently firm on solidification.

    ⊙ While being firm, the wax should also be soft and homogeneous.

    ⊙ It should not crystallize nor should it be coarse.

    ⊙ The wax that is used for microtechnique should not contain water, any other volatile substance or any other scum.

To increase the softness and sectioning quality, beeswax or rubber can be added to the paraffin wax available in the market.

In recent times, Cerasin wax, beeswax, rubber resins, plastic and synthetic materials such as tissue mat are used in the place of paraffin wax. Celloidin is also used. Celloidin is very ideal for taking microsections of hardwood. In certain laboratories, another material called bioloid is used in the place of paraffin wax.

Even though several alternatives for paraffin wax are available and are used, it is paraffin wax that is extensively used in many laboratories on account of its above-mentioned qualities.

Infiltration technique Infiltration of paraffin wax into the tissue should be carried out in gradual steps.

Fine shaves of paraffin wax are to be added in very small quantities to the specimen tube containing the materials in 100% clearing agent (xylol).

Further addition is to be carried out only after the shaves added have completely dissolved. Thus, wax shaves are added in small quantities until the clearing agent becomes saturated with wax.

To hasten dissolution of the paraffin wax, the specimen tubes can be kept in thermostat set at specific temperatures. The specimen tube should be kept open in the thermostat to facilitate evaporation of the clearing agent.

The saturated wax solution is to be decanted and fresh pure molten wax is to be added. This should be done twice or thrice until the smell of clearing agent disappears.

After 8 to 10 hours of keeping the specimen tube in the thermostat, the wax solution is decanted. Pure molten wax is added to the tube. About 6 to 8 hours later, the specimen tube is to be tested for any possible remnants of the clearing agent (by smelling it). If the smell of the clearing agent is still lingering in the specimen tube, the materials are to be changed in pure fresh molten wax twice or thrice until the smell of the clearing agent is not sensed.

Sass suggested a button test to find out if the clearing agent has been totally removed from the material. Using a glass rod a few drops of molten wax from the specimen tube are allowed to fall on a glass petri plate. On cooling, these drops form buttons. If these buttons are greasy or sticky, it denotes the presence of clearing agent. The buttons can also be chewed to find if there is any taste of clearing agent fluid in the wax!

Depending on the clearing agent used, paraffin wax is to be added as recommended in the following paragraphs.

Xylene or dichloroethylene   Paraffin wax shaves can be added in small quantities at intervals. This method facilitates perfect infiltration.

Some recommend transferring the material from xylene, to a specimen tube and adding molten wax to the tube. A thin film of clearing agent may get locked on the surface of the material, hindering perfect infiltration.

Chloroform or benzene   Fine shaves of paraffin wax are to be added to the clearing agent containing materials.

Dioxan   Dioxan is heavier than molten wax. Therefore, dioxan is to be decanted from the specimen tube. Now, add chloroform or benzene to the specimen tube until the materials are immersed. Then add shaves of wax in small quantities gradually.

Normal butyl alcohol   Add chloroform to the butyl alcohol present in the specimen tube containing materials. Now add shaves of wax.

Tertiary butyl alcohol   Shaves of paraffin wax can be added directly to the tertiary butyl alcohol.

The solid wax dissolves slowly and infiltrates into the tissue. Wax should be added further only after what has been earlier has dissolved. This should be continued until the solution becomes saturated.

The wax that is added after the level of saturation will float as a film. This stage is attained in 2 to 4 days time. This kind of slow and gradual infiltration is preferred as tissue damage may result out of rapid infiltration.

EMBEDDING

Klebbs introduced the method of embedding plant and animal tissues in wax for microtoming, in the year 1869.

The tissues (materials) present in the molten wax in the specimen tube are to be embedded in cubical blocks of wax. This is achieved by pouring the molten wax containing the materials from the specimen tube into a reservoir and allowing the wax to solidify. Makeshift reservoirs (tanks) are fabricated using metallic 'L' blocks, paper boats or lids of Coplin jars for this purpose.

Use of 'L' Shaped Metallic or Wooden Blocks

By placing 'L' shaped blocks opposite to each other on even surface, a tank can be created. By placing these 'L' blocks unequally, tanks of desired small size can be created.

Two 'L' blocks (Figure 4.20a) are placed diagonally on a glass plate smeared with oil. A tank or reservoir (Figure 4.20b) of desired size is created. The 'L' blocks should be sufficiently heavy so that they will not move when molten wax is poured.

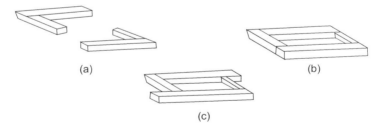

(a)   (b)

(c)

Figure 4.20   Embedding with 'L' shaped blocks (a) Two 'L' blocks (b) Reservoir made by 'L' blocks (c) Size of the reservoir thus varied

The specimen tube containing the materials in molten wax is removed from the thermostat, shaken well and the wax containing the materials is poured suddenly into the tank. Immediately more of molten wax kept ready is to be poured into the tank until the materials are covered with wax.

Using heated scalpel or heated needle, the tissues or materials (flower buds, root tips, etc.) are to be arranged in neat horizontal rows with sufficient space in between.

Wax will continue to solidify gradually. So, the whole exercise is to be done swiftly. Every now and then the scalpel or needle is to be heated.

After the materials are arranged neatly, the wax in the tank is to be allowed to solidify without any disturbance. After solidification is over, the 'L' blocks can be separated. A perfect block of wax with the biological materials embedded in it in neat rows is obtained.

Use of Paper Boat to Embed Materials

If there a large number of tissue bits or materials in the specimen tube or if a large number of blocks are to be made, makeshift (use-and-throw) tanks can be made using thick sheets of paper such as invitation cards, herbarium sheets, etc. Such tanks are called paper boats.

Lines are to be drawn in the card as shown in the Figure 4.21a. The card is to be folded neatly along the lines drawn in the sequence of AA′, BB′, CC′, DD′, EE′ and FF′.

The diagonal lines GE, G′E′, HF, H′F′ are to be folded outwards while all the other foldings are done inwards. As a result, a neat paper boat is obtained. Paper boat can also be made using a wooden block as shown in Figure 4.21b.

Oil or vaseline is to be smeared on the inner surface of the paper boat. The boat is to be kept on a plane surface.

The specimen tube containing the materials in the molten wax should be retrieved from the thermostat, shaken well and the contents poured swiftly into the paper boat. More of molten wax is to be poured immediately until the materials in the paper boat are immersed.

Before the wax solidifies, the materials are to be arranged in neat horizontal rows with sufficient space between the materials on all sides using a heated scalpel or needle.

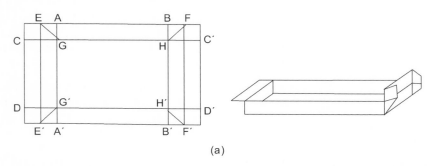

(a)

Figure 4.21   Making a paper boat (a) using pre-determined lines (b) using a wooden block (*Continues*)

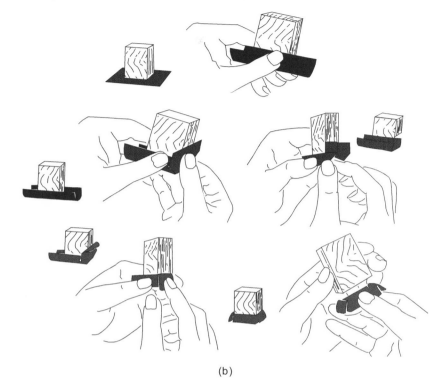

(b)

Figure 4.21   Making a paper boat (a) using pre-determined lines (b) using a wooden block

Solidification of the molten wax in the paper boat can be delayed by carrying out this exercise by keeping the paper boat on a copper table which is heated by a spirit lamp kept underneath (refer earlier section on equipment).

After arranging the materials in neat rows, the boat is left undisturbed until the wax solidifies. The process of solidification can be hastened by floating the boat with the wax in cool water contained in a tray. Care should be taken to avoid flooding the surface of the solidifying wax with water. This will cause undulations in the block.

After solidification is complete, the paper boat can be straightened out and the wax block can be separated.

Use of the Lids of Coplin Jars

If there is a very small number of tissue bits or plant material (say one or two), there is no need for 'L' blocks nor paper boats. The lids of Coplin jars can be used in such cases. Very small blocks are obtained by using them.

Precautions to be Followed while Embedding Materials in Wax

1. While pouring additional molten wax (Figure 4.22a), it should be done very swiftly before the wax poured first along with the materials starts solidifying. Otherwise, the additional wax poured secondly will form a separate layer. The two layers will separate either while the block is being trimmed or during microtoming.

2. Wax in a completely molten state alone is to be poured. If partly molten wax is used for embedding, the block will not be homogeneous.

3. The materials should be arranged in neat horizontal rows. Only then will each individual material be surrounded by sufficient wax on all sides (Figure 4.22b) while cutting the larger block into smaller individual blocks.

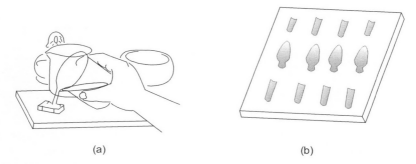

(a)   (b)

Figure 4.22   Embedding specimens in wax (a) Pouring molten wax in the reservoir (b) Wax block containing specimens

FIXING THE WAX BLOCK ON THE SPECIMEN HOLDER

Embedding of a number of materials results in large wax blocks. For microtomy, the large wax blocks are to be cut into small blocks each enclosing a single material (specimen).

In smaller blocks, the specimen should be surrounded by wax equally on all sides. The smaller blocks should be of convenient size to facilitate easy handling. Disproportionately long or stout blocks are not ideal for microtomy.

The small block should be fixed on to the specimen holder supplied along with the microtome. The specimen holder is metallic and it is a circular or square disc (Figure 4.23) with corrugated surface on the outer side and a short handle on the other side.

The corrugated outer surface of the specimen holder should be smeared with molten wax which is allowed to solidify into a bed of wax. By sandwiching a heated scalpel in between the underside of a wax block and the wax smeared on the surface of the holder, and by pulling out the scalpel, the block is firmly fixed on the holder. Wax shaves are added on all sides at the bottom of the wax block. Using a heated scalpel, the wax shaves are fused and this reinforces fusion of the wax block to the wax bed on the surface of the holder.

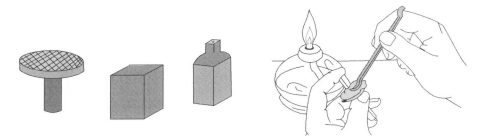

Figure 4.23   Specimen holders

Only a limited number of metallic specimen holders is supplied with the microtome. If there are too many blocks to be fixed, wooden blocks can be used as specimen holders.

The wax blocks containing the embedded material can be left affixed to the specimen holder for several years. To avoid softening of the wax during summer, the holders with the blocks can be kept in refrigerator.

When several blocks are fixed for microtomy, it is advisable to label each holder for easy reference.

The small wax blocks are to be fixed exactly in the centre of the specimen holder. The following are the precautions to be observed while fixing the small blocks on to the specimen holders.

⊙   The block should not be excessively long. While microtoming, excessively long blocks tend to separate from the holder.

⊙   After fixing the blocks on to the holder, the block should be trimmed on all sides. One or two mm of wax can be left on all sides while trimming. This will yield small cute narrow ribbons of serial sections.

⊙   The block of wax containing the material should be oriented on the specimen holder keeping the required plane of section in mind.

MICROTOMING
(TAKING SECTIONS USING A MICROTOME)

Using a microtome, thin sections of desired thickness in microns can be taken from the embedded materials (Figure 4.24).

While taking hand sections, the material is held firmly and the knife is moved forwards and backwards to take sections. Conversely, while using a microtome, the knife is fixed firmly and the wax block is moved up and down against the cutting edge of the knife.

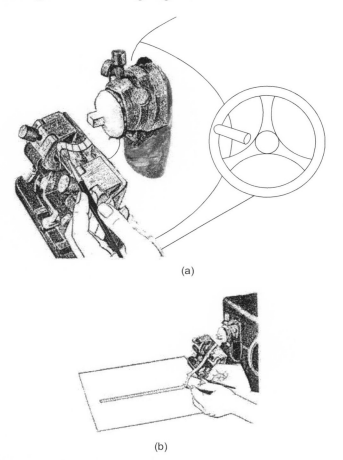

(a)

(b)

Figure 4.24   Cutting sections with a microtome (a) Starting paraffin ribbon
(b) Laying out the paraffin ribbon

Hand sections are obtained as discrete sections (separate sections). But, paraffin-embedded materials, on microtomy, yield serial sections in the form of continuous ribbons. Serial sections are most desirable in biological investigations, as they help in understanding the three-dimensional structure of the part studied.

Problems Met with during Microtomy/
Defects in the Ribbons of Serial Sections and
Rectification of the Defects

During microtomy, serial sections are to be obtained in the form of a straight line. The serial sections obtained in the form of ribbons may show the following types of defects. The reasons for such defects and the methods of rectifying the defects are given.

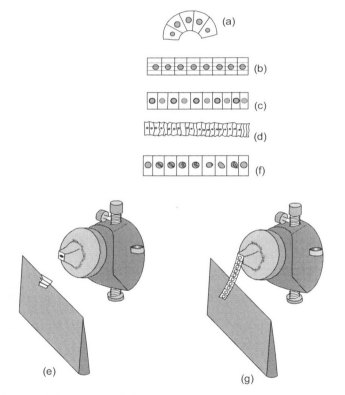

Figure 4.25 Problems met with during sectioning (a) Curved ribbon (b) Longitudinal streaks in the ribbon (c) Alternate thick and thin sections (d) Shrunken sections (e) No ribbon formation (f) Microsection separates from wax (g) Ribbon gets stuck to wax block

1. *The ribbon becomes curved.* If the margins of the paraffin block are not parallel, the ribbon becomes curved (Figure 4.25a). It can be rectified by trimming the margins.

Continual microtomy during summer seasons, may heat up the cutting edge of the knife. The paraffin block that hits the hot edge may also get heated. The lower side of the block may be hotter than the upper side. This also may cause curvature of the ribbons. If this is the reason, the knife is to be cooled down by rubbing the knife with ice cubes. The wax blocks along with the holder may also be immersed in cool water.

2. *Longitudinal streaks appear in the ribbon.* Longitudinal streaks appear in the ribbon (Figure 4.25b), if there are nicks in the knife. It can be rectified by pushing the knife so that the block can meet the knife at other points.

If the defect persists indicating nicks and breaks in all parts of the cutting edge, the knife is to be honed until the entire length of the cutting edge is sharpened.

Sometimes, the cutting edge of the knife may have hard particles such as wax crystals stuck to it. Streaks may also be caused by these particles. If so, the cutting edge of the knife is to be cleaned with a piece of cloth or cotton wool soaked with xylol.

3. *The ribbon presents thick sections and thin sections alternatingly.* Sometimes the ribbons may present very thick sections amidst a series of thin sections alternatingly (Figure 4.25c).

The wax block may have heated up. If so, it is to be cooled by immersing the block along with the holder in cool water.

Sometimes, the specimen holder may be loosely fixed in the microtome. Similarly the knife may be loosely fixed. If so, the screws for the specimen holder and those for the knife are to be set to hold them firmly.

4. *Sections in the ribbon are shrunken.* Sometimes, the sections along with the wax ribbon flakes are shrunken (Figure 4.25d). It may be due to the bluntness of the knife. If so, the knife is to be honed.

Shrinkage may also be due to the fact that the wax block gets heated up. In such an event, the wax block is to be cooled by immersing it in cool water.

5. *Sections get stuck to the cutting edge of the knife—ribbon does not form* (Figure 4.25e). The wax used for making the block may be of high melting point. Apply beeswax or any other soft wax around the wax block and then continue sectioning.

6. *The microsection of the material shrinks and separates from the wax in the ribbon* (Figure 4.25f). Sometimes, the microsection of the material shrinks and separates from the ribbon. This defect is because of incomplete

dehydration and incomplete clearing, both resulting in imperfect infiltration.

Keeping the material in hot molten wax for longer periods may also lead to this kind of defect.

In either case the defect cannot be rectified.

7. *The microsections or the ribbon get stuck to the wax block and get lifted along with the block* (Figure 4.25g). The cutting angle of the knife may be very low. In such a case, the knife is to be fixed properly and the cutting angle be increased.

The surface of the wax blocks might be electrically charged by repeated friction with the knife. This also may cause the defect. In such an event, the ribbon stuck to the block is to be carefully removed and mounted on slides. Cutting is to be stopped for sometime until the block and knife cool down sufficiently. Cutting is to be resumed only afterwards.

Presence of wax stuck to the cutting edge of the knife may also lead to this defect. In such a case, the edge of the knife is to be cleaned perfectly before proceeding with cutting.

FIXING THE RIBBON CONTAINING MICROSECTIONS ON SLIDES

The microsections of the materials embedded in wax are obtained as serial sections in the form of ribbons. These ribbons are to be fixed on clean plain microslides.

Cleaning of Microslides

The plain microslides are to be washed in acid to remove grease or oily contaminations. The acid-treated slides are to be washed in distilled water thoroughly, dried and stored in boxes. When needed, the slides are to be lifted holding them at the edges. If the slides are not cleaned properly, the dirt or dust in them will cause artefacts in the sections. To fix the ribbons on the slides, some kind of adhesive is to be used. The following adhesives are widely used.

Adhesives to Fix the Ribbons on to Slides

Meyer's egg albumin   Meyer's egg albumin is prepared by mixing equal quantities of glycerine and egg albumin. Sodium salicylate is added as a preservative. If it is not available, formalin can be used as a preservative.

Heidenhain's adhesive   Heidenhain introduced this formula in 1905. This is prepared by mixing 25% ethyl alcohol with egg albumin.

The adhesives are stored in Canada balsam bottles (Figure 4.26a). These are wide-mouthed bottles of small capacity with a thin glass rod projecting beyond the rim of the bottle. The lid of the bottle is dome-shaped for easy accommodation of the glass rod.

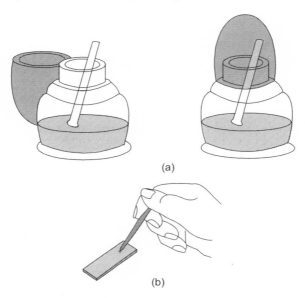

(a)

(b)

Figure 4.26   Adhesive for fixing the ribbons (a) Canada balsam bottle (b) Application of adhesive

Application of Adhesive and Fixing the Ribbons on to the Slide

Place a few drops of adhesive on the surface of a clean microslide. Smear the adhesive on the entire surface on one side of the slide (Figure 4.26b) using an index finger.

Keep the slide smeared with adhesive on a hot plate or show it over a flame. Carefully flood formalin water on the surface of the slide and allow it to stand. Drop bottles fitted with glass fillers with rubber teats can be used to hold formalin water.

As soon as the formalin water on the slide becomes lukewarm, the ribbon is cut to desired length and the segment is carefully lifted using dissecting needles. The segment is carefully floated in the lukewarm formalin water on the slide (Figure 4.27).

As the formalin water gets warmer, the ribbon stretches. The two ends of the segment are gently forced apart so that the segment becomes straight. The wax ribbon segments can be fixed on the slide leaving just enough space for label. Two or three rows of segments can also be fixed on one slide.

Figure 4.27   Mounting the ribbons on slides

The warm formalin water is drained so that the wax ribbon segment gets fixed on the slide. Such slides, to which ribbons have been fixed, are taken to the next stage of staining.

DEWAXING AND STAINING OF THE SECTIONS

⊙ Before staining, the slide and the sections are to be dewaxed.

⊙ Transfer and leave the slide(s) in pure xylol contained in a Coplin jar covered with the lid for about 10 to 15 minutes.

⊙ Take out a slide and check if the wax in and around the sections have dissolved completely. If not, allow sufficient time for the wax to dissolve.

⊙ After dewaxing, take out the slide(s) and wipe the under surface with a clean dry cloth and then very carefully wipe out the area around the sections on the other side.

⊙ Take care not to wipe out the sections.

⊙ Now proceed with a suitable staining schedule (refer detailed stepwise description of various staining schedules).

⊙ All these steps can be carried out by transferring the slides between solutions contained in coplin jars.

⊙ Five sets of slides each with two slides back-to-back can be accommodated in one Coplin jar. While transferring the slides between solutions, each pair is to be wiped clean on the underside and section-side. As the microtome sections are very thin, there are chances that the section-side is wiped out clean. Therefore, it is advisable to pass only five slides at a time and get used to this exercise before attempting to pass ten slides at a time.

⊙ After staining is completed, cover the stained sections carefully with a chosen mounting medium.

MACERATION

Sections of plant parts such as root, stem, leaf, flower, etc. reveal the internal arrangement and interrelationships of the constituent cells as viewed in the plane in which the section has been cut. This may suffice in the case of organs with homogeneous tissue organization.

In the case of secondary vascular tissues (secondary xylem and secondary phloem), the constituent tissues are organized into two systems, namely, vertical system and ray system. In this case sections in transverse plane, radial longitudinal plane and tangential longitudinal plane are to be examined to understand the intercellular relationships.

Sections have a limitation in the sense that they reveal only the two-dimensional details of the cells in that plane. The only reliable method which reveals the cells in their entirety is maceration technique.

Macerating the tissue means dissociating the constituent cells of the tissue so that entire cells can be viewed with the details of their third dimension. Maceration involves treating the organ or part with chemicals to bring about softening of the tissue and dissolution of the intercellular cementing layer (middle lamella/compound middle lamella) so that cells dissociate very easily. Cell wall thickening, pits and other cell wall characteristics are brought out effectively in macerated materials (Figure 4.28).

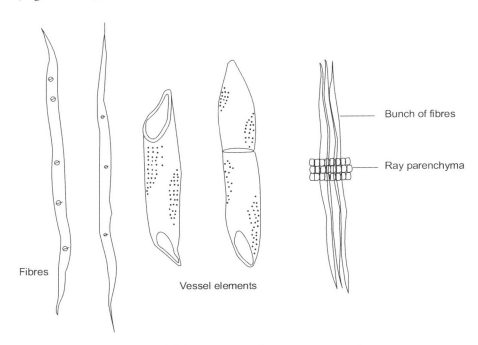

Figure 4.28   Macerated angiosperm wood

Jeffrey's Method

Maceration Fluid

    A. 10% aqueous nitric acid   1 part
    B. 10% chromic acid   1 part

Keep solutions A and B separately and mix equal parts just before use.

Procedure

⊙ Cut the fresh or dry specimen into small slices of about 2 or 3 mm thick.

⊙ In the case of very hard woody specimens, thin shaves can be obtained with the help of a scalpel with a sharp cutting edge.

⊙ Boil the slices until all air has escaped and the slices have sunk to the bottom.

⊙ Take the slices in a specimen tube and pour Jeffrey's maceration fluid to about thrice the volume of the specimen.

⊙ Keep the specimen tube in a hot-air oven.

⊙ Maceration time varies according to the material. Normally, cells begin to separate in 24 hours.

⊙ At the end of 24 hours try to pierce the specimen with a dissecting needle. If maceration has occurred, the needle pierces the tissue very softly. If the tissue is still hard, replace the maceration fluid with a fresh one and allow another day.

⊙ Wash off the maceration fluid from the material thoroughly.

⊙ The macerated material may be stained with safranin for about 6 hours.

⊙ Rinse in water.

⊙ Dehydrate by gradual displacement with hygrobutol.

⊙ Finally give two changes in hygrobutol.

⊙ Infiltrate with balsam highly diluted with hygrobutol. Evaporate the balsam to a mounting consistency.

⊙ If DPX is used for mounting, dehydrate through alcohol series (70%, 80%, 90%, 100%), pass through alcohol : xylol series (3:1, 1:1, 1:3) to pure xylol and mount.

Note Jeffrey's maceration fluid is a harsh mixture and is suitable for hard tissues.

If soft tissues such as root tip, parenchymatous organs, etc. are to be macerated, heat the tissue in dilute HCl (say, 10%) solution. This dissolves the middle layer made of pectic compounds and thus tissue is macerated easily.

FIXING COVERSLIPS AND RINGING (SEALING THE SECTION/BINDING THE COVERSLIP TO THE SLIDE)

The materials mounted on a plain microslide in a mounting medium cannot be viewed through microscope as such. This is because the mounting medium will act as another lens and distort the image. Secondly, the lens of the high-power objective will come into contact with the mounting medium and get spoiled. Therefore, it is necessary to flatten the mounting medium with another transparent material of same refraction index as that of the microslide. Coverslips made of very thin glass sheets of about 0.15 mm thickness serve this purpose.

In the case of temporary micropreparations which serve the purpose of one-time observation, the specimen is mounted either in water or in very dilute glycerine. These are non-adhesive media. After the observation is over, the slide will be washed and the specimen will be wiped out and therefore, no special care is to be taken to bind the coverslip to the slide.

In the case of semi-permanent micropreparations which are to be kept intact for a couple of days to a fortnight, some arrangement is to be made to prevent evaporation of the non-adhesive mounting medium used, through the edges of the coverslip. This is achieved by sealing the coverslip with some sort of resinous medium along the edges. This is also called ringing which if done perfectly helps to keep the slide for a longer time.

If the slide is to be rendered permanent, the coverslip is to be bound to the slide. The specimen in this case is to be dehydrated, cleared and stained and the mounting medium is to be an adhesive medium so that after application, in reasonable time, it will dry and solidify from its liquid form.

In order to choose the suitable mounting medium, one has to understand the mechanism involved in binding the coverslip to the slide.

Mechanism Involved in Binding the Coverslip to the Slide

- ⊙ If a perfect apposition is achieved between two solid objects, they will be drawn towards one another by the same cohesive forces that hold the molecules together in the objects themselves.
- ⊙ However, in microslides, the coverslip and the slide cannot be drawn towards each other and held together by such a force because of the following two reasons.
  1. Their surfaces cannot be made flat enough for perfect apposition.
  2. A section or other microscopical object intervenes between them in microscopical preparations.
- ⊙ Some degree of adhesion will be achieved if a fluid intervenes, provided that the fluid is able to wet both the surfaces concerned.

⊙   Glass can be wetted both by water and by solvents used in hydrophobe mountants.

⊙   The adhesion will be effective only if the liquid not only adheres to the glass but also coheres within itself. In other words, the fluid must be viscous or else be capable of actual conversion into solid.

⊙   The presence of long molecules in the liquids will thus favour adhesion.

⊙   It is desirable that the adhesive liquid is of fairly low viscosity at first and gets converted into a solid either by cooling or by the evaporation of the solvent.

⊙   The adhesive mounting media have the aforesaid properties. Therefore, they combine/serve two purposes, (i) mounting medium and (ii) binding agent.

⊙   Non-adhesive mounting media cannot bind the coverslip on to the slide. In such cases, the coverslip can be sealed using some quick drying resin.

Application of the Coverslip

The coverslip is to be placed very carefully over the specimen mounted on the microslide.

In the case of temporary and semi-permanent preparations where non-adhesive media are used for mounting the specimens, it is possible to remount the specimen. However, in the case of permanent preparations where adhesive media are used, remounting is not possible. Therefore one has to keep the following in mind while attempting this exercise, lest all the efforts put in so far go waste.

⊙   Mounting medium taken on the slide should be enough to spread under the coverslip to the edges.

⊙   If insufficient, air bubbles may get sucked in through the edges as the solvent in the medium evaporates on drying.

⊙   If much more, the medium will spread out of the coverslip and it may be difficult to wipe it clean.

⊙   It is ideal to take a little more than enough-mounting medium for binding the coverslip. It compensates for the evaporation of the solvent in the medium.

Sealing the Coverslip

⊙   Adhesive media harden and bind the coverslip firmly to the slide on drying and therefore, do not require sealing.

⊙ Even in this case, if the specimen mounted in adhesive medium is thick, the coverslip is to be sealed.

⊙ Non-adhesive media do not harden and hence do not bind coverslip to the slide. Therefore, the coverslip has to be sealed.

⊙ Ringing along the periphery of the coverslip with a quick drying resin such as nail polish or gelatin in order to bind it to the slide is called "sealing" (Figure 4.29).

⊙ Sealing is an important exercise in making sections mounted in non-adhesive media (temporary mounts) and in semi-permanent preparations.

⊙ The coverslip has to be bound firmly to the slide with the intervening section and the mounting medium to render the preparation semi-permanent.

⊙ The gelatin gel used for embedding is a good adhesive for sealing. It melts easily in an incubator at 37°C. The slide is dried with a cloth up to the edge of the coverslip and the melted gel is applied with a camel-hair brush. It hardens first by becoming a gel again and subsequently by evaporation of the water. In a day or two, it becomes so hard that it can scarcely be marked/scratched with a finger nail. Both hydrophil and hydrophobe mounting media can be sealed with gelatin.

⊙ As an extra precaution against evaporation of the mounting medium, it is advisable to varnish the hardened gelatine and to extend the varnish beyond the gelatin on to the upper surfaces of the coverslip and the slide.

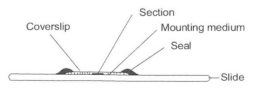

Figure 4.29   Ringed slide

⊙ The varnish chosen for this should be one that makes perfect contact with glass surfaces and is not readily softened or dissolved by the various fluids such as immersion oils used during observation.

⊙ Gold-size is found to be convenient for this purpose. Gilders use this to prepare surfaces to receive gold foil. It consists of gum animi, an oleoresin dissolved in turpentine and linseed oil. (Oleoresin is a resin dissolved in an essential oil. The oleoresin called 'gum animi' is an exudate from the bark of a leguminous tree *Hymaenaea courbaril*, a native of West Indies.)

⊙ In the drying of this varnish, two separate processes are involved.

1. Evaporation of the essential oil.

2. Oxidation of the linoleic acid and other unsaturated fatty acids contained in the essential oil.

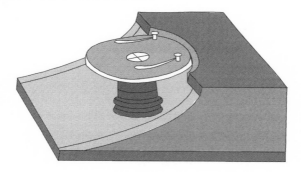

Figure 4.30   Turn table

⊙ The hardening of the varnish takes some days.

⊙ Nail polish is also used as a sealing gel with some satisfactory results.

⊙ DPX mountant itself is also used as a sealing agent.

⊙ Turn table (Figure 4.30) is very useful in sealing the coverslip perfectly. (Refer previous sections for a description of the turn table.)

REVIEW QUESTIONS

Introduction

1. Explain the purpose of microscopic examination.

2. Describe the different kinds of micropreparations.

3. Write notes on:
   i. Smears
   ii. Squashes
   iii. Sections

Glassware

1. Write notes on:
    i. Plain microslides
    ii. Coverslips or cover glass
    iii. Cavity slides (depression slides/culture slides)
    iv. Specimen-transferring tools
    v. Containers for handling specimens or sections
    vi. Coplin jars
    vii. Slide containers

Equipment

1. Write notes on:
    i.   Hot-air oven
    ii. Slide-warming table
2. Describe hand microtome and its uses.
3. Describe a rotary microtome.
4. Describe a sledge microtome.
5. Give a detailed account of microtome knives and their maintenance.
6. Write notes on:
    i.   Operating the rotary microtome
    ii. Sectioning with a sledge microtome

Fixation and Fixatives

1. Why should biological materials be fixed? What are the aims and advantages of fixation?
2. Give an account of the various agents employed in fixing biological materials.
3. Give an account of chemical fixative mixtures.
4. Write notes on:
    i. AA mixtures
    ii. FAA mixtures
    iii. CA mixtures
    iv. Craf mixtures
    v. PA mixtures
    vi. PC mixtures

5. What are the various points to be kept in mind while fixing biological materials for microtechnique?

Stains and Staining

1. Write notes on:
    i. Principles of staining
    ii. Direct and indirect staining
    iii. Differential staining
    iv. Mordants
    v. Solvents for the stains
    vi. Progressive staining
    vii. Regressive staining
    viii. Differential acidification
    ix. General stains and specific stains

Stains used in Plant Microtechnique

1. Give an account of the natural dyes used in plant microtechnique.
2. Give an account of haematoxylin as a natural dye used in plant microtechnique.
3. Give an account of carmin as a natural dye used in pant microtechnique.
4. Give an account of the coal-tar dyes used in plant microtechnique.
5. Write notes on:
    i. Acid fuchsin
    ii. Aniline blue WS
    iii. Crystal violet
    iv. Erythrosin
    v. Fast green FCF
    vi. Light green SF
    vii. Safranin O
    viii. Sudan IV

Staining Schedules

1. Describe the double staining schedule involving safranin and fast green.
2. Describe the double staining schedule involving safranin and haematoxylin.

3. Describe Flemming's triple staining schedule.

4. Describe a quadruple staining schedule known to you.

5. Describe crystal violet and erythrosin staining schedule.

6. Describe Johansen's methyl violet–erythrosin staining schedule.

7. Describe Foster's tannic acid–iron chloride staining schedule.

Dehydration

1. Why should biological materials be dehydrated? Explain the principle involved in dehydration.

2. Give an account of the various alcohols used as dehydrating agents for biological materials.

3. Write notes on:
   i. Hygrobutol
   ii. Acetone as a dehydrant
   iii. Cellosolve as a dehydrating agent
   iv. Dioxan(e) as a dehydrant
   v. Points to be kept in mind while dehydrating biological materials

Clearing or Removal of Dehydrating agent

1. Describe the procedure for using clearing agent (removing dehydrating agent) from/for different kinds of tissues.

2. Give an account of the clearing agents recommended for whole mounts.

3. Give an account of clearing agents recommended for materials to be embedded in wax.

4. Write notes on:
   i. Xylol as a clearing agent
   ii. Points to be kept in mind while clearing the biological material for microtechnique

Mounting and Mountants

1. Give an account of the various types of mounting media available.

2. Write notes on:
   i. Glycerine as a mounting medium
   ii. DPX
   iii. Dammar balsam

    iv. Canada balsam

    v. Styrax and Hyrax

    vi. Cedar wood oil

    vii. Lactophenol as a mounting medium

    viii. Glycerine jelly as a mounting medium

Microslide Preparation

1. Write an account of whole mounts and their preparation.
2. Describe the method of preparing smears of biological materials.
3. Describe the method of preparing squashes of biological materials.
4. Describe any one method of making a smear preparation permanent.
5. Write notes on:

    i. Feulgen's nuclear staining reaction

    ii. Warmke's method of squash preparation

    iii. Hillary's method of squash preparation

    iv. Johansen's methyl violet method of staining the smear

    v. McClintock's acetocarmine method of staining the smear

Sectioning of Biological Specimens

1. Describe the various methods of making free-hand sections.
2. Describe a hand microtome and the method of making free-hand sections using a hand microtome.
3. Describe the method of making free-hand sections using a sledge microtome.
4. Write notes on:

    i. Paraffin infiltration

    ii. Quality requirements of paraffin wax for use in microtomy

5. Describe paraffin infiltration technique in botanical microtechnique.
6. Describe the method of embedding specimens in paraffin wax.
7. Write notes on:

    i. Precautions to be followed while embedding the specimens in paraffin wax

    ii. 'L' blocks

    iii. Fixing the wax block on the specimen holder

8. Describe the problems met with during microtomy, and rectification of the same.

9. Describe the method of fixing the wax ribbon containing sections on to slides.

10. Write notes on:
    i. Adhesives to fix the ribbons on the slides
    ii. Dewaxing and staining of the sections stuck to the slides
    iii. Maceration technique

11. Describe the methods of fixing coverslips and ringing.

12. Write notes on:
    i. Mechanism involved in binding the coverslip to the slide
    ii. Method of applying the coverslip
    iii. Sealing the coverslip

APPENDIX

1. SECTION CUTTING FOR ELECTRON MICROSCOPY

Preparing Specimens for Electron Microscopy

Very small objects like virus particles or molecules can be examined directly under electron microscope without elaborate preparation. All that is needed is to render the object more visible by using negative staining or shadowing technique.

With cells and tissues the situation is totally different in the following aspects.

- ⊙ Living cells and tissues contain at least 70% water. If living cells are placed in the high vacuum in which the electron microscope operates, they would be dehydrated by evaporation and consequently collapse. Their intricate structure would be destroyed.

- ⊙ Cells are nearly a thousand times thicker than the virus particles. A virus particle is not more than a few hundred Å units whereas a cell is usually between 10 and 100 μ. The thicker the object, greater will be the electron scattering rendering the image uniformly dark. In order to obtain a clear image in electron microscopy, the section or object should not be more than 0.1 μ (=1000 Å) and ideally they should be more nearer to 500 Å.

- ⊙ Living cells are fragile, watery objects, easily damaged by unfavourable conditions. The first step in sectioning is to stabilize their structure, so that they will stand the rigours of further treatments. This is done by treating the cell with a suitable reagent called a fixative.

Fixation of the Specimen

- ⊙ Out of the several chemicals that have been tried as fixatives, osmium tetroxide (OsO_4) and certain aldehydes such as glutaraldehyde are favoured by most technicians as fixatives for electron microscopy.

- ⊙ Fixation of a cell or tissue depends on formation of chemical bonds or cross-linkages between some of the molecules which make it up.

Though a cell contains a number of varieties of molecules, it is chiefly the proteins and lipids that are involved in fixation.

⊙ Aldehydes used as fixatives react with the amino ($-NH_2$) groups of the side chains of protein molecules. For example, if a di-aldehyde such as glutaraldehyde is used as a fixative, this reaction takes place between amino groups of two different protein molecules so that the fixative forms a cross link between them. Since almost every protein molecule will have many sites at which aldehydes can react, multiple links can be formed involving many molecules and the proteins of the cell are converted into a stable, cross-linked network.

⊙ Osmium tetroxide reacts, among other things, with double bonds in unsaturated lipids and also in proteins, and it can cross-link these molecules.

⊙ Thus, fixation results in the stabilization of structure by formation of cross-links, chiefly involving proteins and lipids. Other constituents of the cell which do not react with fixatives will not necessarily be preserved and may be washed out during subsequent processing. This is particularly liable to happen with small, soluble molecules. Ultimately only the macromolecular skeleton of the cell is likely to be preserved.

⊙ The samples meant for ultratomy are to be not more than one or two mm in thickness so that the fixative can penetrate rapidly.

⊙ Fixation time lasts for about an hour or two. After fixation is over, excessive fixative is to be washed off.

Embedding

⊙ The fixed material is still too fragile to stand the rigours of sectioning. Therefore, it is to be embedded in some material which will give some sort of support to the material. Praffin wax is not ideal for ultratomy because paraffin-embedded specimens cannot be sectioned to thickness of less than $2\ \mu$. Therefore, the specimen is to be fixed in some harder types of materials. Various plastics are used for embedding.

⊙ The principles involved are the same as those involved in paraffin embedding. The specimen is to be dehydrated prior to embedding. The dehydrated specimen is immersed in unpolymerized form of the plastic allowing infiltration. When it has penetrated the object completely, the plastic is polymerized, usually by application of heat. The plastics used are various methacrylates (some of which are also the basis of perspex) and certain epoxy resins (e.g. araldite) which are complex substances originally developed for use as adhesives.

Both of these are strong materials and yet soft enough for sectioning. They also polymerize without substantial change in volume, so that distortion is kept to the minimum.

Microtomy for Electron Microscopy

⊙ The same methods adopted for cutting sections for light microscopy are followed in ultratomy also. A microtome is used, but the knife edge used for cutting is a glass edge that is prepared by carefully breaking up a plate glass. Polished diamond edges are also used and these have longer life than glass. Only, the microtome used in ultratomy is to be constructed to a very high degree of perfection.

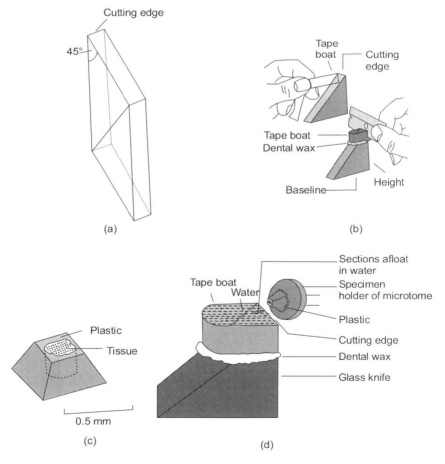

Figure A. I   Section cutting for electron microscopy (a) Plate Glass (b) Making tape boat (c) Specimen in the plastic block (d) Sectioning

⊙   The plastic block is to be trimmed carefully using sharp razor blade while watching through a low-power dissecting microscope. The sections obtained are usually very small (less than 0.5 mm) and very thin (less than 2 μ) and therefore are likely to be blown away even by a delicate draught of air such as the breath of the technician. It is impossible to handle such sections using hands. This problem is overcome by fitting a small container (tape boat) to one side of the knife and filling it with water, the level of which is adjusted so that the meniscus exactly meets the knife edge (Figure A.1b and d). As sections are cut, they float on the water surface. The sections can be easily picked up on grids. With practice it is possible to obtain sections in the form of continuous ribbons. The whole process is observed under a dissecting microscope so that sections can be examined as they are cut.

Staining the Ultrasection

⊙   Cells and tissues have low intrinsic electron-scattering power. So in unstained sections, little detail of their structure can be made out in the EM. It is therefore essential to increase electron-scattering ability artificially, and heavy metals are used to achieve this. Instead of using them for negative staining, these are applied directly to the sections. Different parts of the cells and tissues take them up to different degrees. For example, uranyl salts are taken up strongly by lipid-containing membranes. The embedding plastic remains in position in the sections and is not removed. Fortunately, the embedding materials used are permeable to water to allow staining to occur, and themselves do not take up the stains.

2. STAINS RECOMMENDED FOR SPECIFIC STRUCTURES

Structures	Stains recommended
Callose	Aniline blue*
	Resorcin blue (specific)
Cellulose cell walls	Acid fuchsin
	Aniline blue
	Bismarck brown Y**
	Congo red
	Haematoxylin** (Delafield's formula)
	Fast green FCF*
	Light green*
Chitin	Safranin
Cutinized cells walls	Acid fuchsin
	Crystal or methyl violet*
	Erythrosin*
	Methyl green
	Methylene blue
	Safranin (specific)
Cytoplasm	Acid fuchsin
	Aniline blue
	Eosin Y
	Erythrosin B
	Fast green FCF
	Indigocarmine
	Light green
	Malachite green

* Achromatic stains   ** Bulk stains

(Contd.)

Structures	Stains recommended
	Methyl orange
	Nigrosin
	Orange G
	Phloxin
Dividing chromatin (chromosomes)	Brazilin
	Carmine**
	Carminic acid**
	Haematoxylin
	Iodine green
	Methyl green
	Safranin
Fats	Sudan II or IV (specific)
Lignified cell walls	Crystal violet
	Iodine green
	Methyl green
	Safranin
Middle lamella	Iron haematoxylin
	Ruthenium red (specific)
Mitrochondria	Acid fuchsin
	Aurantia
	Iron haematoxylin
	Janus green B (vital)
Nuclear (general)	Carmine
	Crystal and methyl violet
	Haematoxylin
	Iodine green
	Methyl green
	Methylene blue

** Bulk stains

(Contd.)

Structures	Stains recommended
Plant mucin	Bismarck brown Y
	Congo red
	Pararosaniline
Plastids	Crystal or methyl violet
	Iron haematoxylin
Proteins	Safranin
Suberized cells walls	Safranin
	Sudan III or IV (specific)
	Crystal violet

3. DIAPHRAGM

Diaphragm is a circular ringlike path that allows light to pass through.

In light microscopes, the path of light is controlled at all stages right from the stage of illuminating the object through to the stage of formation of the image I_3 in the ocular lens system. (Refer Working of the light compound microscope in Chapter 2)

The purpose of controlling the light path is twofold:

1. To delimit the diameter of the path of light
2. To control the amount of light

The circular ringlike passage that allows light into the condenser and into the ocular lens system serves these two purposes and is called **diaphragm.**

The circular ring diaphragm of the ocular lens system delimits the field of view, which is the extent of the area of the specimen that can be seen under that ocular/objective combination.

The diaphragm provided in the substage condenser performs additional functions of helping increase the resolution by increasing the numerical aperture (NA) and also increasing the contrast in the image!

The substage condenser is provided with iris diaphragm, which provides adjustable opening to the condenser. By closing and opening the iris diaphragm, the diameter of the light path and the amount of light used for illuminating the object can be controlled.

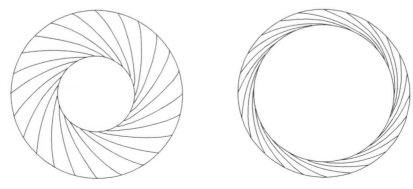

Figure A.2   Recommended range of condenser iris

For any objective in use, Figure A.2 shows the range of the condenser iris that gives acceptable results, from minimum (left) to maximum (right). Contrast decreases whilst resolution increases from left to right. It is the task of the observer/user of the microscope to find the best position depending on what one wishes to see and he/she will have to vary it during the observation, as the fine focus is varied. One will also regularly take out the eyepiece and check the aperture.

4. SIZE AND NATURE OF THE IMAGE FOR VARIOUS POSITIONS OF THE OBJECT

Nature of lens	Position of the object	Image Position	Size	Nature
Convex lens	At infinity on one side	At the focus on the other side.	Point	Real and inverted
	Beyond 2F.	Between F and 2F on the other side.	Diminished	Real and inverted
	At 2F.	At 2F on the other side.	Same size	Real and inverted
	Between F and 2F.	Beyond 2F on the other side.	Magnified	Real and inverted
	At focus on one side.	At infinity.	Refracted rays	Rendered parallel
	Between the focus and the optic centre.	On the same side of the object.	Magnified	Virtual and erect
Concave lens	At infinity	At the focus on the same side.	Diminished	Virtual and erect
	For all positions	Between the lens and the focus on the same side.	Diminished	Virtual and erect

GLOSSARY

Abbe type condenser   The simplest type of two-lens condenser. It is capable of passing bright light and is not corrected for spherical or chromatic aberrations. An Abbe condenser normally can have a numerical aperture (NA) of 1.25 (up to 1.4 in high-end models with three or more internal lens elements).

Aberrations (of lens)   Distortions in shape and colour of the images formed by lenses. (*See also* Chromatic aberration and Spherical aberration.)

Achromatic condenser   A condenser having a biconvex lens along with a biconcave lens. In this type of condenser, both chromatic and spherical aberrations are corrected. It is most ideal for observations that require accuracy.

Achromatic objective   A composite lens system consisting of two lenses made of two different types of materials. Such a composite lens system helps in focusing (converging) all the different wavelengths at the same point on the other side of the lens, thus rectifying the chromatic aberrations. Achromatic objectives yield best results with light passed through a green filter (often called interference filter) and using black-and-white film when these objectives are employed for photomicrography.

Airy disc   The central maximum of the airy patterns, and is defined as the region enclosed by the first minimum of the airy pattern and contains 84 per cent of the luminous energy. These airy discs consist of small concentric light and dark circles (*See also* Diffraction pattern/Airy Pattern.)

Amplitude   The depth of the troughs in the light waves. It is felt as brightness by our eyes.

Amplitude contrast   The ability to see one object superimposed on another because one object is brighter or darker than the other.

Angstrom   Equal to 0.0000000001 metres or 0.1 nanometres.

Angular aperture (AA)   The number of degrees associated with the angle of light accepted by an objective when in focus on an object. (*See also* Numerical aperture.)

Annular Diaphragm   An opaque disc inside a phase-contrast microscope's condenser, containing a clear ring through which the illumination may pass.

Annulus   A ring.

Antipoints   The various points in the image corresponding to the various respective points of the specimen.

Apochromats (Apochromatic objective lens systems)   Objective lens systems that are capable of separating the colours very effectively.

Beam splitter   An optical device for dividing a beam into two or more separate beams.

Beckline artefact   When a transparent object is mounted in a medium of much lower or higher refraction index than its own, 'Becke lines' are formed in the image in areas where the object meets the medium. Images obtained by higher power magnifications present exaggerated 'Becke line' artefacts.

Body tube (of microscope)   (*See* Head.) In most cases these terms are used interchangeably   (functionally synonymous).

Cavity slides   Also known as depression slides or culture slides, these are plain microslides with one or two hollow cavities to hold bulky specimens.

Chromatic aberration   An image defect produced from dispersion within a lens. Varying colours are focused at different planes causing an image to be "fuzzy with colour fringing". The overall effect is that the microscope image is not as "sharp" as it could be. It suffers from low resolution and contrast. (*See also* Aberrations of lens.)

Coarse focus (knob)   Coarse focus means getting the image in approximate focus. It is achieved using the larger "coarse –focus" knob. This control alters the specimen-to-objective distance to a considerable amount for a small amount of knob rotation. At medium to high magnifications, the coarse focus knob should be used very carefully (if at all).

Coddington lens   Coddington lens is obtained by grinding a lens on each end of a cylindrical piece of glass. It is in fact the central part of a biconvex lens in which the peripheral parts are removed. Use of Coddington lens effectively corrects the spherical aberration.

Compensative oculars   These are oculars which introduce an equal but opposite chromatic error in lens elements to compensate the excessive separation of colours caused by apochromatic and achromatic objectives. Compensating eyepieces may be either of the positive or negative type, and must be used at all magnifications with fluorite, apochromatic and all variations of plan objectives They can also be used to advantage with achromatic objectives of 40× and higher. (Huygenian and Ramsden oculars cannot compensate this condition and therefore they are called simple oculars as against the compensating oculars.)

Component (of a microscope)   A part of the microscope such as an objective, a stage, an ocular, body tube, etc.

Concave   Denotes a spherically shaped surface, curved inward.

Condenser   A substage optic that converts the relatively broad beam of light coming from the illuminator into a conical beam of light. The cone enables light to pass through the specimen at many different angles, limited by the condenser's NA. In general, the focal point of the cone should be adjusted to occur at the specimen plane.

Condenser iris   An adjustable opening consisting of overlapping blades which alter the angular aperture (AA) of the condenser (i.e., change the angle of light that the condenser is bringing to a focus).

Conjugate foci When two objects at different planes are imaged at one plane somewhere within an optical system, the images are said to be "in conjugate foci". An example is the **graticule** image sharply focused within the **ocular** when the ocular is in focus on the specimen's image produced by the objective. In reality, the specimen and the graticule might be even inches apart but, through the ocular, both are in focus at the same visual plane.

Contrast The ability to see one object or feature against another because of differences in brightness or colour. Generally, the greater the differences in brightness and between objects, object boundaries, other objects, and the general background, the easier it is to interpret the image. (*See also* Amplitude contrast and Colour contrast.)

Convex Denotes a spherically shaped surface, curved outward.

Coplin jar A rectangular glass jar furnished with a series of vertical grooves that hold a number of slides apart. Coplin jar is meant for use when many slides with sections stuck to them are to be transferred between solutions simultaneously.

Correction collars These are collars that are incorporated in the objective to change the spacing between critical elements inside the objective barrel. The correction collar is utilized to adjust for these subtle differences to ensure the optimum objective performance.

Counterstain The stain that is used in the second and a subsequent step in the staining schedule.

Cover glass A thin piece of glass used to protect the objective from the specimen (and vice-versa). At medium to high magnifications, the thickness is important with 0.17 mm (11/2) being a common criterion. Cover glass can be thought of as a parallel lens. The quality of cover glass is important, as it is the first optical element through which the specimen's image passes. Cover glass of improper thickness contributes to spherical aberration as it acts as a parallel lens.

Coverslips Very thin glass circles, squares or rectangles used for covering the biological material mounted on the slide.

Critical Mordant Quotient (CMQ) The mordant quotient of a mordant/dye solution that neither increases nor decreases the intensity of colouring of a stained section.

Depth of field The axial range through which an objective can be focused without any appreciable change in image sharpness is referred to as the objective depth of field. This value is inversely related to numerical aperture (NA).

Depth of focus Also known as sharpness or penetration, it depends on the NA and the magnification and is inversely proportional to both.

De-staining Removal of the excess of primary stain from the microsection prior to counterstaining. Solutions which reduce the affinity between the primary stain and the structures stained are used for de-staining.

Diaphragm Term used in context of a plate or disc mounted inside of a condenser. Diaphragm is a device used to delimit the diameter of the light path (as for example the iris in human eye does).

Diffraction   Bending of light as it passes very close to the edge of an object.

Diffraction pattern   When light from the various points of a specimen passes through the objective and an image is created, the various points in the specimen appear as small patterns in the image. These are known as **airy patterns**. This phenomenon is caused by diffraction of light as it passes through the minute spaces and parts in the specimen and circular back aperture of the objective. (*See also* Airy disc.)

Direct staining   A method of applying the stain to the tissue or the object and removing it when sufficient dye has been absorbed.

Disc diaphragm   A circular substage plate with circular holes of different diameters cut into it. Any of these holes can be brought in line with the path of light by rotating the disc. The disc helps to control the diameter of the light path. Hence the name Disc diaphragm. (*See also* Iris diaphragm.)

Dispersion   For a given material, it is a change in **refraction index** as measured in differing colours of light. A given substance having a sizeable change in refraction index as measured in both red and blue light would be said to have a "high dispersion".

Dry objective   Objectives meant for use in the medium of air. Generally all low-power objectives (up to $45\times$) are designed to work with their front lens elements in airy medium. Since these front lenses do not need to be "immersed in any fluid medium, they are referred to as dry objectives.

Eccentric iris diaphragm   A type of iris diaphragm in which the blades close down the path of light in an eccentric manner to provide inclined or unilateral illumination.

Element   In a microscope, it is usually a component of a lens system. The element might or might not be a lens. (*See* Phase shifting and cover glass.)

Exit pupil   (*See* Ramsden disc.)

Eye point   (*See* Ramsden disc.)

Eyepiece   (*See* Ocular.)

Field diameter   In an optical microscope, field diameter is the diameter of the viewfield expressed in millimetres and measured at the intermediate image plane. It is expressed by the field-of-view number or simply field number, which is the diameter of the viewfield expressed in millimetres and measured at the intermediate image plane.

Field iris   An adjustable opening (consisting of overlapping blades) located in the illuminating system. This is not the condenser iris. The field iris adjusts the diameter of the illumination beam.

Field number   (*See* Field diameter.)

Field-of-view number   (*See* Field diameter.)

Filimicroscopes   The magnifying lenses used in the 15th and 16th centuries (fili = insects). Lenses were largely used to study insects during this period.

Fine focus (knob)   Fine focus (getting the image in exact focus) is achieved using the smaller "fine-focus" knob. This controls only changes in the specimen-to-objective distance a small amount for a considerable amount of knob rotation. At medium to high magnifications, the fine focus knob is the primary specimen-focus control.

Finite tube length In the designing of microscopes, it is assumed that the specimen at focus was placed at a distance a "little" further than the front focal plane of the objective. For many years, almost all prominent microscope manufacturers designed their objectives for this finite **tube length.** The objective then projects a magnified image of the specimen and converges the same at the level of the eyepiece diaphragm, located ten millimetres below the top edge of the openings of the microscope observation tube–where the eyepieces are inserted. The early versions of microscopes had a tube length of 250 mm and such models were too unwieldy to hand. As per the recommendations of The Royal Microscopical Society (RMS), the tube length was later standardized to 160 millimetres for finite-corrected transmitted light microscopes. Objectives designed for a 160-millimetre finite tube length microscope bear the inscription "160" (mm) on the barrel (as outlined in Structural Description of Objectives). In the modern infinity-corrected microscopes, optical tube length is referred to as Reference focal length. (*See also* Tube length.)

Fixation Inactivating or immobilizing the organism, organ or tissues, killing them instantly. Fixation is the first step in microtechnique.

Fixative A chemical known to have the property of killing the tissues instantly and used for fixing biological materials in microtechnique.

Focal length The distance from the lens to the principal focus.

Focal point The point where the light rays entering a convex lens converge on the other side and is also called principal focus. In a concave lens however, the light rays do not converge but diverge on the other side. If the divergent rays are traced back, they will appear to meet at a point which is called **virtual focus.** (*See also* Principal focus.)

Fresnel lens A plastic-moulded lens offering aspheric surface. It is a thin sheet with the lens curvature placed in a series of concentric grooves on the surface of the sheet. This is said to be a better approach in correcting aberrations in lenses.

Fuzzy As applied to an image, a somewhat indistinct, out-of-focus image suffering from absence of image detail and reduced contrast.

Graticule Normally located inside of an ocular, a graticule is usually a glass disc containing an image. The image usually contains markings that a microscopist can use to measure dimensions, area, angular characteristics, etc. Graticules (**ocular micrometers)** measuring linear dimension are calibrated using a **stage micrometer.**

Green fluorescent protein (GFP) A natural protein produced by the jellyfish *Aequorea victoria.* This is an accessory pigment found along with aequorin, a calcium-activated photoprotein. These proteins are bioluminescent. Aequorin emits blue-green light. GFP accepts energy from aequorin and re-emits it as green light. This jellyfish glows around the margin of its umbrella. The light arises from the yellow tissue masses each of which consists of about 6000–7000 photogenic cells. These cells generate light by a process of bioluminescence, whose components include a calcium-activated photoprotein (aequorin) that emits blue-green light and an accessory green fluorescent protein (GFP), which accepts energy from aequorin and re-emits it as green light.

Hand microtome A very simple mechanical device designed to hold the specimen firm against the razor blade to cut sections of pre-set thickness.

Head A sizeable component of a microscope that physically connects the **oculars** to the **nosepiece (turret)** region of the stand. A monocular head holds one ocular, binocular head holds two ocular and trinocular head three oculars.

Huygenian telescope An arrangement to reduce/correct chromatic aberration as well as spherical aberration to a great extent. It consists of two planoconvex lenses spaced apart by their focal length.

Illuminator An apparatus, usually part of the base of a microscope, containing a light bulb, projection lenses and mirrors. The purpose of illuminator is to supply a beam of light having sufficient diameter so as to fill the **condenser** (if needed) and having sufficient brightness to sufficiently illuminate the specimen for observation under given conditions.

Immersion objective Objective lens system designed for use with immersion oil.

Immersion oil A special oil used in microscope work with the highest power objective lenses (i.e., 100× lens). There are two basic types of immersion oil, type A and type B, the only difference between them being viscosity. Use of immersion oil as a "bridge " between the cover glass and the front lens of the 100× objective enhances resolution. In a **positive** phase-contrast objective, the phase-shifting material is deposited on top of (or may be underneath) the intensity-reducing material.

Index of refraction The ratio of the velocity of light in air to the velocity of light in refraction material for a given wavelength.

Indirect staining A method of staining in which the tissue is soaked in the stain and then differentiated in an acid or mordant, until the stain has been removed from unwanted regions.

Infiltration In biological microtechnique, infiltration means reinforcing the fixed biological material with a soft-solid material such as paraffin wax so that it can withstand the force of the cutting edge of the knife.

Infinity-corrected objectives Such objectives project an image of the specimen to infinity.

Infinity space The space between the objective and tube lens of modern infinity-corrected microscopes, where intermediate attachments are placed in the light path.

Interference The constructive and destructive superposition of two wavefronts that have different phases. In an **interferometer**, two wavefronts are produced by the reference surface and the test sample surface.

Interference filter   Green and blue filters used in the light path of light microscopy.

Interferometer   An instrument that employs the interference of light waves to measure the wavefront.

Interferometric objective   An optical component attached to a microscope that gathers light from the object, forms an interference pattern as a real image.

Intermediate image plane   The fixed plane within the optical light microscope at which the objective lens system projects a real, inverted, and magnified image (I_1) of the specimen.

Interpupillary distance   The distance between a person's pupils (the openings in the eye). Interpupillary distance also applies to adjustment of the distance between the oculars so a person can see through both oculars and merge the two images into one (a mental process).

Iris diaphragm   A thin circular pliable metallic plate which is cut into several leaves along obliquely running curved radii. The leaves are fitted in such a way that they can be made to move in an overlapping manner and function like the iris of the human eye. Iris diaphragm enables a continuous variation of the diameter of light path. This is in contrast to the discontinuous variation in the diameter of light path characteristic of disc diaphragm.

Kohler illumination   An approach that averages the non-uniformities in the light source so that a clear image is obtained. Lenses work at their best if the image of

a self-luminous object is superimposed on the transparent object that is actually under observation. This theoretical objective was achieved with ease in the olden days when oil lamps were used to illuminate the object in microscopy. In the present times of electric bulbs, this is achieved by Kohler illumination.

Laser   An acronym for "Light Amplification by Stimulated Emission of Radiation". A laser is a cavity, with mirror that is filled with a gas or gas mixture, such as helium and neon.

Lens   Usually a clear glass or plastic structure designed to converge or diverge a beam of light. A **simple lens** is just one lens, illustrated by a common magnifying glass. A **compound lens** consists of a connected system of more than one lens, illustrated by camera lenses, **objective** lenses, most **condensers**, and **oculars**.

Maceration   In microtechnique, maceration means the separation of the tissue into its constituent cells.

Magnification   The ratio of the size of the focused image, produced by a lens, to the actual size of the object. (*See also* Total visual magnification.)

Mechanical stage   An assembly connected to the **stage**, having two knobs which move the slide in the X, Y directions (visually, through the microscope, this is equal to left/right and up/down).

Mechanical tube length   The distance between the nosepiece (where the objective is mounted) to the top edge of the observation tubes where the eyepieces (oculars) are inserted.

Meniscus lens   A lens with one side convex and the other concave. Meniscus lens is devoid of spherical aberration as one surface compensates for the effect of the other surface.

Micro   The   prefix   meaning one-millionth.

Micro-inch   Equal to 0.0254 micrometre.

Micrometre (or Micron)   Equals 0.000001 metres (formerly micron) or 39.3701 microinches.

Micropreparation   Denotes microslide containing a section or whole mount, squash, smear or macerated material meant   for   observation   under microscope.

Microscope   An optical instrument designed to see very minute microscopic objects. Just as telescopes were developed as a visual aid for the observation of the distant objects in "outer space", so also microscopes (Gr. *Micros*= little; *skopein*= to look at) were developed to aid the eye in visualizing the finest details of 'inner space' invisible to naked unaided eyes.

Microsection   A very thin section of any biological material cut for observation under microscope. For comfortable microscopy, sections are required to be very thin in the range of a few μm thicknesses.

Microtechnique   The serial steps involved in making microslides of biological materials for microscopic observation.

Microtome   A mechanical device for cutting sections of biological specimens to uniform and pre-set thickness (in microns).

Millimetre   One thousandth of a metre.

Millimicron   *(See* **nanometre.**)

Mordant   An intermediary substance used to increase the degree of adhesion of dyes that are weakly charged.

Mordant quotient   The relative abundance of the dye and mordant that decides whether a mordant/dye solution dyes or extracts (removes) the dye from the section (or material).

Mountant/Mounting medium   The medium in which the section/whole mount is mounted on a slide.

Nanometre (nm)   Equal to 0.000000001 metres, (formerly millimicron), or 0.03937 microinch.

Negative ocular   In the negative type ocular, the secondary image (I_2) is formed at the focal point of the field lens (in between FL and EL) of the ocular. (*See also* **Huygenian ocular.**)

Noise   Any random or periodic non-data signal in the measurement.

Nosepiece   A component of the microscope, which allows physical connection of one or more objective lenses. It is also called turret. It revolves around its central axis and therefore is also called revolving nosepiece. A nosepiece can hold up to three objectives in the circular holes provided for them and is called triple nosepiece. That which can hold four objectives is called quadruple nosepiece.

Numerical aperture (NA)   A number that expresses the ability of a lens to resolve fine detail in an object being observed. It is derived by a mathematical formula (n sin u) and is related to the angular aperture of the lens and the index of refraction of the medium found between the lens and the specimen. The physical size of the lens is important in determining the NA of the lens. A numerical aperture value of 0.65 – 0.75 is typical for a 40× objective.

Objective Also called objective lens or objective lens system it is the optic that first collects the light that has passed through the specimen. The objective provides the first stage of magnification. The following types are available achromatic objective, apochromatic objective, aplanatic objective and oil-immersion objective.

Oblique illumination Light passing at an angle through a specimen. In the angular cone of light from an open condenser, very little light waves are passing straight through. Most light waves are passing through the sample at a variety of oblique angles limited by the **condenser's** angular aperture.

Ocular An optic that collects and further magnifies the image created by the objective lens. Normally, the ocular is the **optic** through which the user observes the microscopic image.

Optical path The mathematical product of a material's refraction index and thickness.

Optical tube length The distance between the back focal plane of the objective and the intermediate image. This value is different from the mechanical tube length of a microscope.

Overall magnification The mathematical product of the magnification "powers" of the **objective** lens, **ocular**, and **tube**

length (for example: $40 \times 10 \times 1.000 = 400\times$ respectively)

Parcentricity This is another attribute offering convenience and safety in focusing under high power. Matched sets of objectives are also designed to be parcentric, so that a specimen centred in the field of view for one objective remains centred when the nosepiece is rotated to bring another objective into use.

Parfocal distance International standard for parfocal distance has been determined as 45.0 mm. A majority of objectives manufactured in yester years had a parfocal distance of 45.0 millimetres and were considered interchangeable.

Parfocality A phenomenon of convenience and safety offered by objectives that are manufactured in sets, so that a set of matched objectives, (e.g. all achromatic objectives of various magnifications) mounted on the nosepiece, project an image to approximately the same plane in the body tube. Thus, changing objectives by rotating the nosepiece usually requires only minimal use of the fine adjustment knob to re-establish sharp focus. Such a set of objectives is described as being parfocal.

Permanent micropreparation Micropreparation made for use over extended period of time.

Phase A term illustrating how, in case of two light waves travelling in the same direction, one light wave is moving as compared to the other. If light waves travelling together in the same direction are vibrating in a synchronous manner (i.e., vibrating up and down together), the waves are said to be "in phase". If otherwise, they are "out of phase".

Phase contrast microscope A special light microscope that allows visualization of transparent preparations (that are similar to the refraction index of the surrounding medium) by altering the phase relationships of light that passes through and around the object.

Phase rings A phase contrast microscope contains two rings: a **phase shifting element** inside the objective and an **annular diaphragm** ring inside the condenser.

Phase shift The difference in wavelengths of light waves that are "out of phase " with each other (e.g. one wave is ¼ of a wavelength behind the other) or degrees (e.g. one wave is 90 degrees out of phase or this wave has a 90 degree phase shift relative to the other).

Phase shifting element A dark **ring,** found at the back focal plane of a phase contrast **objective** lens, containing a thin layer of phase-shifting material and a thin layer of material that reduces the intensity of the light passing through the ring.

Pixel Shortened form of "picture element".

Plain microslides A piece of thin glass usually of size 3 " × 1 " × 1 mm. Slides of size 3 " × 1½ " or even 3 " × 2 " are also sometimes used to accommodate a big series of sections such as fossil sections.

Primary magnification The magnification of the primary image.

Primary stain The stain that is used first in the differential staining process and which is a general stain, which attaches to all the structures.

Principal focus The point where a bundle of light rays (which are parallel to the axis of the lens) appear to converge after passing through the lens.

Progressive staining Staining method in which the desired colour intensity is attained by observing the staining under the microscope from time to time. The staining reaction is stopped once this is achieved.

Raleigh resolution The resolving power of an objective given by $1.221/NA$.

Ramsden disc Light rays emanating from the eyepiece intersect at the exit pupil or eye point, often referred to as the Ramsden disc, where the pupil of the microscopist's eye is to be placed in order for her to see the entire field of view (usually 8−10 mm from the eye lens).

Real image A real image exists in a certain plane and can be caught on a screen. Lens of a slide/film projector takes a small transparency and projects an enlarged image on a screen on the other side. A camera lens can take a huge scenic view and condense the real image of the same onto a small reactive surface (photographic film).

Reference focal length The intermediate image in an infinity-corrected system appears at the reference focal length (formerly, the optical tube length) behind the tube lens in the optical pathway. This length varies between 160 and 250 millimetres, depending upon design constraints imposed by the manufacturer. The magnification of an infinity-corrected objective is calculated by dividing the reference focal length by the focal length of the objective lens. (*See also* **Finite tube length.**)

Refraction   The bending of light on passing from one medium to another.

Refraction index   A term and number (often expressed as four-figure numbers e.g. 1.645). Refraction index is the ratio of the velocity of light in vacuum (or air) to the velocity of light in a particular medium.

Regressive staining   Staining method in which the section or micropreparation is overstained considerably and then de-stained until a satisfactory optimum is reached. This is the most commonly followed staining method.

Resultant light   A combination of deviated and undeviated light rays. In reality natural daylight is the resultant light.

Residual colour   The limited correction of achromatic objectives can lead to substantial artefacts when specimens are examined and imaged with colour microscopy and photomicrography. If the specimen is focused in the green region of the spectrum, images will have a reddish magenta halo often termed **residual colour.**

Resolution   Generally, the ability to distinguish detail in an image. Resolution is the amount of detail that can be seen. It is usually expressed in terms of the minimum distance observable between two objects. The smaller the distance that can be seen between two objects, the better the magnification. Resolution is a measure of clarity. Resolution is always limited by factors such as wavelength of the illuminating light, **numerical aperture** of the lens used to image the object, optical defects of the lens system such as **chromatic** and **spherical** aberration, and overall image **contrast.**

Resolving distance   Resolution is defined by resolving distance. Resolving distance is the smallest distance between two points that allows the observer to see these points as distinctly separate.

Retraction stopper   A spring-loaded device that allows the front lens assembly to be retracted by pushing it into the objective body and twisting to lock it into place. Such an accessory incorporated in many objectives designed for close working is convenient when the objective is rotated in the nosepiece so it will not drag immersion oil across the surface of a clean slide. Twisting the retraction stopper in the opposite direction releases the lens assembly for use.

Rotary microtome   A microtome in which the specimen holder is moved forward against the fixed knife by the movement of a circular rotary wheel.

Sections   Thin slices of biological materials cut with the help of a razor blade or a mechanical device called microtome. They are also referred to as microsections as they are often extremely thin (in the range of a few microns in thickness).

Semi-apochromats   These are objectives corrected for optical correction. They are also called fluorites after the mineral fluorite, which was originally used in their construction.

Semi-permanent(Micro) Preparation Micropreparation made for use for a short period of time.

Sharpness (of image) Implies distinct, realistic image detail and contrast.

Simple positive ocular (also known as Ramsden ocular) This eyepiece has an eye lens and field lens that are planoconvex. The eye lens has its flat side towards the observer's eye. But the field lens is mounted with the curved surface facing the eye lens. The front focal plane of this eyepiece lies just below the field lens, at the level of the eyepiece diaphragm, making this eyepiece readily adaptable for mounting reticles.

Single point resolution In some cases, single-point resolution is appropriate when imaging isolated objects. Individual isolated points, smaller than those predicted by a two-point resolution definition, can be distinctly imaged. This criterion applies to fibre samples having disperse, isolated particles and fibres.

Sledge microtome A microtome in which the specimen remains fixed and the knife slides forward and back on a sledge against the specimen.

Smear Micropreparation in which the biological material is smeared so that the loose cells are conveniently spread over the surface of the slide rendering easy observation.

Specimen tube Also called specimen phials, these are used to store biological specimens for any length of time.

Spherical aberration An image defect produced by lens imperfections that cause waves of light passing through the outer regions of a lens to be focused at slightly different planes than waves passing through central regions. Spherical aberration causes a point to be focused as an enlarged and fuzzy spot. The greater the spherical aberration, the larger, fuzzier, and more "washed out" the spot (and *vice versa*). The overall effect is that the microscope image will have less **resolution**.

Square petri dish Petri dishes that are ideal for processing the smear micropreparations.

Squash Micropreparation in which loosely packed or held cells are separated from each other by application of gentle pressure.

Stage A flat platform onto which the slide containing the (biological) specimen is placed for observation in a microscope.

Stage micrometer A ruling etched, photographically deposited, etc., on a glass slide and covered with a sealed **cover glass**. The most detailed rulings (lines) are 0.01 mm apart. This is marked on the stage micrometer.

Stain A dye or a substance in solution that impregnates the object, and imparts colour to it.

Stand The primary frame of the microscope onto which a **stage**, **nosepiece (turret)**, and **head** are attached.

Stender dish A circular tublike container made of quality glass to contain biological specimen.

Substage The region just beneath the **stage.**

Temporary (Micro) Preparation Micropreparation made for the purpose of one-time use.

Total visual magnification (of a microscope) Total visual magnification of the microscope is derived by multiplying the magnification values of the objective and the eyepiece.

Tube factor This is the additional magnification factor introduced by the additional lenses built into the body tube of modern research microscopes. This is usually around 1.25–1.5×. Tube factor is a design characteristic relating to the tube length. When an ocular is physically located at the prescribed tube-length distance, the tube factor is 1.000. If the mechanical configuration of the microscope is such that the ocular is closer to or further away from the objective, the tube factor is less than or greater than 1.000 respectively.

Tube length A design characteristic relating to the focal length of the objective lens (i.e. 160 mm, 200 mm, etc.). For a given make of microscope, a 40× objective provides an image forty times larger than life size when the image is at the designated tube-length distance above the objective.

Tube lens In modern infinity-corrected systems, the tube lens is a multi-element optic (to prevent introduction of coma or astigmatism even with increased "infinity light path space") built into and sealed in the observation tube.

Turret *(See* Nosepiece.)

Two-point resolution The conventional perspective of resolution is "Two point resolution" and it means distinguishing the space between two minuscule objects that are close together or in other words, recognizing two very closely aligned points/line/objects as separate entities.

This is a common criterion for observation of intricate cellular details in a tissue sample.

Vertical resolution The smallest measurable increment normal to the plane of measurement. A function of the resolution of interferometric phase.

Vignetting In photography and optics, **vignetting** is a reduction in image brightness in the image periphery compared to the image centre.

Virtual focus In case of a concave lens, this is the point on the other side of the lens where the divergent rays if traced back will appear to meet.

Virtual image An image that does not actually exist except for the perception of viewer. An image reflected in the mirror is a virtual image. The overall image seen through a microscope is a virtual image.

Watch glass Very shallow circular containers made of glass to contain biological specimens during sectioning and/or staining.

Whole mounts Micropreparations in which the biological specimen is mounted as a whole.

Working distance (WD) The clearance distance between the closest surface of the cover glass and the objective front lens. In situations where the specimen is designed to be imaged without a cover glass, the working distance is measured at the actual surface of the specimen. Generally, working distance decreases in a series of matched objectives as the magnification and numerical aperture increase. For example, an objective lens system of 0.65 NA and 40× has a working distance of approximately 0.4 mm. (*See also* Depth of focus.)

X axis   Horizontal or left and right direction. Refers to left-to-right movement. Orthogonal to **Y** and **Z**.

Y axis   Horizontal or back and forward direction, but 90° to **X**. Refers to the front-to-back movement of the stage or to the up-and-down direction on the video monitor.

Z axis   Vertical direction of the microscope relative to the fixture stage. Refers to the up-and-down movement of the head. Parallel to the optical axis and normal to the X-Y plane.

REFERENCES

Bradbury, S. and Evennett, P. (1996). *Fluorescence Microscopy, Contrast Techniques in Light Microscopy.* BIOS Scientific Publishers, Ltd., Oxford, United Kingdom.

Grimstone, A.V. (1970). *The Electron Microscope in Biology.* Edward Arnold, U.K. p. 54.

John, R. Baker. (1969). *Cytological Technique (Principle Underlying Routine Method).* Methuen & Co. Ltd. and Science Paperback. p. 149.

Johansen, D.A. (1964). *Plant Microtechnique.* Tata McGraw-Hill, New Delhi. p. 523.

Murphy, D. (2001). *Fundamentals of Light Microscopy and Digital Imaging.* Wiley-Liss, NY.

Peter Gray. (1964). *Handbook of Basic Microtechnique.* McGraw-Hill, NY. p. 302.

Rost, F. and Oldfield, R. (2000). *Fluorescence Microscopy, Photography with a Microscope.* Cambridge University Press, Cambridge, United Kingdom.

Sass, J.E. (1964). *Botanical Microtechnic.* Oxford IBH. pp. 228.

Sluder, G. and Wolf, D. (eds.). (1998). *Video Microscopy.* Academic Press, NY.

Sharma, P.D. (1996). *Microbiology.* Rastogi & Co., Meerut. p. 359.

Vinita, V. Kale and Kishore, P. Bhusari. (2001). *Applied Microbiology.* Himalaya Publishing House, Mumbai. p. 42.

INDEX

120-format film 213
35-mm film 212
4 × 5-sheet film 213

A

AA mixtures 280
Aberrations 9
Accelerating voltage 186
Acetaldehyde 142
Acetic acid 142
Acetone 323
Acid fuchsin 304
Adhesive mounting media 339
Aeschynomene aspera 361
Airy disc 204
Albert Prebus 192
Allen's modifications
    of Bouin's fluid 285
Amplitude 137
Analytical TEM 197
Angular aperture (AA) 123
Aniline blue 304
Annular stop 140
Antoni von Leeuwenhoek 110
ASA designation 209
Attributes of digital cameras 226
Attributes of SLR camera 221
Autofluorescence 142
Automatic camera
    tamer software (ACT) 227

B

BAO 142
Basic fuchsin 142
Beechwood creosote 329
Bergamot oil 329
Binocular loupes 115
Birefringence 152

Black/white films 211
Blade 273
Bleaching 294
Body tube 126
Bonannes 112
Bouin's picric acid
    fixative mixture 284
Brazilin 298
Butyl alcohol 321

C

Calibration 240
    of ocular scale 240
    of microscope 240
Camera adapters 219
CA mixtures 282
Camera lucida 203, 204
Campini 110
Canada balsam 343
Carbolxylene 333
Cardioid condenser 149
Carnoy's acetic
    acid–alcohol fixative 281
Cavity slides 257
Cedar wood oil 329, 344
Cellosolve 323
Charge-coupled
    device (CCD) 171, 217
Chicago FAA 281
China blue 304
Chloroform 333
Chlorophylls 142
Chromatic aberrations 9, 10
Circular rotary stage 154
Clarite 344
Cleaning of microslides 377
Clearance angle 273
Clove oil 328

Coal-tar dyes 303
Cochineal 302
    derivatives of 302
Coddington lens 11
Coldfinger 189, 196
Colour films 211
Complementary filters 144
Condenser 123
Confocal microscopy 163
Congo red 142
Contrast 208
Contrast plate 118
Coons *et al.* 143
Coplin jar 259
Cotton blue 304
Coverslips 255
    of different shapes and
        dimensions 256
    of various thicknesses 256
Craf-1 fixative 284
Craf-2 fixative 284
Craf mixtures 283
Crossover 173
Crosstalk 173
Crystal violet 305
Crystal violet and
    erythrosin combination 315
Culture slides 257
Cutting facet 273

D

Dammar balsam 342
Dark-field condenser 146
Dark-field microscopy 148
Daylight-balanced films 212
Deconvolution 225
Dehydrating agents 319
    clearing of 325
Dehydration 318
Delafield's haematoxylin 300
Depression slides 257
Dewaxing of sections 380
Dextro-rotatory 153
Dichroic mirror
    (dichromatic beam splitter) 144

Differential acidification 297
Differential interference
    contrast (DIC) microscope 158
Differential
    interference microscopy 158
Digital imaging 225
DIN speed ratings 209
Dioxan(e) 323
Direct and indirect staining 290
Disc diaphragm 124
Dissection microscope 117, 119
Documentation 203
Dovetail 178
DPX 341
Drawtube 122
Drift 178

E

Ehrlich's haematoxylin 301
Electromagnetic lenses 187
Electron gun 185
Electron microscopy 183
Embedding 369
Embryo cup 258
Embryological watch glass 258
Emission chamber 193
Emission filter 144
Emulsion speed 209
Eosin 142
Epi-illumination
    fluorescence microscope 146
Ernst Ruska 185, 192
Erythrosine 306
Ethyl alcohol 320
Excitation filter 144
Eye lens (EL) 129
Eye loupes 114
Eyepiece 119
Eyepiece camera system 224
Eyepiece reticle 236
Eyepoint 207

F

FAA mixtures 281
Farmer's fixative 280
Fast films 211

Fast green FCF 306
Fat ponceau R 308
Ferrant's medium 340
Feulgen's nuclear
   staining method 359
Field lenses 114, 129
Field of view 116
Filimicroscopes 109
Film size formats 212
Film speed 209
Fixative 276
Fixed stage and movable
   body tube 177
Fixing coverslips 382
Fixing the ribbon on the slide 377
Flemming's triple stain 310
Fluoresamine 142
Fluorescence lifetime 143
Fluorochromes 142
Fluoro-micro-chromy 148
Focusing knob 117
Formaldehyde 142
Foster's tannic acid–iron chloride
   staining schedule 317
Fourth image 129
Frederick Zernike 139
Free-hand sections 362

G

Galileo 110
Gate's fluid 282
General stains 297
Gentian violet 305
George G. Stokes 141
Giant pipette 259
Glycerine jelly 345
Glycerine–xylol method 351
Glyoxylic acid 142
Gold-size 348
Gum arabic 342

H

Haematein 302
Haematoxylin 298
Half ground blade 273

Hand microtome 266
Hand-rest 118
Hans 110
Head-band magnifiers 115
Heidenhain's adhesive 378
Herbarium 203
Hillary's method 358
Histochemistry 251
Hollow cone of light 146
Hollow ground blade 273
Honing stones 275
Hot-air oven 262
Hydrogen peroxide 295
Hydrophil media 337
Hydrophobe media 338
Hygrobutol 322
Hygrobutol method 349
Hyrax 344

I

Illuminated loupe 114
Image-degrading noise 170
Immunofluorescence 147
Improved Mayer's haemalum 301
Induced fluorescence 142
Infiltration technique 367
Integral lens camera 219
Integral metering system 222
Interference microscopy 157
Iris diaphragm 123
Isopropyl alcohol 320

J

James Hillier 192
Jeffrey's method 381
Jeweller's loupes 114
Johansen's methyl violet–erythrosin
   schedule 316
Johansen's methyl violet method 355

K

Koehler 143

L

Lactophenol 344

L-adapter 221
Laevo-rotatory 153
Laser scanning confocal
    microscopy (LSCFM) 164
Leather strops 275
Lens coil 187
Leonardo da Vinci 109
Light green SF 306
Louis-Victor de Broglie 184
'L' shaped blocks 369

M

Max Knoll 185, 192
Maceration 380
Magnification 129
Magnifying power 116
Maintenance 273
Marvin Minsky 163
Measuring and inspecting
    magnifiers 114
Medium-speed films 210
Meniscus lens 12
Methyl alcohol 321
Methyl salicylate 341
Meyer's egg albumin 377
Microgrid 195
Micrometers 236
Micrometry 235
Microslide preparation 345
Microtechnique 251
Microtome 265
Microtome knives 273
Microtome sections 366
Microtoming 374
Mirror type 204
Moderate chrome–acetic
    acid mixture 282
Mounting and mountants 335
Movable stage and fixed body tube 177

N

Natural dyes 298
Navaschin's fixative 283
Negative films 211
Nicol prism 153

Nicol prism of calcite 154
Nipkow disc 171
Noise 171
Nomarski-modified
    Wollaston prism 158
Non-adhesive mounting media 339
Nosepiece 127

O

Oatley C.W. 198
Ocular 119
Ocular micrometer 236
Oil diffusion pump 189, 196
Ontogeny 251
Opaque 150
Optical differentiation 161
Optically anisotropic substances 152
Optically isotropic substances 152
Optical property 152

P

PA mixtures 284
Paired objectives 121
Paper boat 370
Paraboloid condenser 149
Paraffin infiltration 366
Parcentricity 178
Parfocality 176, 178
Patch stop 150
PC mixtures 285
Permanent microslide 252
Permanent preparation 252
Phase-contrast microscopy 137
Phase shift 137
Phenylalanine 142
Photoeyepiece 208
Photographic films 209
Photomicrography 206
Photomicroscopy 207
Photomultiplier tube (PMT) 163
Pinion 126
Pinion wheel 117
Plain microslides 255
Plate camera 196
Polarimeter 153

Polarimetry 153
Polarized light microscopy 151
Polarizer 152
Polaroid film 154, 215
Pole pieces 187
Porphyrenes 142
Positive films 211
Prebus and Miller 185
Preservation 216
Primary fluorescence 142
Primary image 128
Principal focus 7
Principle of differential staining 289
Principles of staining 288
Progressive and
    regressive staining 296
Projection lens 208

R

Rack 126
Rack-and-pinion 122
    backlash in operation of 178
Rack stop 128
Ralinin's FAA 281
Ramsden disc 129, 204
Reflector 117
Resolution 208
Resolving power 1
Resultant light 138
Reticle retainer ring 235
Rhieta 112
Ringing 382
Robert Hooke 110
Rotary microtome 267
Rotary pump 196

S

S. nigra 361
Safranin and fast green 308
Safranin and
    haematoxylin 310
Safranin O 307
Sambucus canadensis 361
Scanning electron
    microscope (SEM) 191, 198
Scanning transmission electron
    microscope (STEM) 197
Sealing the section 382
Secondary image 129
Sections 253
Semi-permanent preparation 252
Setting the cutting facet 274
Signal-to-noise considerations 171
Signal-to-noise ratio 166, 169
Single "intermediate"
    focusing knob 178
Single lens reflex (SLR) cameras 220
Sledge microtome 270
Slide containers 261
Slide jar with a slide rack 259
Slide storage cabinets 262
Slide-warming table 264
Slip clutch (check nut) 178
Slow films 210
Smearing technique 353
Smears 253, 352
Specific stains 297
Specimen chamber 195
Specimen phial 258
Specimen tube 258
Spectral bleed-through 173
Spherical aberrations 9, 10
Split cylinder 273
Square ground blade 273
Square petri dish 259
Squashes 253, 357
Stage micrometer 238
Staining schedules 308
Staining the smear 354
Stamp loupes 114
Standard rotary pump 189
Stender dish 258
Stereo-binocular 119
Stereoscopic
    microscope 119
Strong chrome–acetic
    acid mixture 282
Stropping 275
Styrax 344
Sudan IV 308

Scharlach R 308
Syracuse dish 258
Syracuse watch glass 258

T

Temporary preparation 252
Terpineol 328
Tertiary butyl alcohol 322
Tertiary image 129
Thermionic emission 186
Thioflavin-T 142
Thompson 184
T-mount adapter 221
Toluol 331
Total internal reflection fluorescence
   (TIRF) microscope 147
Trans-illumination fluorescence
   microscope 145
Transmission electron
   microscope (TEM) 191, 192
Transparencies 211, 216
Trichloroethylene 333
Triple nosepiece 128
Tryptophan 142
Turn table 386
Tyrosine 142

U

Use of mordants 290
UV microscopy 156

V

Vacuum system 189
Virtual focus 7

W

Warmke's method 357
Watch glass 257
Water blue 304
Wavelength 137
Weak chrome–acetic mixture 282
Wehnalt cylinder 186
Wehnalt cap 186
Whole mounts 253
William Hyde Wollaston 203
Wilson 113
Wollaston prism 158
Working diameter of the lens 116

X

Xylol 331

Z

Zacharias Jansen 110

Made in the USA
Coppell, TX
23 November 2021

66336124R00268